INQUIRIES IN PSYCHIATRY

By the same Author

THE STATE OF PSYCHIATRY

Essays and Addresses

SIR AUBREY LEWIS

A Monochrome reproduction of a portrait
by Ruskin Spear

INQUIRIES IN PSYCHIATRY

Clinical and Social Investigations

by
Sir Aubrey Lewis
Emeritus Professor of Psychiatry
University of London

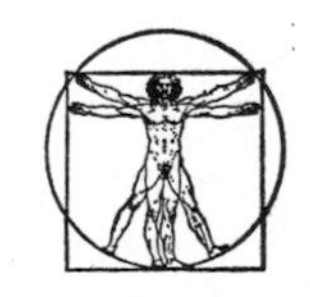

SCIENCE HOUSE, INC.
NEW YORK

First published 1967
by Routledge & Kegan Paul Limited
London E.C.4

Printed in Great Britain

CONTENTS

INTRODUCTION

IN OCTOBER 1966, Professor Sir Aubrey Lewis, a leading figure in the world of psychiatry for more than a generation, retired from the Maudsley Hospital, where he had joined Dr Edward Mapother's staff in 1928. After qualifying in medicine in his native Australia, he had first made some anthropological studies of aborigines and then turned to psychiatry, working in some of the most famous clinics in America and Europe before coming to London. In 1936, he was appointed Clinical Director of the Maudsley Hospital, and, in 1945, Professor of Psychiatry in the University of London. He was knighted in 1959. During these years, the healthy development of psychiatry, in Britain and abroad, has owed much to his guidance and encouragement: while the Maudsley Hospital, which was combined with the Bethlem Royal Hospital in 1948, has flourished and expanded into a psychiatric centre of international renown.

To mark his retirement, his present students have arranged for the publication of some of his best-known writings. These have ranged considerably beyond the confines of clinical psychiatry, wherein many of his contributions are now recognized as classics. Two volumes have been prepared. The first contains articles on the history of psychiatry, the ways in which it should be taught, and some of the important general issues with which every psychiatrist must inevitably concern himself, but which very few can clarify. Professor Lewis's closely argued essays have always been highly valued by those interested in these fascinating and complex topics for providing some firm ground in an area notorious for soft generalizations. This volume is devoted to clinical and social psychiatry. Both include a complete bibliography of all Professor Lewis's publications.

Our selection, as the bibliography shows, is only a small sample, but it reflects the breadth of his scholarship and the vigour of his critical mind. For his past students, now scattered throughout the world, these essays will, we hope, be something more: refreshing reminders of their training. For athletes training involves not only a gain of muscular strength, but a loss of excess fat. For psychiatrists Professor Lewis provided its intellectual equivalent. It has been through his teaching, with its challenging mixture of scholarship and common sense, that his influence has been most widely felt, and it is this which we, his present students, gratefully commemorate.

THE EDITORS

The Junior Common Room
The Bethlem Royal and the Maudsley Hospital
November 1966

ACKNOWLEDGMENTS

IN the collection of these papers invaluable help has been given by Miss Helen Marshall, M.A., secretary to Professor Lewis for nearly twenty years. Her exceptional range of precise information and her constant readiness to assist immensely facilitated the task of preparing the books.

We thank the Editors of the following publications for permission to reproduce these articles:

Acta Genetica, Acta Neuropsiquiatrica Argentina, Athlone Press, *British Journal of Medical Psychology, British Medical Journal, Eugenics Review, Journal of Mental Science, Lancet, Proceedings of the Royal Society, Proceedings of the Royal Society of Medicine, Recenti Progressi in Medicina, Sociological Review.*

ACKNOWLEDGMENTS

CLINICAL PSYCHIATRY

I

THE EXPERIENCE OF TIME IN MENTAL DISORDER

THE IDEA of evolution in time has been the main influence in biology for many decades; and in philosophy the universe is a four-dimensional continuum of which time is an essential aspect. In narrower fields it is the same. That disease is a matter of time relations was the opinion of Clifford Allbutt. Hughlings Jackson and von Monakow have insisted on the importance of a time-factor in all the normal and pathological changes of the nervous system; while investigations such as those of the physiologists into chronaxy are another recognition of its significance. It would be strange if psychology and psychopathology, always responsive to current modes of thought, should here be lacking. Nor are they, but one can still comfortably read through all the available literature, written by a handful of German and French psychiatrists, on time-phenomena in mental disorder. There are two aspects of this subject. The first is the time factor as a determinant of the duration of illness: a factor too often ignored by psychotherapists of the thaumaturgic kind—this I do not propose to consider. The second is of time as a modality of personal experience, an immediate or derivative datum of consciousness. Gross disorders of this occur in organic psychoses, where disorientation in time is a familiar feature, but it is also found in the 'functional' psychoses, and it is with the latter than I am here concerned.

An extract from the case record of one of my patients will illustrate the matter.

'Everything seems very much longer. I should have said it was afternoon, though they say it is midday. They always tell me it is earlier than I think . . . and it looks as if I'm wrong and I can't help feeling I'm right . . . I cannot see any end to anything, any end to the world . . . I don't know whether I shall die quickly within what we call time and then have no more feeling . . . Time has a limit, but I don't know what limit . . . Time certainly passes, there is progression but not in the

---

This paper was read to the section of psychiatry, Royal Society of Medicine in December 1931. It is reprinted from the *Proceedings of the Royal Society of Medicine* (March) 1932, **25**, 15–24.

ordinary way now; there seem to be long pauses and then it goes on in the ordinary way . . . I've felt twice that time is standing still . . . I suppose I judge my time by the way I feel where the sun is; I noticed it very suddenly changes as though at the will of someone . . . I think no one will ever die.'

This is fairly typical of one kind of time disorder: and one hears such accounts not only from the highly educated or philosophically minded but also from unintelligent, illiterate or matter-of-fact patients. In such a patient as the above there are unquestionable changes in the sense of time. To examine these one must have some notion of the psychology of time, i.e., of the mental happenings which permit us to recognize the present, judge the duration and passage of time, and bring it into relation with other contents of consciousness.

Time is a word of several meanings. There is objective physical time, clock time, calendar time, and there is personal time, experiential time, in short, psychological time. The former, which may be called world time, is the arbitrary standard, a fictional construction. The latter is time that we live in. They are usually more or less in agreement, more especially where no disturbing factors enter, as in sleep, hypnosis, and in certain waking states. But psychologically they are quite separate. Time-consciousness is a matter of immediate experience: it is an aspect of all conscious activity: it is essential to all reality: whatever we call it, *durée vécue* or what not, it is inescapable in every reality-experience: we live in time. J. S. Haldane puts it summarily: 'When we perceive things they are perceived as related to a past and future, and as related spatially to one another . . . Past, future, and contemporary present are thus given in each experience . . . our perceptions express our interest. In other words our perceived world is no mere picture independent of our presence in it, but the embodiment of our personal interest which reaches back over the past and forward to the future, so that past and future are represented in the present. Each of our perceptions, and each of our actions, embodies learning from experience, and therefore both retrospect and foresight; . . .; when we see evidence of this we interpret the behaviour as being conscious. Unity extending over events in time as well as space is expressed in conscious behaviour.'

Time is by no means an attribute of sensation, though probably of perception. Those who consider time from a genetic point of view hold that the elementary primitive phenomenon was duration: this, in its dependent relation to conduct, was developed into the idea of stability which was extended and objectivated so as to become a feature of the environment, otherwise so changeable and manifold. Beginning and ending are indispensable integral parts of duration; rhythm, so important in biology and art, is a mixture of stability and change. The conception of the present is a later development; with it comes the conception of the absent, to which we adapt ourselves by expectation. Memory has developed in order to integrate past experience with the living present. The present is set apart as a particular point, 'now', in relation to which the succession of happenings can be put in order as past and future. Otherwise one has pure and simple succession, as in children who mix up the order of events. Thus the present has a constant relation to action and striving. This setting up of a notion of the present is possibly a complex, not a primitive, mental process; through it meaning is given to the present. In *déjà vu* there is a brief inability to actualize the present which in consequence is projected into the past. The present and the past are not uniform: there is an immediate past, a recent, a remote, and an indefinite past (and future), graded according to their closeness to the present and intimacy with it, as it were, and according to their explicit emotional character. The immediate past is not a matter of recollection: it is a progressive reality, almost continuous with the present, but shading off into the more remote, the mass of forgotten but available past from which can be evoked clearer recollections by bringing them up into the immediate past. Our conception of the past is like our consciousness in general: the totality of both consists in a global feeling of which only certain modalities attain to clear presentation.

With the penetration of the notion of time by the idea of reality the essential features of the process are arrived at. Instead of giving the same reality to past, present and future, the present is now regarded as real, past and future as unreal: diminishing degrees of reality attach to the immediate, near and remote past, as to the immediate near and remote future, but the indefinite past and future are almost entirely unreal, and such remoteness as is implicit in eternity is for us ordinarily an abstract fiction.

As a form of philosophical organization of time, the general and universal idea of time has developed, like the corresponding idea of space—something independent of ourselves; something external, unitary and abstract; a time which passes and destroys. A scientific mode of organization of time has led to the introduction of objective measures as well as to a determinist conception of time, as the conservative, yet always dynamic, transmitter of past forms of energy into forms yet to come. The objective measures of time are familiar divisions of 'world time', in which the present is a travelling point—not a brief brightest area in a scale of brightness shading off as it recedes at either end: in it the past disappears. Personal time is often brought into relation with world time. We have a consciousness that time is passing quickly or slowly in an absolute sense: also we may conclude that it is passing quickly or slowly in relation to world time; the two are commonly associated but by no means identical. In boredom, for example, time is said to pass slowly, because it is not possible to give it the content one would choose; hence, secondarily, comes distressing attention to the passage of time. Interesting changing occupation gives one the time consciousness 'how fast it goes', though after it one has the impression of a long day, full of incident: a dull tiresome day seems, to retrospection, short. But this time consciousness is different from 'time sense', which enables us to guess at the duration of an interval in terms of world time. Some would limit this as a simple perceptual process to very brief intervals (one and a half to two seconds), and regard the appreciation of longer intervals as a matter of judgment: they talk further of memory images, and of intervals with and without stimuli, but these notions and experiments and this element in the process, if it be one, need not detain us. What is the basis of this quantitative awareness of time, whether it be of long intervals or short ones? Several explanations are current among experimental psychologists: some referring to feelings of tension, others to contents of sensation, and so on; generally they mistake the factors which hinder it or alter it for those which are its basis. Others speak of 'psycho-energetic' processes which appear in consciousness as a feeling of activity; thus they connect the quantitative appreciation of time with the psychic concomitants of action. But this alone is not helpful. One must consider, I submit, two elements: (1) an immediate awareness of the magnitude of duration or of speed of succession; and (2), an ability to recall similar former experiences for comparison. I do not suggest that the latter are simple memory images or engrams, plucked out of their pigeon-holes for the purpose, as schematizers would have it, but as representing particular aspects of memory, to which I have already alluded. As to the former, it is carried out best in sleep and allied states; in waking hours the less of affective interest and direct attention to it, the better it is performed. The psycho-analysts say it is a function of the preconscious part of the psyche. It is, I would suggest, a particular manifestation of the general time sense of the integrated organism, also manifested in such periodic activities as cardiac and respiratory function, sexual activities, e.g., menstruation, the alternation of metabolic changes associated with sleep and waking. Various writers pick out particular activities of this kind and hold them responsible for the special capacity: it is better to consider it as deeply rooted in biological changes of the whole organism. I would refer, in passing, to the work of Pawlow's school in regard to the conditioned time-reflex. It is not appropriate to discuss the relation of rhythm to time in further detail here: one psycho-analyst of repute thinks that time feeling is unconscious and depends on unconscious rhythm being an endopsychic perception of fluctuation of libido-distribution.

Only with some general notions, such as the above summary of views on the psychology of time, can one set about an analysis of the disorders of time processes that we meet in our patients.

What are these disorders? First let us consider depersonalization and the sense of unreality. The following is a description of his time disorder by a young man with a striking clinical picture of this sort:

'As I went about everything seemed unreal. There is no break of time. I'm passing through time, there is no day and no night. There's nothing divided between my getting up and coming here and going back. It's all joined into one. I have no definite recollection of going to Australia, though I'm only just back. . . . There's something gone from me—the spirit: I have no life. . . . I'm dead already. I can't die. The mind is alive. You can't kill that. You could hurt the physical body, but if you were to shoot me, I would drop to the ground. But "I" would still be sitting here, it must go on and on . . . it's a trance, a dreadful dream. My mind is there for eternity, nothing can alter it. . . . You can't imagine yourself different from the present, can you? Well, I'm that, accentuated a hundredfold.'

Here is another, also from a young man:

'Everything seems just a painted picture, deathly quiet. . . . I want to get something back to my mind that seems to have gone, to let me see the present and the future . . . everything seems ages ago. Even getting up in the morning, I feel I've forgotten it; it seems ages ago. And yet time seems to go faster. If anybody had asked me at this time (12.30 p.m.) I'd have thought it was only half an hour since I got up. It simply means that time is going quicker than I realized. . . . Time does drag naturally, having nothing to do. I can't visualize; I can't picture anything at all. Everything comes new to me and fresh. . . . The future to me is remote. I feel hopeless. . . . Before I could look to the future, but I can't now. There's something won't let me (actually continually worrying about the future). Time just doesn't appeal to me. I look up and see it is twelve o'clock, and think, "What's twelve o'clock?" . . . I've got no idea of time or what the day is or anything, unless somebody tells me. I mean, I couldn't tell you how long I've been sitting here; an hour seems like a minute. Time doesn't seem to go at all; the whole day seems exactly the same. If I look at the clock it doesn't mean anything to me at all. . . . I couldn't give you the remotest idea now what the time is [asked, said it was twelve o'clock, actually 11.50]. It's difficult to think of the past at all . . . everything seems to have gone out of my head.'

These are not rarities or exceptions. They are typical of numerous accounts that I have collected. They illustrate many of the outstanding features of the disorder: the inability to evoke the past readily or clearly, to distinguish the present from the past and the future ('I think about them all three at once, past, present and future,' said another patient), to seize the present, to look into the future or to anticipate a future for oneself; there is paradoxically the increased quickness with which time passes, though it seems also to drag along; the seeming remoteness of the recent past; the unconfirmed feeling of inability to judge length of time.

The point-by-point application to these phenomena of the considerations presented earlier in this paper is, no doubt, sufficiently apparent. I will, however, put forward some more general considerations. The influence of MacCurdy, or an itch for causality-explanations in terms of comprehensible *einfühlbare* psychic processes, has led to this syndrome being regarded as a sequel or 'manifestation of loss of interest which is in turn related to the loss of energy and stimulus susceptibility'. I have elsewhere put forward evidence against this view. I would regard the syndrome as indicative of the disturbed state of consciousness in which the immediate data of perception—an active, not a passive process—are so changed as to have lost their primary attribute of reality. There is a change in space- and time-consciousness which may be expressed in various forms: simply, as in the above instances, or less clearly in general feelings of a change in the environment, or of complex rearrangements of space and time relations. In short, clinically one finds the syndrome of unreality and depersonalization, in various guises but none the less unmistakable, in many kinds of mental disorder—in manic and depressive states, in schizophrenia, in obsessive-ruminative tension states, encephalitis lethargica, toxic confusional and delirious forms, epilepsy and hysterical dissociations. That is easily demonstrable clinically; without going into all its implications I suggest that in all mental disorder there may be more or less disturbance of consciousness *in this sense*, and that this disorder of consciousness, in affective as well as other forms of mental disorder, may manifest itself only in a trifling time and reality disorder, hardly distinguishable from the variations we are aware of in ourselves (who are presumably normal) up through a growing obviousness to the grossest forms of disorientation and distortion. I have not referred to the disturbance of space appreciation in this syndrome, but it is of the same order.

The clearest analogue to depersonalization and unreality in ourselves, if indeed it is not the same thing, is the *déjà vu* or *déjà raconté* phenomenon. I think immediate premonitions also must be included here; in this connexion I would recall what was said about expectation in the earlier part of the paper. I have been impressed in reading a large number of records of the unreality syndrome to find how regularly it is associated with a feeling of imminent disaster. I cannot here consider its relation to anxiety, but I mention it, and refer also to the statement which patients make that 'there is no future': this invariably refers only to the personal future, sometimes only to a pleasant or tolerable future: 'I feel nothing will change in so far as I shall never be better,' said one patient; 'I feel as if there's no future,' said another, yet at the same interview he said, 'I dread everything: I picture all sorts of terrible things, that I shall go to asylums, and all sorts of things.'

There are variations in the manner of description: there is sometimes conscious elaboration, but in the main, the uniformity in essentials is amazing. One variation is in the attitude towards recollections. Some insist on the remoteness and vagueness of the past, others on its sharpness and clarity in comparison with the present; they say they have lively pictures coming up:

> 'Everything seemed suddenly to go backwards. The future seemed to go and the memory came forward. My memory became vivid, my childhood became vivid. It seemed to come automatically. I came to form mental pictures. From that I went back and back. It seemed as though everything was changing. The present and the future didn't worry me. Vivid pictures kept coming.'

This variation is commoner in depressives, in whom the deterministic force of the past is strongly felt: things are occurring now, will occur in the future, which are only continuing evidences of past happenings; the future is closed to new action but an irrevocable process has been set in train. (In schizophrenics it is sometimes stated in the form, 'I feel that what I say now will influence the future.')

This brings us to the depressives. Here emphasis must be laid on the inhibition or 'retardation'. This inhibition, which von Monakow calls 'apathetic anastole', is a total change, affecting experience and determining conduct. I would bring into relation the altered time-consciousness which exists alongside unimpaired time-judgment (or time-perception, *sensu strictiori*), and altered activity-feelings which exist alongside unimpaired psychomotor capacity. 'Retardation' is a personal experience, not an objectively demonstrable slowing or diminution of psychic or psychomotor performance; for this there is clinical and experimental evidence. In the case of the time-disorder, I have carried out on depressives a number of experiments in time-appreciation, using mainly the same tests as Bouchard set forth in his monograph, and I have found, as others have, ever since Revault d'Allonnes' work on the Korsakow syndrome in 1903, that the patients' professed incapacity to estimate duration is not borne out by objective tests for short intervals, and scarcely at all for longer intervals, though here other factors come in. I think that this inconsistency in both psychomotor and temporal experience can be referred to a common factor, which I should also hold responsible, in part, for that obstinate and ominous symptom—a belief that one has spent a sleepless night when it is not so: the distinction between this symptom and true sleeplessness is important and too often overlooked. In these depressive patients the rapidity with which time passes is felt, as well as its painful heaviness: the sufferer is beset with a press of memories, vivid and insistent.

The following is the account of his time disorder given by a recurrent depressive, self-reproachful and anergic, seen in his fourth attack:—

> 'I'm an absolute blank; I can't imagine what it is like outside. It seems as though the end is coming to me, dreadful. I can't imagine tomorrow. The days seem to fly by like magic, but I can't look forward, I look backward all the time, all my childhood. I feel I can't do anything correctly, somehow.'

Another, a young girl, said:

> 'I can't think of the past and the future; it all seems a blank. Thoughts and memories will keep going round and round in my head: they are all of things I have seen and done during the last few years. They are like little pictures inside my head.'

Only in so far as experiences acquire full meaning and reality, can they be incorporated into one's individual life history, and contribute to the development and unfolding of one's personality. It is inevitable that with the closing off of the individual future, i.e., anticipated activity, the past shall become torturing and intolerable: in a certain measure also the present. This is important in connexion with compulsive states, to which I now come.

The intimate relation between compulsive and manic-depressive types of reaction is generally acknowledged, and is clinically and psychopathologically so manifest that it is unnecessary to consider the older view that one was a 'psychosis' and the other a 'neurosis', and that they were essentially different. The real problem is in many cases how to account for the development in, say, one depressive patient of delusions and in another of compulsions—compulsive thinking and compulsive acts.

Compulsive phenomena, considered not so much according to their content (which is symbolic), but according to their form, commonly show time components. This observation was made so long ago as 1874 in a paper in the *Journal of Mental Science*. As far as content is concerned, compulsive doubts and questions are sometimes taken up with time, especially in patients preoccupied with creation and causality, primeval chaos and suchlike metaphysical expense of spirit in a waste of thought. One patient, for example, with gross obsessional symptoms, said:

'I keep worrying about the origin of God. I think about eternity. There is one thing that worries me: I can't get it off my mind. These eternal years trouble me a bit. My imagination is set going, and gets on numbers and eternal numbers, and eternity. Immensity, too....'

Another patient with obsessional attacks of the cyclic variety said:

'I have to reason everything out. I seem right up against a blank wall, and I feel I can't go on existing like that.... Do you think if I read some books about it would I get some rest? I have to just think and think about things like that. I can't get any satisfaction. I keep worrying about thousands of years ago, about the beginning of things. I feel I must know. If I don't know everything like that I don't want to go on.... I can't understand about the chaos that there was in the beginning and what was before that.'

Time and eternity, the beginning of things and their end, are here the content of the compulsive phenomena; but what of their form? The main characteristic of this so far as compulsive thinking is concerned—and it applies equally to compulsive ideas and impulses—were referred to also in the foregoing examples: the inability to stop, to get satisfaction, the feeling of incompleteness, of lack of finality. One patient who said of her thinking 'I feel as if I'm all mind, as if I'm mind altogether, and I don't get anywhere with my thinking,' said also: 'Sometimes when I am writing something I can't get past a full-stop. I keep making it bigger and bigger.'

Many examples support the familiar view that it is in the incapacity to complete the particular act and so dispose of it, that the essence of morbid 'compulsion' lies. Many psychologists now regard thinking also as an act, as internal conduct. Be this as it may, thinking and conduct are both carried out in constant reference to the future which is the arena in which the personality expresses or unfolds itself; but this time-attitude is altered where general inhibition has occurred. For the normal person the past and the present are carried on into the future satisfactorily only when completed and dealt with; the less this is so the more there is of regret and return to the past: there is difficulty in completing an act, i.e., there is indecision, where the particular act will gravely affect the future. But in the inhibited obsessional patient it is not concern about effects in the future that hinders action; for him the future is barred, and so in his acts he is continually struggling against this check, hindered in completion and disposal, and thrust back to his starting point. Both the inhibited *depressed* patient and the inhibited *obsessional* do no effectual acts, but in the one it is by refraining from action at all, and in the other by indeterminateness and vain repetition of acts. I am sensible of certain difficulties in this and of its limited application; and I emphasize that one is here concerned with the form, not the content of the compulsions.

Compulsive phenomena of various kinds are prominent in encephalitics.

In them, too, one finds disturbances in time-appreciation; thus a patient with oculogyric crises said:

'My eyes turn up and I get sentences like "What is what?" going through my mind. Time seems to go quickly. And yet it seems to drag. When I look at the clock the time has passed more quickly than I thought . . . It was one o'clock when I started reading and I'd read two pages by three o'clock and I expected it to be about half-past one . . . During these attacks I feel I can't see how I can come right. While I'm in it I seem to be thinking of the past the whole time, but these thoughts like "What is what?" come in between. . . . During the attacks I feel older: I feel as if I've had a lot of experience.'

Another said:

'Time seems to hang a bit but especially when it (the oculogyric attack) is coming on. I feel terrible, right down ill. You know it'll stop, but sometimes you feel it'll go on for ever. In the old attacks (more severe) you used to feel you'd never get to the end of it.'

I am omitting the toxic-organic disorders, in which there are much grosser disturbances of consciousness, especially evident in regard to orientation in space and time, where there is often not merely a change in time consciousness and time appreciation but also an ignorance of world time which rests on complicated disorders of judgment and memory. I am also omitting the drug-made time-disorders.

The large group of presenile or presbyo-phrenic patients presents some of the most striking of time-disorders. I do not regard them as a unitary or distinctive group but as showing combinations of the various reaction types. There are no features of this disorder ('involutional melancholia') beyond its greater frequency at this time of life—the climacteric and after—which may not be found in other age periods. There is nothing absolutely distinctive in the time-disorder; nothing which may not be found in younger people with similar nihilistic ideas, paranoid attitudes and somatic hallucinations or delusions. I therefore quote without comment passages from a full account of striking time-disorder by a patient with 'involutional melancholia':

'Of course I realize I'm quite finished now: my faculties are all gone. I'm completely wrecked. I can't lose consciousness. I can't sleep, no sleep at all. I shall never really die . . . I know I shall be physically conscious for ever . . . I can't estimate time. I can't say what time it is because it's an artificial day; what you call a day with the artificial day is very much shorter than the ordinary day. The time goes very much quicker . . . I noticed my watch was accelerated . . . What I mean is this; since we had breakfast this morning, according to your time it is eight hours, isn't it? Well, we haven't had eight hours since this morning by Greenwich time. The time you keep here isn't Greenwich time. Yours is only a quarter of the real time . . . Probably in my months it'd be a couple of months since I came here, in what I call the ordinary time. But of course in your reckoning it'd be eight months, what you call a month . . . Time in the sense of being heavy on your hands is terrible here, I can't do anything. By Greenwich time it goes very quick. But (considering) whether you find the moments interesting, time passes very slowly: every moment that passes is, you know, tedious and wearisome. Time in the sense of a period, though, is very quick. It would be about August 1930, now by Greenwich time. I'm certain because I know Greenwich time couldn't have gone as quickly as July 1931 (the date of the interview). The past seems a long way off, but that is only the tremendous tedium since. Figuratively speaking it seems years since I was out in the normal world . . . I never know any moment what is going to happen. It's the most terrible outlook I've ever had to look to. It's all perpetual. I've got to suffer perpetually.'

There is little need for comment on that typical account. In some the change is interpreted, not in the personal sense, but, like the unreality, it is projected and the patient declares that she must die but that no one else will ever die.

There were schizophrenic elements in that patient's account of his experience. In some 'involutional' patients they are obtrusive. What then are the disorders of time found in the schizophrenic? In addition to the usual unreality-accompaniments there are some distinctive features. One of these is the feeling of previous death and rebirth, as in this patient, a young woman:

'I should say it was the beginning of a new world. I think I shall die at a certain time and live again. It seems as if I have died, not recently. I used to ponder over it, and think I'd been living a long time . . . I think there has been a break in my life . . . I feel things may slow up a little more; more evenly, that's all . . . I think the world stops and goes on so quickly that it's only noticed by certain people . . . In here the time goes much more evenly than anywhere else I know . . . Sometimes I've got up in the morning and wondered if it is night-time. It has seemed strange. I looked out of the window and saw the sun and it certainly looked like evening and it was really morning.'

The feeling of an interruption in time occurs frequently in the records; thus one patient had said that 'somebody was playing with the clocks'. When talked to about it he said:

'It's very bewildering. I don't seem to know how the date's going . . . It stands still for some time and then goes on again. I'm sure it does. Look at watch at half-past four and then look again an hour after and it's still half-past four. Guess a long interval has elapsed . . . Seems something wrong with the time here. It's later than it appears. Seem to sleep the night right round including the next day somehow . . . It seems as though a day's gone by and I'm still in bed . . . The elections were held on the 27th October' [actually two days before interview]. 'I should imagine that was two or three weeks ago, judging by the days that have been missed.

Another, a young man, said:

'There's a constant altering of perspective. I feel I'm not continuous. I seem to be reborn every moment. Although I remember things, I can't seem to exist to myself for a long time together. . . . I know that everything is the same as it always was. At odd moments I can reconcile my mind to the new. . . . I can see the continuity of events. . . . People's faces seem to open up to me fresh every time. I seem to have to arouse myself and accept the world again every moment. I have no continuity in my way of seeing things, and I have difficulty in bringing it back to a constant one.'

This may be regarded as attributable to irregular changes in consciousness, i.e., occurrence of varying intermittent states of unreality; it has considerable bearing on other symptoms of schizophrenia. Another common feature in schizophrenia is the particular change in time experience often referred to as 'thinking backwards', e.g.:

'It's as though I had everything all mixed up with the present. Whenever anyone said anything to me, it referred back to some part of my life, numbers and colours. One mind was living back and one mind forward, living present-like. . . . I died three times; I seemed to go right back. . . . I think it's the backward reflex of the brain. . . . I wish they would bring me forward in my mind. . . . I know I've got to die soon.'

Another said:

'I dream backwards. . . . I've run past myself.'

Still others have anticipations of the 'premonition' type:

'When I am thinking about something, other people say just what I'm thinking. I think there must be some special significance.'

Another:

'Before a door opens I know it's going to open. I can tell what's going to happen.'

Another:

'Quick changes happen. I've noticed that when I do anything or when I'm going to do anything, people seem to imitate me.'

Another schizophrenic patient, who has profound disorder of time-consciousness, though his personality is so far well preserved, and who weaves ingenious metaphysical speculations to account for these phenomena, declares that he is able to prophesy anything that may happen within the next few years; this patient considers that the weeks this year are only as long as three days of former years: it is all controlled by a machine in the basement of the hospital which regulates the physical universe; he has devised a new calendar to cope with the situation. In other patients, duration seems affected in the opposite sense: one said:

'I can't believe there are twelve hours in a day. I live twenty-five years in one year.'

The contradiction here is only apparent: the full statement would be, 'I live twenty-five years of my time in one year of world time, your time.' In others the fragmentation is impenetrable, e.g., 'Seems as if something in the air went by, you see what's next going to happen; puts me in distress. . . . What we've been talking, what we've been writing down, have to pull it up into Time, time, the clock'. And once she wrote spontaneously the words 'clock-time' though I had never used the expression to her. In these patients I could not demonstrate any objective time-disorder, again making use of Bouchard's tests.

A few words about mania and hysteria. In mania there is the subjective experience of capacity for rapid thinking and moving which is not confirmed by objective tests, with corresponding disproportion between personal time and world-time: 'I can think faster, I do everything faster. I feel as strong as a lion. . . . I asked just now what time it was and he said quarter past eleven. I expected it was twelve . . . it seems more than twelve days since I came here.'

Another patient: 'I think too quickly. Thousands and thousands of thoughts run through my mind. People don't seem to think quickly enough for me. I've always wanted to move quickly and other people move very slowly to my idea. I'm so full of beans and vitality. Time passes terribly quickly; only thing is it seems the opposite; at night I don't get to sleep and I long for life. . . . It seems rather long and monotonous.'

In mania the not infrequent disturbance of consciousness manifests itself in misidentification of the environment and setting up of secondary temporal relations:

'I know who you are; you're Mr Williams. You took my teeth out ten years ago.'

In the speech and conduct of the patient there are frequent reminders of the playful fantasy activity of children, already referred to. With regard to hysteria; in dissociation there may be a secondary time disorder; for example a patient with puerilism said:

'People all seem grown up and older. And my Mum, I'm sure I know her from a long time ago. I look at her, but I can't make it out.'

As to other hysterical manifestations, I may quote a patient who said when questioned about *déjà vu*:

'Oh, yes, I've noticed that. Tell you what I do have. Horrible feeling of the bed moving. Lasts about five or ten minutes, seems ages. As soon as I close my eyes I feel I'm either drifting along or going round and round. I feel it'll go on and on, it's like a trance. It seems a long time while I'm in it.'

Many hysterical patients report premonitions:

'Many times I know what people are going to say just before they say it, and if I go up to a crowd in the street I know what's happened. Yesterday I was in the street and I said to myself, "That lorry's going to turn over", and that very minute it ran into a 'bus in Exwell Street and fell over.'

These are, of course, not infrequent experiences in normal people, but when one asks hysterics routine vague questions about time, they commonly report this experience more frequently than other people. One of the striking features in the hysteric is that, although completely idle, many of them say that time goes quickly:

'Time seems to pass very quickly, to me it do. I get up of a morning and it seems no time before I go to bed again,'

said a man with gross conversion symptoms, who lived a day as devoid of outward incident as sitting on a chair by the fire could make it. This is comprehensible if one considers that it is an inability to fill time with the contents of choice that makes for boredom, or a slow passage of time; in the hysteric these conditions do not obtain.

I have endeavoured to give a very brief if superficial account of the main features that have emerged in an investigation of rather wide range. The whole matter seems to me one of great importance in psychopathology; and though I would not be understood to refer all morbid phenomena to a disorder of time-consciousness, I think it appears in and colours most of the manifold changes of the functional unity, which we agree to subdivide into perception, affect, and the rest of our fictions. It is a primary alteration of consciousness and may be found almost as often as it is looked for in mental disorder.

2

THE PSYCHOPATHOLOGY OF INSIGHT

ABOUT INSIGHT as a psychiatric problem little has been written; but in many places more or less casual evidence may be met with of prevalent notions which seem loose or ill-founded. In order to clear the ground a formal and necessarily incomplete essay is offered as a basis for further clinical study.

Insight is not a word of plain and single meaning. For a Gestalt psychologist it is an act or an ability to effect a direct configuration, a connected whole which is evident in the meaningful reaction to a stimulus-structure. Spearman seems to mean by it the quality in consciousness that attaches to belief based on adequate (self-experienced) evidence. In ordinary speech it refers to the quality by which we penetrate into the essence of things or happenings. In psychiatry, it is none of these things. Where its meaning is not assumed to be self-evident—and vague; or restricted to delusions, in which *ex hypothesi* it is impaired, it is said to cover 'the amount of realization the patient has of his own condition'—a quantitative relative judgment by the physician, expressed in such terms as 'total lack of insight', 'little real insight'; or a, often implicitly all-or-nothing, quality, a realization of the mental or 'nervous' nature of the illness, something which psychotics have not and neurotics have. A further usage, rare among psychiatrists, is to denote an appreciation by the patient of the presumed motives and genesis of his symptoms; this is sometimes called 'psychological insight'. In the textbooks the diversity of meaning attached to the word appears in the form of discrepant statements and even polemics.

It is therefore especially desirable to consider the antecedents of the word and the meaning to be attached to it. Originally it meant internal sight, i.e., seeing with the eyes of the mind, having inner vision and discernment. This is closely akin to the earlier meaning of the word 'consciousness' as the mind's immediate cognition of its own experiences. The French still use the same word for both. Later it was turned outwards and meant a mental regard or consideration of things, and so arose its current meaning 'the power of penetrating with the eyes of the understanding into the inner character or hidden nature of things'. Clearly the psychiatric usage is closer to the early

---

This article is reprinted from the *British Journal of Medical Psychology* (1934), **14**, 332–48.

than to the current meaning. It is concerned with looking inwards rather than looking outwards. I would offer as a temporary definition of insight for purposes of medical psychology and clinical medicine, that it is 'a correct attitude to a morbid change in oneself'. This definition is by no means final, needs much explanation and is here used chiefly as a convenient text. Each of the four terms—correct, attitude, morbid, change in oneself—calls for discussion.

For a patient to have an attitude towards changes in himself it is necessary that evidence of these changes shall be available to him. One could not have an attitude towards gangrenous changes in a limb, if the sources of information were cut off—if the affected limb were anaesthetic, one could not see or smell it, and no one spoke of it. Where there is a mental change—I use the dualistic word for obvious reasons—it must likewise be accessible to consciousness in some way if one is to have an attitude towards it. It may be said that consciousness has little to do with it; but we can judge insight only by the patient's behaviour and especially his utterances, i.e., his expressed attitude towards what is accessible to his knowledge—accessible but not necessarily present in consciousness. Of physical changes, there may be an immediate perception making use of the usual channels, or there may be judgments on secondary data, e.g., comments by others (as in ozaena) or difficulties in performance; reference to the two kinds of data may be expressed as 'there is a change' and 'there must be a change'.

Are morbid mental changes similarly accessible to consciousness? It is an old and familiar observation that we have an attitude—one of notice or regard—towards our own mental experiences; in other words, that they have a tendency to appear in consciousness, though not always, nor necessarily, nor in a differentiated form. We not only think or see but know that we think or see. Various factors have been invoked—a self-observing tendency such as Schilder and others described has been given various names—and there are philosophic and psychological battle grounds of all ages in this territory. I shall not enter into Professor Spearman's masterly presentation, nor into the subtle windings of some Theseus tracking the super-ego. I would only emphasize the possibility that with every mental activity—or act—there is an observing and registering of its apprehended quality apart from the material upon which the function in question is being exercised. Since of course mental activity is a fluid continuous happening, the observation may be correspondingly continuous, but subject to secondary isolation of temporally limited experiences; much of the dispute as to whether introspection must always be retrospective turns on this last point. It is relevant to the question of insight into past psychosis which I shall touch on later. At this point I would speak only of present mental happening. To take an example, I not only see a horse but I have a cognition of my seeing—a particular and to me familiar experience to which ordinarily I pay no heed. If I am a practised introspectionist, in certain circumstances I pay tremendous heed to this happening, ignoring for the most part the material of the function, i.e., the horse. If I have a mental disorder, the function may be disturbed, as is most strikingly seen in depersonalization: it is no longer the familiar happening but a changed one; the more sudden or extreme or unpleasant the change the more I will be perplexed by it or the more will I attend to it. Here the apprehension of the experience is an immediate datum of change. The apprehension of it in consciousness is not necessarily full, but it tells me a great deal of what the experience is, the changed experience; I am aware of it in itself as well as of its effects in the form of particular perceptions, thoughts, etc. To separate a psychic tendency from its material is as difficult as to distinguish form from content or function from structure, but it is the only way, I think, of doing justice to the experience of a dynamic process: in so far as the change extends to all experiences of the kind, the common quality of these represents the function. Restating what I have said: where there is a change of quality in mental functions there will also be a tendency to an awareness of this change (I say 'tendency' for much the same reasons as those of Spearman in the statement of his first noegenetic law). It is often said in discussing the findings of Külpe's pupils, and other introspection based on the Würzburg methods, that experience must be objectivated in order that it may be cognized, but I would prefer to say that for the apprehension of change, the immediate experience is subjective, and only with the attempt to describe it is there objectivation and so approximation to the secondary data to be referred to below.

There are, then, in some forms of mental disorder immediate data of change—some of them of somatic origin, others psychic, though developmentally all must be referred to bodily experience, and commonly both are experienced together and not differentiated. I know it may be urged that in mental disorder there is no change in quality of functions but only rearrangement, modification or regression. I do not accept this view, finding it unsatisfactory, or at any rate premature, to account for the phenomena of perverted function in terms of earlier stages of normal development; but even if it were so the change would still be experienced as a change from the familiar established happenings. I am not going so far, however, as to say that there is some change in quality of function in every mental disorder, nor even that it is invariably apprehended consciously in some degree when it exists. A lengthy clinical study such as I may later have opportunity of presenting in connexion with depersonalization and related states could alone deal with the range of such disturbances. I think the range is a very wide one. There are disorders in which the change is quantitative; there are others in which it has come on so gradually that there is no more awareness of it as change than we ordinarily have of our own non-abrupt developmental changes, say, of affect or cognition. It is a matter of general psychopathology. I said earlier that the suddenness and extent of the change and the unpleasantness accompanying it would be important in determining how far it reached consciousness. This is not a precise or exhaustive statement, but I have intentionally excluded as a factor the possible unconscious symbolic value and meaning of the function, because

I do not know of any evidence in favour of it, though of course there is a great deal to be said for the influence of this on the presentation in consciousness of the material of a function.

I have dealt with this question of immediate data at length because it is customary to assume that the acquiring or having insight is a matter of judgment. That is quite true, but it is also assumed that the judgment is exercised only on the same material as the physician or other observer uses for forming his opinion of illness or mental illness—which is false. That material is no doubt also available to the patient in large measure. But he has also these immediate data, accessible only to himself, and their importance is, I think, worth labouring. Insight is concerned primarily with the awareness of the change, and secondarily with the judging of this change, as to whether it is illness or demoniacal possession or insanity (which may not for him be the same thing as illness affecting chiefly his mind) or religious conversion or some other remarkable intervention.

In addition then to the immediate apprehension of a change in mode of function, it is possible to have what might be called secondary evidence of change in oneself—a lessened capacity to calculate, let us say (borne in upon one by mistakes at work or rebukes), or to make people interested in what one is saying—though I hope that is not always a sign of mental illness. The behaviour and social or other effects of this from which we ordinarily recognize a change in another person—all this is potentially available to the patient and is to be regarded as secondary evidence of change so far as he can observe and objectivate it.

From such data then, somatic and psychic together, the patient may arrive at a knowledge that he is changed. His communication of this knowledge is our first ground for assessing his insight or, more correctly, his requisite for insight. Much of his difficulty in describing the change will be due to the inadequacy of words to cover such unfamiliar experiences.

What is a correct attitude towards this change? It is commonly taken to consist of a realization of illness and, since it is psychiatry we are concerned with, a realization that the illness is mental. If we require this of the patient we must be clear as to what we mean ourselves when we speak of illness, mental or nervous abnormality, and what he means by it. Different groups of people have divergent conceptions in this matter.

The normal is either a statistical or an ideal conception. In neither case does it necessarily tally with the healthy. The statistical norm of mind is for the most part almost impossible of description because of the difficulty of measuring mental attributes. The ideal norm, say of Kant, would set up a canon of harmony, dependent on fluctuating non-experiential values, ethical or aesthetic, which would serve as a standard for comparison but not as an immediate empirical criterion of normality; it might be that no man would by such a standard be judged normal. If biological or social values be used for the ideal norm, it comes very close indeed to the conception of being healthy. Those qualities of reaction would then be regarded as normal which serve the end of appropriate adaptation to the environment. The better the adaptation the more definite the normality. Normality will then vary with local and temporal social conditions. Its scientific value is therefore restricted. A third view, to which Kronfeld calls attention, is that everything which follows natural laws is regarded as normal. But since the abnormal follows its own laws one must then say that that is abnormal which does not correspond to the laws determined for the majority of phenomena or for the commonest, the laws found to have the widest validity.

These are the three, on the whole unsatisfactory, norms—the statistical, the teleological and physical; it need hardly be said that in ordinary usage all enter into the words 'normal' and 'abnormal', and that they roughly cover each other. It is a normal attribute to consider oneself, one's permanent whole self, as approximately normal, though not necessarily as to detail. The changes referred to earlier in this paper will be regarded as deviations from this norm.

Abnormality, however, is not disease. A genius is abnormal, but he is not ill. A tiny well-set-up dwarf and a mystic have this in common, that they may be quite healthy but are quite abnormal. What then is the conception of the morbid, this variety of the abnormal? Let us consider first the higher ranges—the views of theorists and careful thinkers. Of physical conditions—and it is of these that most people think when they speak of illness—those will be called morbid in which abnormal cellular or humoral phenomena are accompanied or followed by discomfort, limitation of activity or danger to life. It is a teleological conception, arbitrarily making use of biological values. It does not admit of strict definition. What then is morbidity in the mental field? For some psychiatric theorists it is a matter of quantity—a mental anomaly becomes morbid only when it reaches a certain degree (Wilmanns); for others it is a value-concept (Wertbegriff): to be ill is to be from some point of view harmful, undesirable, inferior (Jaspers). Both these views may be combined as in Krapeelin's opinion that personal variations from the normal line of development can be called morbid when they acquire considerable (harmful) meaning for somatic or psychic life. Bleuler also arrives at this conclusion, putting emphasis on the social criterion. Clearly these are not precise definitions, any more than Allbutt's 'absolute health is an ideal conception . . . it is a positive conception of a perfect balance of the moving equilibrium which we call systemic life: disease is a negative conception and signifies something less than this perfect balance'. The difficulties of comprehensive, yet sharp, definition are well illustrated by the numerous controversies as to whether the psychopathies are to be regarded as mental disorders. The heated assertions about psychosis and neurosis are equally good evidence of the different and vague conceptions prevailing among psychiatrists regarding mental illness. It is clearly not otiose to discuss it now, since it is the psychiatrist who must judge a patient's insight by his realization of mental illness.

There is a discrepancy, not to say confusion, between everyday usage and scientific requirements. Neither has any time for the third or metaphysical conception, a denial of any distinction between health and illness, allied to which is the 'metapsychological' notion that 'normality may be a form of madness which goes unrecognized because it happens to be a good adaptation to reality'.

In ordinary life phenomena, whether physical or mental, are judged to be morbid on other than biological, or somatic pathological, or 'metapsychological' grounds. Physicians occupy an intermediate position, I think, between the public and the thinkers. Except in so far as they are captured by the current lay attitude, they regard those phenomena as morbid which conform to the descriptions in textbooks and the experience gained in hospitals and consulting rooms, reinforced by special knowledge or theories concerning the bodily changes and mental 'mechanisms' or developments; symptoms are signals to be evaluated according to their setting. But the non-medical layman has rather different attitudes towards illness, different notions of what is morbid. Moreover, his attitude towards physical disorders is not by any means the same as towards 'mental' ones. So far as the former are concerned he is an adherent of the school of Cnidos: the disease, the thing that comes from without, is the essential; it attacks, and symptoms are the means by which the victim becomes aware of its ravages. If one feels pretty well, without pain, able to do one's work, then one is healthy. Each disease is fixed by nature and is characterized by certain symptoms as an animal or a plant is characterized by its particular qualities. It is conceded that diseases may 'lurk in the system', but even in such cases a really good doctor would discover the appropriate symptoms. At any rate, many hold that until the disease makes itself felt by the patient in the sense of discomfort or limitation of activity he is not ill. Such a view has this much soundness in it, that it pays regard to the whole man, who is considered ill only when his full life is interfered with through bodily discomfort.

So much for the everyday, or everyman, view of physical illness. Mental illness is judged on different grounds. So far as madness is concerned it is doubtful whether, except among the better informed or the more reflective, it is regarded as illness at all in the sense commonly used, though lip service may be paid to the medical conception of it. It is still looked upon by large sections of civilized people as an obscure visitation often with implicit moral or social obloquy, to be ignored, laughed at, shunned or euphemized. Its manifestations are referred to an empirical standard of normality qualified by social criteria, and made up of daily experience of one's own mental activities and one's inferences as to the ordinary range of behaviour and the motives underlying it in the majority. Neither the murderer for gain nor the malingerer are commonly regarded as mad, since most persons can enter readily into their supposed or possible motives. It is useless to deny the existence of this everyday psychology. It is of course really a matter of *Uneinfühlbarkeit*: it is difficult to enter into strange kinds of mental activity or extreme exaggerations of familiar kinds. If the person's behaviour, though *uneinfühlbar*, be in conformity with that of a group of socially useful people, or have socially useful fruits, or even be socially unobtrusive, he is not described or (more correctly) stigmatized as insane. For the vulgar to say of a particular mystic that he is also insane is not to make parallel diagnoses using different values but to belittle his achievements. Intoxication with alcohol is not regarded as morbid because it is sufficiently common and within the range of personal experience to be easily entered into and 'understood'. When, however, it results in gross antisocial conduct the view of it as temporary insanity may be entertained, unless routed by ethical considerations. Similarly, odd types of personality are described as eccentric rather than mad unless extreme, incomprehensible or antisocial. Since these are the conceptions of madness which most patients bring to a consideration of changes in others or in themselves, it is not idle to consider them fully in a paper on insight.

It may be urged by some that a primitive experience of madness lingers in us as a trailing cloud from our 'panpsychotic' babyhood, and that it is not at all an attitude such as we have towards others that we use in judgments of ourselves when insane, but rather a primitive dark knowledge which comes more or less to consciousness. Such intimations of insanity from recollections of early childhood are a theme which I find it profitless to pursue.

So much for the popular notions of physical illness, and of madness. There is, however, the intermediate notion—'nervous'. Here structural changes in the nervous system, or varieties of personality are included: or the occurrence of symptoms familiar in disease where there is local structural damage, but here declared by doctors to be unaccompanied by such local lesions; or finally the term 'nervous' refers to mental abnormality either mild and more or less understandable in form, frequency and persistence, or else unaccompanied by striking changes in the personality. In short, it covers pronounced types of personality, mild mental abnormalities, and symptoms suggesting physical change but competently judged not to be due to them, i.e., symptoms without that concrete and palpable menace to life that there is in physical illness. Also of course it covers definite disease of the nervous system. If then we expect a patient to arrive at a conclusion that his illness is nervous, we are in many cases expecting a very remarkable exercise from him.

In asking for complete insight in any mental disorder we are setting the patient a very remarkable exercise indeed. It is an ideal requirement, impossible of attainment. What is complete insight?—'a correct attitude towards a morbid change in oneself'. We have considered what is a morbid change (in the patient's use of the related words for this), and how he may become aware of the change: also it is clear that we cannot expect of him anything more than that he should stand over against these changes, and with or without guidance arrive at an attitude towards them which lies somewhere between that of his associates or his former healthy self, and that of the physician: such an attitude is a 'correct' attitude. The psycho-analyst may expect an attitude ultimately much more like his own than would a psychiatrist whose treatment had been unlikely to make the patient acquainted with the particular theory of psychopathology illustrated in himself, and who would expect little more than that the patient's attitude should be that of an ordinary layman of his own sort, socially, intellectually, etc. But for everyone the criterion of the correctness of insight is the attitude of a non-affected person, whether it be physician, layman, or the patient when he is healthy. This I repeat is an ideal requirement.

Let us consider first the easier instance of a physical illness. It is commonly assumed that the ordinary person with a physical illness has 'complete insight', i.e., that he views his symptoms objectively as another person would. But everybody knows that this is not so and that people vary widely and inevitably in this respect. An identity of bare statement may be the only common ground—'I have such and such a physical illness,' 'He has such and such a physical illness': the attitudes, however, are necessarily far apart. The data on which opinion is formed are not the same for the sufferer as for others, nor can the phenomena be viewed with the same kind of detachment by him—I am sorry to labour anything so obvious. The familiar forces which are at work in one's attitude to oneself must here be effective—forces which are only in limited measure present in consciousness. There is no theory of psychopathology which can neglect the preponderant rôle of one's body in giving substance to consciousness and relevance to reality. It is not to be supposed that a significant change in the body can leave the mind just as it would be if there were no such change. The patient's deference to the opinion of others, especially doctors, his concern about the effects of an avowal of his attitude in the face of what he recognizes to be a different attitude on the part of those round him, and his inadequacy or economy of language, may give a false impression of complete insight. But there are numerous instances of grossly defective insight in physical disorders. Spes phthisica may be the last rare striking manifestation of a year-long peculiarity of attitude to chronic tuberculosis. A physician (L. P. Mark) has related how for fifteen or twenty years he remained blind to the patent acromegaly which confronted him every morning in the mirror as he shaved, and of which all his friends were aware. Gibbon thought nobody knew of the hernia and hydrocele which hung conspicuously down to his knees. Failure to appreciate hemianopsia or monocular blindness is fairly common—I saw only recently a boy with advanced optic atrophy who insisted, in spite of evidence, that he had some vision in the blind eye, and that it was improving. Such failure to appreciate blindness, deafness or paralysis has been reported in focal lesions of the brain by many observers, and the condition has its own name among neurologists. Phantom arm is a relevant phenomenon. Guttman has referred, and so has Mayer-Gross, to the defective appreciation of symptoms that is common in frontal lesions. It is not sufficient to explain such phenomena only as psychogenic: there is a physiological disturbance of cerebral function, interfering with the integration of the contributory or part function. This is not to deny the concomitant familiar psychic influences such as have been described in innumerable books and papers.

Now it may be said that physical illness is commonly a response to an external noxa, and the patient has an attitude only to the (physiological) effects in himself of this noxa, whereas in mental illness it is from himself that the symptoms spring, from his mind and its appetencies as it were, and that his attitude to such mental happenings will be influenced by his unconscious knowledge of the motivation of the symptoms. Brill has written a paper on unconscious insight. Hollós and Ferenczi have investigated it in general paralysis. This would be paralleled as to physical disorders by the extreme views, say, of Groddeck. But this view has no force unless a coherent and comprehensible psychopathology, in terms of unconscious and conscious, is available and is held to represent the whole of the psychic happenings. This is a view I do not hold. The distinction is fundamental. If all psychic phenomena are the expression of forces which transform experience, invest it with equivalent (symbolic) significance in a vast 'unconscious' which is at any rate a field of 'knowing' in some sense, and of storing, then apprehension including judgment of illness will be through a more or less distorted arrival into consciousness of an 'unconscious' presentation of these 'unconscious' happenings. This is not what I have supposed to be the case. In the literature of psycho-analysis I can find no clear expression of the supposed relations in such a case, and even if there were such a clear view its clarity would not argue cogency.

The data of change are limited, I think, to those I have mentioned earlier. So far as immediate vague awareness of a mental change is expressed—'I don't know what's come over me', 'I feel my mind is going'—these, I would emphasize, refer to a contrast or change in the quality of experienced function, not to the appearance of a lasting unconscious capacity for the recognition of certain 'psychotic' motivations. Also in mental disorder there are the data not so immediate, which are in some measure available to the patient as they are to others, e.g. paralysis, stammer, perverse behaviour, etc.

The way in which the patient describes these data or communicates his judgment on their significance will depend of course partly on his words. I saw lately, for example, an obsessional patient who assured me that his trouble must be 'mental'—'it's not natural thinking, all these foreign thoughts oughtn't to enter a man's mind, or he ought to be able to fling them off. It's as if I was possessed. And I am asking myself all the time why, when and wherefore. I feel different. I am not as other men are. I think it's mental because I do such silly tricks. It's a slight form of insanity of course; I think there's a very small margin between sanity and insanity.' Here is a man offering two interpretations of his changed experience—insanity, or possession; he chooses the former, as in other days and countries he might have chosen the latter. But when I went on to express surprise that he should regard himself as crazy, he repudiated this and said that by 'mental' and 'insane' he didn't mean that at all, he was very far from considering himself mad. Another patient, who spoke both languages, called his condition in English 'some obsessional trouble', but in German he called it 'Verfolgungswahn'. Into the patient's verbal expression of his attitude to his condition will enter all the modifying influences familiar in Aussage-psychology and in psycho-analytic studies.

But it is not only to his verbal expression we will pay heed; we will observe his demeanour and see how far it corroborates or gives the lie to his statements. It is to his total attitude, possibly over a long period, and not to his verbal statements or his so-called intellectual acceptance of a point of view that we pay attention.

To summarize the modifying factors above alluded to is not easy. Nor are they only those familiar in Aussage-psychology or psycho-analytic studies. That would be to accept the view that the whole of disturbed mental function is describable in terms of so-called normal or more properly healthy functions.

In any mental disorder, whether mild or severe, continued or brief, alien or comprehensible, it is with his whole disordered mind that the patient contemplates his state or his individual symptoms, and in this disorder there are disturbances which are different from the healthy function either in degree, combination or kind. The hysteric brings to bear on his symptoms, or on his whole illness, a hysterical mind, not a healthy mind with a limited separable disturbance; in such a condition as a Ganser syndrome, the necessity for this view is evident. The obsessional brings his repetitive self-torturing mind to bear on his condition and his individual symptoms. The schizophrenic, the manic or depressive patient, the general paralytic, all contemplate their apprehensive change with that disturbed mind which we subdivide into disturbed memory, disturbed thinking, disturbed affectivity, disturbed perception, disturbed will or what not. The emphasis may lie more on one than another disturbed function, but always there will be a disturbance which makes it impossible for the patient to look at his data and judge them as we, the dispassionate, presumably healthy outsiders do. His judgments and attitude can therefore never be the same as ours because his data are different, and his machine for judging is different in some respects. You will see that if one undertakes to discuss insight in schizophrenia, say, in any detail, one must consider not only data of change in this condition, but also the whole psychopathology of schizophrenia, especially where it enters into the judgment of reality. All questions of the judgment of reality, such as are often introduced into the consideration of insight, go to the root of the psychopathology of different conditions and it is not possible to discuss them here.

You will also see that statements about a person with some mental disorder having 'complete insight' are loose and almost extravagant, except as clinical shorthand. If it be said that they are approximations and that a verbal concordance with the physician's or the unaffected comparable layman's opinion about the disorder is all that has been required, or that 'a rough notion of the patient's sanity of judgment, or commonsense attitude towards his illness, is all one wants', well and good. But it must be recognized that that is no more than convenient clinical practice and has only qualified right of admission into psychopathology.

I have been so remiss in giving any of the clinical material or particular investigations on which my views rest that I should like now to make slight amend by a few purely clinical observations. An eminent English psychiatrist has said that insight is an absolutely infallible and subtle touchstone for distinguishing neurosis from psychosis. Since I regard this distinction between neurosis and psychosis as false in principle and sometimes misleading in practice, I should not examine the use of insight in making it if I did not find the view so often the parent of confusion to beginners in psychiatry. They stumble over insight and then ask posers about whether something is not 'really psychotic' or 'only a neurosis'. It is I think correct to say that gross disorders of insight are often found in neuroses—to use the familiar word. The obsessional's attitude towards his illness or to any special symptoms is vastly different from that of his wife, or his friend, or his doctor: and one must, like Stoddart, narrow down insight to a mere question of delusion and coherence of thought, if one is going to say that the obsessional's insight is complete. As for the hysteric—who would suppose that a girl with dermatitis artefacta has a healthy or normal attitude towards her symptom? the same may be said of the man with a 'shell shock' tremor, or of any other of the manifold exhibitors of hysterical illness. Similarly with patients whose anxiety is extreme. If on the other hand one considers the familiar psychoses—schizophrenia and the affective group—one often finds a relatively good insight, in the usual clinical usage of the term. Thus in a patient with severe acute mania, whose record I selected at random, I found the following statements, 'You see, I haven't been sleeping very well, that's sheer excitement you know, and, I went to my bath, I was shoebathed by my father. I am muddled. I've got such a lot to think about. I want to do a tremendous lot on very little. There's no time like the present. I'm a bit nervous, of course I am, examination, pulling yourself to bits.' Another recurrent manic patient said, 'I am hot, hot, strong . . . beware, where. Don't know what I'm doing again. . . . Have to keep on, oh the numbers. Have to keep on, one to be ready, two to be steady, three to be off. . . . You're going too quickly now, you're going too slowly now, look out . . . the answer is three words, don't be silly, don't be absurd. You're saying it too quickly. Oh Lord I'm awful. . . . I've lost my own self. I feel it in my chin. Don't look at me so hard, don't, listen. To listen you've got to stop yourself. Didn't I tell you, you've got to tread on it. Oh you fool, and using the bull. The wrong end of the stick I've got hold of it, you are a fool today.' Deron, among several instances in his monograph on mania, quotes Mlle Et. who, after expressing her satisfaction at the great activity of her mind, added 'Je ne suis pas normale, je pense tout haut'. On the other hand I had a depressed patient who talked a lot, and continually commented on her own loquacity, e.g., 'I was talking all night. I'm like a clock. I stop for a while and then I start again.' As regards depressive states I may quote here from an investigation published elsewhere, which I made into a number of such patients. Of sixty-one, selected at random, twenty declared or even protested that they were not ill, that there was no need whatever for them to be in hospital; nine said they had physical ailments but not mental or nervous ones; eighteen conceded illness but would not discuss its nature, and fourteen considered they had some mental or nervous disorder. But such figures in themselves mean little. One patient said 'I'm not ill. My nerves are very strong, it's not nerves,' and she also said 'Perhaps I'm a little mad, hadn't I better be put in an asylum?'; another said 'There isn't really anything the matter with me,' but also 'I wonder if I shall get all right again'; another 'I'm not ill, I just have this nervous breakdown'; another 'I didn't come here as a patient', yet almost in the same breath she added 'I imagined things'; another 'I'm not ill at all, there's nothing wrong with me', and yet also 'I must be daft'; still another, 'It's not illness but I am afraid I'll lose my reason.'

A statement 'I must be mad' or 'I ought to be in an asylum' is, however, not necessarily evidence of good insight: it may rest on characteristic disturbances of affect, severe anxiety, self-reproach; and is not far from the other interpretation, offered by one of these patients, 'It's not illness but sin, or perhaps possession.' One may get such convoluted statements as 'The whole truth is, the brain's all right but the nerves aren't. I haven't any control over it. I feigned I was mad. It's an imaginative complaint, hysteria,' or 'My head's gone wrong but I am sane enough to talk of it. I ought to be killed like a mad dog.' Sometimes in depressed patients a clear and painful insight takes the place of some illusion with which they have lived happily, and their judgment of themselves as well as of their present state has nothing to controvert it except the limiting effect upon their daily activity. I am tempted to go into details of depressed patients' attitudes towards individual symptoms, especially delusion, but it is recorded elsewhere.

Similarly the clinical aspects of insight in schizophrenia call for most detailed consideration, such as I must deny myself in this paper. The phenomenological studies into this disorder contain many arresting examples of insight. It is, moreover, the common experience of psychiatrists that, at the onset of the disorder, the insight of the patient is sometimes considerable and is associated with a struggle against the illness that is tragic. Here is an account written by a boy of 18 years who has had a definite schizophrenic illness for at least a year; he has much depersonalization also. He writes:

'I am more and more losing contact with my environment and with myself; instead of taking an interest in what goes on and caring about what happens with my illness, I am all the time losing my emotional contact with everything, including myself: what remains is only an abstract knowledge of what goes on around me and of the internal happenings in myself. . . . Even this illness which pierces to the centre of my whole life I can regard only objectively. But on rare occasions I am overwhelmed with the sudden realization of the ghastly destruction that is caused by this creeping uncanny disease that I have fallen a victim to. . . . My life has something unreal, strangely unnatural about it now. . . . This dead emotionless attitude towards myself is almost as though I were protecting my nature against myself. With the numbing of my feelings I am as though half drugged: only in the rare accesses of anxiety I awake from this dream life and with torturing clearness I become aware of my actual state. . . . My despair sometimes floods over me. But after each such outburst I become more indifferent. I lose myself more in the disease,

I sink into an almost oblivious existence. My fate when I reflect upon it is the most horrible one can conceive of. I cannot picture anything more frightful than for a well-endowed cultivated human being to live through his own gradual deterioration fully aware of it all the time. But that is what is happening to me.'

I should like to quote briefly from a record of another schizophrenic patient, who showed very well the changes in insight that can occur within the space of a single interview. He said:

'I thought I heard voices saying always the same thing, wondering whether I was a Jew, or whether I was a fool. It worried me. There have been days lately when I have felt these voices. I seem to hear some sort of a voice in the distance calling. I have often thought they were obsessions, that I had thought myself into it: that I was looking out for the voices. I could never really realize. . . . My nerves were in such a bad state that I really could not, what shall I say, couldn't find the mental background to force these obsessions out of my head. I think I'd call it 'Verfolgungswahu.' . . . I thought people from the boat had come along and told that story that I was a Jew and I was a fool. I never knew whether that was an obsession of mine or whether it actually existed. . . . This morning I felt as if I was hypnotized. . . . The man in the next bed. I thought it was him and then I thought he had changed completely, then I thought "Oh yes it is", but in a minute I thought "No it couldn't be. . . ." My illness is purely mental. I got into such a nervous state. I got terribly sensitive to outside influences. I feel the voices throb through my brain.'

A few minutes later in the middle of a conversation about banking—he was a banker—he asked me if I had heard someone call out 'Otto' just then, asked me if I was a police doctor; his appearance changed greatly, he appeared frightened and dejected and said, 'I had a terrible feeling, I thought my mother was dead. I heard a voice say in my ear "Mother."' Asked if there was anything in it really, he answered, 'No, I just got that impression. I do get these funny sort of feelings, sometimes.' A few minutes later in great agitation he said, 'I want to give myself up to the police at once, I feel I am not safe, I'll not leave this house alive.'

And here we have at brief intervals a considerable change in the immediate data associated with a change of attitude. It is closely connected with the primary uprush of beliefs, with immediate convictions—autochthonous ideas, such as Wernicke described and to which Targowla has recently devoted an interesting monograph *L'intuition délirante*. It would be going too far afield to discuss the factors which effect the change of attitude. But what is seen here, in the moments of what one would call clinically 'more insight', can be regarded as indicating a retrospective attitude towards recent morbid data. This question of retrospective insight is of great importance clinically, since upon it often depend questions of recovery and further prognosis. Willis, over a century ago, said that no one could be regarded as healthy until he voluntarily acknowledged his aberration. Such a view is still widely held not only with regard to schizophrenia but also to depressive states, paranoid ones, toxic confusional episodes and others. It has repeatedly been pointed out that such a general view is not justified, but it has sufficient truth in many cases to ensure its continuance, though sometimes harsh and cruel results follow its application. Neither the true clinical state of affairs, nor the psychopathology of retrospective insight can be gone into now. I have made investigations into it in affective states which I may later be able to communicate.

Omitting the complicated issues that arise in organic psychoses—and who can deny that they will be complicated when it is considered that aphasia enters into them, the very emblem of much-explored obscurity—omitting these and any discussion of the remarkable material which states of depersonalization offer, I would close these prolegomena with a reference to a common assumption that is not entirely justified. The bearing of insight on treatment has been stressed by many. It has been maintained that where there is good insight, psychotherapy is likely to be successful and the converse is held also to obtain. But the patients who complain most of their symptoms, or have the most 'objective' attitude towards them, are by no means those who co-operate best, or, co-operating, ride into harbour. Far be it from me at this hour to lay down criteria for successful psycho-therapy, but one might say in the most general way that defective insight in itself is no criterion for this purpose, and may be even the sign of an attitude towards health, a turning away from the evidence of ill-health, a repudiation of disease, which is an advantage in treatment. In such issues, however, as turn on the patient's willingness to come into hospital or to stay there, his insight may be an important, and even a determining factor.

As is perhaps clear from my little clinical orgy at the end, I have imposed a reluctant self-denial on myself in the earlier theoretical part of this paper. Such self-denial seemed necessary if the basis for any clinical study of insight was to be stated within the limits of a paper along the general lines that appear to me indispensable. I should be the last to suggest for these views finality or completeness.

3

MELANCHOLIA: A CLINICAL SURVEY OF DEPRESSIVE STATES

THE FOLLOWING examination of the clinical features of depressive states is based on the detailed study of 61 cases examined and treated by the writer at the Maudsley Hospital, London.

The diagnosis of 'depressive state' had been made finally after the discharge of the patient; each of them had been seen first either in the out-patient department, or in private by a competent psychiatrist, the case had been presented at a clinical conference, and a diagnosis reached after discussion; in many cases the patient had been presented on more than one occasion, the ultimate diagnosis representing the considered view of the medical staff of the hospital. By 'depressive state' has been understood a condition in which the clinical picture is dominated by an unpleasant affect, not transitory, without evidence of schizophrenic disorder (other than slight or subordinate) or organic disorder of the brain, and in which, moreover, the affective change appears primary, not secondary to other symptoms of ill-health. It was therefore in part diagnosis by exclusion; in so much as symptomatic depressive states, occurring in the course of such disorders as general paralysis of the insane, present no positive characters, *qua* depressive, to distinguish them from the depressive reactions here considered, it seemed preferable to limit the inquiry to those in which the disorder seemed primary.

This is essentially an examination of the clinical features of depression. It has formed part of a larger investigation in which especial attention has been paid to the relation of pre- and post-psychotic personality to the symptoms of the actual illness, and in which genetic, constitutional and prognostic factors have been considered. Many aspects of this have called for a much larger series of cases, to permit of statistical examination, but the present cases were selected for special study of the clinical features; they include all the depressive patients who were examined and treated by the writer during

---

This paper was reprinted from the *Journal of Mental Science* (April 1934), **80**, 277–378. For reasons of space the detailed case histories which are referred to in the text by initials have been omitted.

part of the years 1928 and 1929. The purpose of the investigations having at first been towards the investigation of personality, special studies, mainly along the lines suggested by Hoch and Amsden, were made by the writer and by social workers under his direction; in no other respect was the investigation and observation of the patients governed by any concern with particular aspects of the illness; the records may therefore be considered to reflect only the general attitude and preconceptions of American and English psychiatrists, and at such points as the conclusions differ from these, it has been because the data imposed the divergence rather than because it was expected or sought after.

The studies, above alluded to, of personality and the genetic and prognostic aspects of depressive illness are not included here. The separation is a difficult one, and it has frequently proved necessary to introduce such matters. The general attitude of the writer to the dynamic aspect of the disorder may be gathered from the concluding section on 'Reaction, Psychogenesis'. There seems, however, still to be much that calls for investigation in the actual clinical picture; one must collect one's data before one sets about accounting for them or interpreting them, and it is to this preliminary object that the following is devoted.

MOOD

The affective change is justly regarded as the central feature of depression. Mania and melancholia are the 'affect-psychoses' which 'possess as a common fundamental element a pathological variation of the affective tone which reveals itself in the two contrasted syndromes' (Lugaro). This view, common to English and American psychiatrists and generally accepted in Germany, is scarcely held in France: Benon, for example, writes: 'Pour nous le mot dépression a la même signification que le mot "asthénie". Il s'agit là de troubles non pas d'ordre "thymique", mais d'ordre "sténique"; la clinique, notre unique secours, est sur ce point claire, précise, démonstrative' ('For us the word depression has the same meaning as the word asthenia. It is a question of sthenic, not of thymic, disorders. Clinical experience, which is here our only help, is clear, precise and conclusive on this point'). Delmas defines melancholia as a psychosis characterized clinically by 'la dépression de l'activité psychique et motrice, se manifestant sur un fond d'humeur triste' ('depression of psychic and motor activity, showing itself on a basis of sad mood'), but of this 'humeur triste' he remarks that it is essentially a disorder of coenaesthesia; the painful coenaesthetic state is the fundamental and primitive symptom of the affection; all the feelings of sad mood come from this, and on the other hand the mood change may be insignificant in relation to other manifestations of disordered coenaesthesia. In order that such apparently diverse views may be reconciled, it is necessary to consider that affectivity (Bleuler), like other more or less arbitrary divisions of psychic life, is only a special aspect of the total activity of the organism; and the less one attempts to analyse or define the total 'feeling', the 'biotonus' (Ewald) of the organism, and to separate mental and bodily functions, emotional and vegetative, the more natural is the observation, and the freer from implications of any theory. However much psychologists may dispute about 'emotion', 'feeling', 'affect', 'coenaesthesia', and other words—the Wittenberg symposium on 'Feelings and Emotions' is sufficient evidence of their divergent view—the plain man is in no doubt of what is meant when he is asked how he feels, what his mood is, whether he is in good spirits or low-spirited, nor has he uncertainty about the meaning of such words as 'miserable', 'sad', 'downhearted', 'down in the dumps'. In the following account only the patient's spontaneous utterances about his mood, or his reply to the neutral questions 'How do you feel?' 'What is your mood?' 'How are your spirits?' 'How do you feel in your spirits?' are given. Such questions as 'Are you happy?' 'Are you sad or melancholy or out of sorts or worried?' (suggested by Henderson and Gillespie) have been eschewed since they offer the patient a choice of words, instead of letting him find his own description.

18 patients said that they were 'miserable'; some said 'utterly miserable' ; others 'more miserable than ever'. Many said, 'I feel dreadful, I'm so miserable,' W. C. said, 'I feel miserable; I don't want to talk much.' L. C. added that she was worried, F. H. that she felt a failure and didn't want to live, R. H. that he felt helpless, abandoned, hopeless; R. J. that she felt lonely, I. M. that she was 'so low-spirited', A. E. N. that she had nothing to live for, and felt she just wanted to go to sleep and never wake up, D. N. that she was broken-hearted, and another that he felt run down. 10 patients' main complaint was that they felt 'worried'. To this, various other statements were added: Of being sad, of 'feeling like crying all day long', of feeling frightened, of being muddled; D. C. said also: 'I feel dreadful. I've been badgered and worried and shut up in myself and irritated and frightened. I'm frightened because I'm afraid I'm mad.' Hopelessness was the chief complaint of 5 patients. 'I don't want to live; I've got nothing to live for; I'd like to die' was the chief feeling expressed by 9 cases. Other words used to describe how the patient felt were 'sad and lonely', 'unhappy', 'low-spirited', 'despondent' or 'down-hearted', 'discontented', 'fed-up', 'melancholy', 'awful in myself, in agony'. I. W. said only, 'I feel dirty.' Many would only answer to the above questions, 'I feel I want to go home; I want to be at home'; others that they felt dazed, dizzy, muddled, and two said that they felt 'queer'.

As Lange remarks, patients rarely complain of anxiety, compared with the frequency of its presence, judged by other criteria than the patient's description of his mood: 'Anxiety in some form or other is part of the mood very often, oftener indeed than one would gather from the spontaneous utterances of the patient.' A great number of the patients also described themselves as 'depressed', but one is inclined to think that this is a 'doctor's word', one like 'neurasthenic' or 'deluded', which would not spring to the lips of most people unless they had learnt from medical books and doctor's questions to think it the sort of word one should use in talking to a doctor. It is certainly much more commonly used among in-patients and old out-patients than among out-patients at their first visit. Some of the patients use minimizing expressions or litotes—'I'm not very bright, really'; 'I'm a bit low-spirited' —though their demeanour betrays the extreme of dejection and gloom.

Most writers lay stress on feelings of unreality and loss of interest as part of the mood change; few patients in this series, however, mentioned them in this connexion, unless directly questioned on the point; they are considered in another connexion below.

E. R. F., however, said: 'I seem to be different, to have no feeling at all. My body is tense. I'm frightened and nervous of something happening.' R. D. said: 'I don't really feel myself. I feel lonely.' H. D. H.: 'I feel shut up in myself. I feel things have come to a climax.' E. A.: 'It's this nervous feeling I've got in my stomach, like I've had when I was frightened. This awful nervous feeling as if I shall go out of my mind. I feel unhappy. I shall never be happy again. I've lost control.' E. J. F. said: 'I feel restless, I feel nervous, I feel I'm not wanted.' F. B. declared herself 'desperate, miserable. I'd rather be out of the world. When I speak to anyone, I feel better.' A. H. said: 'I feel miserable; the other patients hate me and make life miserable.' L. W., whose manner was hostile and resentful, said: 'Everything gets on my nerves.' M. B.: 'I'm fed up with work and everything else. I'm thoroughly miserable. Life is too much bother.' J. G.: 'I'm utterly miserable, of course, beyond description.' B. J.: 'I'm depressed, I've conflicting emotions.'

These are, in detail, the patients' statements about how they felt. The other and complementary method of judging mood is by observing the patient's expression and behaviour. Facial expression of emotion is more easily recognized than described; analysis of it, feature by feature, omega-figures, Veraguth folds, and such details, after the manner of Kirchhoff, is less informative than a single glance or a word of description. Behaviour is, so far as depression goes, a matter of posture and motor activity; the latter will be considered in connexion with 'retardation', 'agitation' and 'stupor'; the posture is drooping and slack for the most part, unless there be also agitation or apprehension. It has not seemed necessary to reproduce at length from the records the detailed descriptions of the emotional expression in the patients here considered, but to extract from them a few descriptive terms which connote familiar pictures.

Thus, in 10 cases, the patient's expression was predominantly apprehensive or scared; E. J. F. sat up habitually, looked startled, with wide eyes and half-open mouth; A. C. sat up in bed, looking gloomily expectant; anxiety, tenseness, disquiet was evident in the face and bearing of 21 cases. R. J. looked forlorn, E. G. D. and F. N. were gloomy, D. P. and C. W. were glum; dejection was striking in 7 cases ('a picture of misery') and unsmiling solemnity ('deadly serious') described the expression of 5; in 3 there was an aspect of weary resignation; bewildered, puzzled, irresolute is the description at times of another 6; M. H. and E. T. looked absorbed 'turned inwards', while there was mostly an expression of alertness in 7 patients, as though they were well in touch with their surroundings, interested.

Weeping is mentioned as occurring in 33 patients. This list includes only two of the twelve male patients—R. D., a boy, and A. H., who was effeminate in other respects. B. J. in moments of the utmost grief and misery clenched his hands and groaned and clutched his hair, but did not weep. Lessing, whose *Laokoon* might be used as a Thesaurus of classical descriptions of grief, has written of this sexual difference, 'I know we Europeans of a more refined age know how to control our mouths and eyes better. Politeness and decorum forbid screaming and tears. The active bravery of an earlier, rougher age has changed to a more passive fortitude' and he goes on to compare the attitude of the Greeks and Romans to our own in this matter of men weeping. The general rule that in severe melancholic states there is no secretion of tears (Doering) was exemplified in many cases of this series not included in the above list. Thc only one, however, actually to complain of her inability to shed tears was E. R. F.; M. B. said at the beginning of her illness that if she could have cried, she would not have got into such a state. G. S. whined continually, and J. C. moaned. Smiling is not usually associated with sadness, but there were many patients who would give a mirthless smile, either of social response if one smiled at them, or of unamused recognition of the funny side of something that was said or that happened; e.g., J. G. had said that people looked like monkeys; when the physician replied, 'Look at me, then; do I look like a monkey?' she smiled. Similarly M. S. and E. B.; whereas in M. B. it was a much more bitter smile, of the kind that Kraepelin has described, 'The patients at times develop a certain grim humour; they jeer and mock at their own complaints, and with an angry laugh call themselves dolts and donkeys,' the others of whom he wrote 'we are often taken aback by a forlorn smile, a sudden gaiety' were more numerous—10 cases. One of them, D. P., at a time when she was very depressed and hopeless, played the trick on a stiff and stand-offish nurse of putting her boiled egg-shell upside down in the egg-cup to make it appear she had not eaten the egg.

It is of importance to see what relation the patient's statements about his mood bear to the expression of it in face and bearing. There are such wide variations in normal people between their appearance and their statement of how they feel that it is only where the discrepancy is pronounced that one could draw any conclusion in morbid depression. Such a discrepancy was observed in 5 patients. W. G. thumped the table and looked angry while declaring he was wicked and worthless and a coward; R. H. waved his arms about and declaimed like a stump orator, 'I feel miserable; what is there in life for me? I wish I were dead. . . . I ought to be killed like a mad dog.' F. N., though looking very gloomy, would become alert and attentive when addressed, and always appeared cheerful to the nurses; while still saying he felt miserable, he fell in love with one of the nurses and made himself so agreeable to her that she thought him quite recovered. R. S., while saying that he could not get a moment's peace of mind, that he felt all of a stew, that he couldn't keep still, actually lay quietly in bed, resigned-looking but calm and able to smile at a joke, though without amusement. E. W. looked less apprehensive than a person should who was expecting to be tried and put to death, though one had to make allowance for the grandiose strain in her talk. In the opposite way, L. W. would declare she was all right when her aspect belied it, sullen, almost mute, making no other movements of expression than a shrug of the shoulder or a lifting of the eyebrows. H. C., though he professed himself, and in his face looked, depressed, had a self-possessed easy manner, put his feet on the rung of the physician's chair and leant on the table. There was another group of patients who said they felt very miserable, but there were times when they would laugh and look quite cheerful; also they would weep copiously; this lability of mood, with emphasis by the patient on its depressive features, was seen in 5 patients.

It is clearly necessary to consider both what the patient says and how he looks before deciding on the mood change; there may be a quantitative discrepancy (due to exaggerated language or to an unexpressive face, immobile or wooden, as in I. M.) or a qualitative difference (as in W. G.); there is not the qualitative difference, however, that may be observed in schizophrenia; instead of humility and sadness the demeanour may proclaim resentment and self-assertion, but there is no smiling when talking of misery and persecution, nor apathy in the face of impending horrors.

The affect in depressive states is always unpleasant, lasting and apparently primary; it is the expression of the whole state of the organism, or in more psychological terms, 'the complex qualities of the experienced totality' ('Erlebnisqualitäten des Gesamtganzen', Krueger), and distinctions between its 'mental' and 'physical' aspects are artificial. The visceral and autonomic changes are part of a total reaction in which the 'psychical' elements are equally primary, and one hesitates to accept such views of emotion as that explicit in Aveling's definition; 'Emotion is the massive and generally wholly unclear experience of coenaesthesio-kinaesthetic sensation.' Intellectual and affective changes are too closely intermingled to permit in psychopathology of that abstraction of single elements which psychologists make; the ordinary man says, 'I feel run-down', 'I feel rotten', 'I feel good for nothing today', and he is making no distinction between his body and his mind; he is describing the whole of himself as he is aware of it; nor can we impute fundamental importance either to the changes in his vegetative system, adrenalin output, kinaesthetic sensation, or to his appreciation of difficult environmental situations recently experienced or now confronting him. In this sense the change in the process of thought and the change in motor activity of the depressed patient are parts of his total affective state, only for purposes of exposition and description to be regarded as secondary; just as much parts of his facial and general expression, his visceral changes, his feeling of gloom or apprehension. Pleasure and discomfort ('unpleasure'), tension and relaxation, excitement and depression are the general features to which, as it were, content and differentiation are given by the external and internal situation. An undifferentiated anxiety is so often met with in these patients, presently given form and individuality by personal experience; the vague dread becomes a dread of being tortured on the rack, or of having a cancer in the gut. The attribution of energy to emotion making it the dynamic force of the organism is common; the most detailed development of this 'economic' view along special lines is the psycho-analytic theory. It is not appropriate here to consider this highly conceptualized structure. It must be pointed out that in the opposition 'excitement' and 'depression' there is no implication that in one energy is most manifest, and in the other least; any but superficial observation reveals in the melancholic an increase of affective excitability (for painful affect) in which only the motor component is lacking; and if agitation be also evident, then even the motor component is seen. A patient like M. B. continually gave the impression, for all her quietness, of energy thwarted and misdirected, if such vague words and impressions may be used; there was neither in her nor in the others that apathy which appears to betoken a withdrawal or damping down of energy, but rather an energy (of self-reproach and striving or resenting) which could not be overlooked. So far as energy is concerned—allowing for the vagueness of the concept—there is nothing surprising in a change from melancholia to mania. Kretschmer, however, has pointed out that melancholics may lose their excitability for painful stimuli: 'In contrast to mania the melancholic does not always, as his mood becomes gloomier, show a greater responsiveness to sad events; the depressive inhibition usually overlies this excitability, and so often makes him peculiarly and paradoxically unresponsive to painful external experiences (e.g., deaths and the like), while the patient's subjective feeling is one of emotional unresponsiveness, of inward dullness and deadness'. But there is here some confusion of thought. The 'painful external experiences' must be sad happenings not in the eyes of the observer or for the healthy person, but for the patient in his present state; and if this distinction be remembered, there is nothing paradoxical in the patient's apparent unconcern on learning of the death of someone for whom he now feels only hatred, or who is of little moment to him amid the tremendous and catastrophic happenings on which he is now centred. If one tries to force food on such a patient, or otherwise impose experiences that are painful in the sense of running counter to his present tendencies and wishes, there is no lack of evidence that he is excessively responsive; it will presently be seen that, in this series at any rate, so-called depressive stupor never manifested itself in a complete submissiveness and failure in motor response. As for the patients who complain that they have no feeling, in the sense of emotional response to visits from relatives, etc. (or even in the other meaning of the word, bodily sensation, depersonalization), there is still a distress over this 'absence of feeling' which marks it as something other than a mere withdrawal or lack of response.

As to affective nuances, such as may be gathered from the above record of the patient's statements and expression, these are individual colourings given to the general states of unpleasantness and tension; the latter may be regarded as the primitive and constant feature of all depressive states. 'Psychologists still speak of the emotions as if they were discrete entities. . . . This is, of course, an anachronistic view. The emotions constitute a polydimensional continuum, in which we arbitrarily and for convenience designate certain ranges by certain names and ignore the remaining ranges. Fear, for example, is a qualitatively variable emotion. . . . The limitations of language are probably responsible for the consideration of the more common names as if they designated unique emotional elements' (Knight Dunlap).

Anxiety and feelings of unreality, loss of interest and depersonalization are considered separately later.

OUTPUT OF TALK

There is here a wide range, from constant chatter to complete muteness. There are 22 patients who talked a great deal. It is a common observation, at any rate upon those with mental disorder, that women talk more than men; the female 'acute ward' is usually by far noisier than the male, and the preponderance of women among these 61 cases may account in part for so high a proportion of loquacious patients.

In the earlier controversies about 'mixed states' it was often maintained that a greater output of activity, both in general movements and in talk, indicated a manic admixture in the depressive state (Specht, Thalbitzer, Dreyfus), and in at least two of the cases reported here a diagnosis of mania had been made by a competent observer. This can, however, not be conceded; where the content of the talk is depressive, where the form is mainly reiterative, the object apparently to importune rather than to amuse, attract or stimulate, where confession or reproach is more evident than ebullience, it is not just to use the term 'manic' or 'hypomanic'. This and related points are discussed later. It has also been suggested that these so-called 'mixed states' are characteristic of 'involutional melancholia'. The adjoined cases show that the same picture may be seen in earlier periods of life.

In M. B., H. C., J. G., L. C. and A. F. the patients were passing through the menopause or in the involutional period. The output of the first three was very great; they muttered or talked aloud the whole time they were awake, irrespective of whether anybody was there to listen. M. B. and J. G. kept repeating the remarks of other patients and applying them to themselves, with a running commentary, or dealing in a similar way with remarks addressed to them by the doctors or nurses, which they repeated, distorted, commented on and played with, even making puns, but always in the sense of self-reproach, etc. They commented on their own behaviour e.g., 'I was talking all night. I'm like a clock; I stop for a while and then I start again'. 'I came here for talking.' 'I'm more troubled than the others that keep getting out of bed. I stay in bed.' They would both stop if requested, but only for a few minutes. Their language was rather extravagant, 'utterly miserable, of course, beyond description'.

H. C. whimpered all the time; occasionally she would utter a sharp comment or rebuke, but most of her almost inaudible talk was in the nature of comment on herself and those around her.

A. F., however, was different. Importunate, with very few topics, she beset all the nurses and doctors whom she saw with inquiries, requests for reassurance and complaints, without paying any heed to suitability of time and place. Left to herself, she became silent. In this she resembled L. C., who was constantly asking for interviews, and who then talked a great deal, but at other times was quiet.

Among the younger women of this group, importunity was striking, with the exception of E. B., who, during one period of her illness, talked constantly about her own behaviour and that of the other patients in a low, scarcely audible voice, much like the three older women mentioned above. She continued with this even when there was no audience. At an earlier stage she had talked profusely, but only when addressed.

Four cases insisted on being noticed. J. C. called one, whenever one appeared, to draw attention to her pains and discomforts. If no one was near her, except other patients, she remained silent. She would continue talking so that one had difficulty in getting away from her bedside. She repeated the same set of phrases over and over, as did also L. C., who would call out 'May I stay here, may I stay here' hundreds of times in a day, i.e., as often as a nurse or a doctor walked by her bed. D. N. remained quiet until someone came near her; she would then call out, and if it were the doctor ask for a private interview; during such interviews she would talk at great speed, running over the same ground in almost the same words, often refusing to leave the room when the interview was over, but persisting with her old requests for reassurance and her protestations.

G. S. talked incessantly, audience or no audience, on a few topics with verbal reiteration, mostly in a loud, whining voice, with a formal precision of phrase, like a school-mistress. It is noteworthy that in her, as in M. B., J. G. or J. C. and E. P., to all of whom somnifaine and other sedative drugs were given to produce continuous narcosis, the talking continued during the period of drowsiness, though reduced to an incoherent whining or mumbling. Under somnifaine E. P. and J. G. whimpered more.

E. P., just referred to, repeated over and over the same two or three phrases in a rather loud voice, with much whining and tearless sobbing. She would not, during this period, answer questions relevantly unless they bore on the burden of her complaint. A little earlier she had been able to give an account of her life and illness.

L. H. was incessantly proclaiming her difficulties and wrongs, protesting against unjust accusations. She would do this in a loud voice until midnight sometimes; she would follow one about in the ward, demanding reassurance or promises, and she did not talk if there was no audience. She would converse only on these few topics (the reasons for including this patient in the series are given elsewhere).

I. M. was continually asking for interviews, at which she reiterated the same few complaints, and at the end of which she was most reluctant to leave the room, going on with her declarations of unhappiness, headache, etc. She did not talk unless she had an audience. She would stop, moreover, if interrupted, and it was possible to carry on a conversation with her and to direct its course. Though in importunity, therefore, she belongs to the preceding group, in the form of her loquacity, or perhaps garrulousness, she suggests the group of patients now to be discussed.

In this group, though they talk tremendously and at times override interruption or talk down one's attempts to change the subject, though they revert often to a few topics, there is a clear appreciation of what one says to them. Their answers, if they do answer, are relevant, and their sentences consecutive; one can always with persistence assert a dominance more or less brief in the trend of the conversation, and one can at all times during the illness obtain from them a clear and full account of their history. To their talk may be applied the brief description, written in the notes of one of them (E. N.), 'plain, connected, profuse'. Much of their talk is spontaneous; they often remark on one's having to write so much about them, on their regret for taking up so much of one's time, and even on their own talkativeness. In none of them was it a new feature, but had been their habit for many years; their husbands had remarked on it. The significance of it lies, therefore, chiefly in its persistence, even though the patients are depressed, and at a time when they complain of weariness and disinclination for any effort.

The patients included in this group are E. A., A. C., M. F., F. H., R. J.—the last four were Jewesses—and E. N. In A. C. and R. J. the talking had led to domestic quarrels, because the former chattered and the latter nagged, long before the onset of the present illness. Probably belonging also to this group is E. R. who had always been quarrelsome and talkative, and during her illness talked freely and even at times impudently to patients and members of the staff alike, though at the time she declared herself dejected, exhausted, unable to concentrate, a degraded woman.

There are only two men who talked a lot. One, A. H., was continually asking for an interview, and harped on a few topics—his wickedness and his ill-health—but he did not talk much to the other patients or to the nurses, and his conversation could be deflected; he may be referred, therefore, to the importunate group, with features similar to those of L. C. and I. M. The other loquacious man, R. H., railed loudly and vehemently about his misery, hopelessness, cowardice. In him alone, however, hypomanic features might be recognized: he surrounded himself with books, which he read rapidly; he waved his arms when talking and otherwise gesticulated; he gave the impression of gusto, of enjoying his tirades against himself and fate.

Among the above, those who had an attitude of protest or resentment include R. H., E. R., J. C., L. H. and D. N.; in the others who were importunate, complaints against the nurses, other patients, the ward or the environment generally were not infrequent. These features occur so commonly among depressed patients (as discussed elsewhere) that one cannot draw any more definite conclusion than that the paranoid egotistical features (including scratching, biting and spitefulness generally) are well in evidence among those with a considerable output of talk.

In all, there is great limitation of the number of topics, much reiteration, and impatience or ignoring of interruption. In these, however, the interruption is utilized, as are other words overheard, as material for self-application, to be repeated, and even punned on in this sense; it is in form what one calls distractability in the manic patient—a taking notice of the irrelevant and making comment on it—but so far is the patient from being distracted by it that the irrelevant remark or even happening is here taken up and carried along in the stream of self-reproachful talk, etc. Finally, there is a group in whom garrulousness has always been a feature, and in whom it is not diminished during depression.

As to those who said little: there is a division into those who said little even when interviewed about their life and illness, and others who discussed these matters freely when alone with the physician, but conversed very little with the other patients or with the nurses.

If one examines the former group, there are first B. S., M. S., M. C. and R. D. All of them looked frightened, and said they were muddled. B. S. gave at times irrelevant answers, in accordance with her preoccupations. M. S. answered only when spoken to, and then briefly; for a few weeks she did not speak at all, and for several months no more than monosyllables. M. C. was curt and repetitive, often gave no answer when addressed. R. D., a boy, made no spontaneous remarks, except to interject 'Dadda is good'; his replies were relevant, but he would break off in the middle of the answer; if pressed, he would finish the sentence; often he gave no answer at all.

One could not doubt that apprehension and bewilderment in these patients was closely associated with their taciturnity. In all, there was considerable delay before they answered questions (see under 'Retardation').

M. R. illustrated another form of importunity. Saying very little and only on the two topics of her wickedness and her poverty, she would start to speak and break off after the first or second word, to finish the sentence only as one was leaving her; another sentence would be begun, only to be completed as one moved away, and by this, one was detained for a long time at her bedside. Here, as in the loquacious importunate, the seizing and holding of the listener's attention appears to be strongly desired (this patient, like A. C. and I. W. presently to be described, became voluble in a subsequent state of elation and excitement). The difficulty in finishing sentences, present in M. R., was also seen in R. D., and was observed in other depressed patients who were not sparing of speech, such as M. L.; it differed from schizophrenic blocking in that there was no sudden change of topic, and the sentence, if presently continued, was consecutive and made sense.

B. S., at all times reserved and sparing of words, became, during periods of great agitation, unable to finish his sentences so long as they referred to the subjects of his distressful thoughts; neutral questions he would answer briefly, after recollecting himself, but otherwise he became quite silent, though apparently making great efforts to utter his unhappy reflections; he would open his mouth to speak, then groan and beat his forehead, or ejaculate 'My God', or an initial word or two of a sentence.

E. J. and A. C. were 'disinclined to talk'; a very few topics and much reiteration, a weary level tone and an expressed desire not to be bothered were the chief features. M. B. did not reiterate, would answer questions on any matter (even on one occasion about the position of women in the Athenian state, and at another time about blue-books on the Reform Act period), but never spoke spontaneously, never brought the conversation round to any particular topics, said as little as possible, and professed herself tired and averse from any conversation; she would lie all day without speaking to anyone. Another like her in this respect was D. P., whose talk was concise, apt, free from reiteration and never spontaneous.

E. T. said little, reiterated the same round of despairing beliefs, and never addressed her neighbours.

M. A., a very reserved woman, had always been so, was so again after recovery, and could be got to answer questions, though she said very little spontaneously; she uttered no sentences longer than ten words, and seldom answered with more than one sentence; she showed much bewilderment, in this resembling B. S., M. S., M. C. and R. D., while in the respect of taciturnity as a feature of her pre-psychotic personality she may be compared with B. J. In I. W. apprehension and resentment were evident when she was first interviewed; she remained silent though questioned, said she would not speak to the physician, and went abruptly and unbidden from the room; she said that this was not a hospital nor I a doctor; later her attitude changed from this, and she became less taciturn. Resentment was also strong in L. W., who rarely made a spontaneous remark, who answered curtly or not at all, said she should not be here, and afterwards said she 'hated every moment' she spent in hospital.

Of the remaining cases, A. N. and E. H., alike in this as in other respects, volunteered little, answered questions relevantly after a pause, hardly talked at all to the other patients. A. G. was such another. E. R. F. and A. H., though very agitated and constantly out of bed or bath, said little, unless maudlin with sedative drugs. M. C., also agitated, said little, the content of her talk being repeated anxious inquiries. E. J. F. was neither copious nor sparse in conversation during her depression; now, possibly recovered, she talks a great deal, e.g., for an hour without questioning or interrupting, though she is not hypomanic as far as one can tell. E. W. D. was taciturn here, during each of his two depressive attacks, speaking curtly, irritably or evasively; at home he was voluble and argumentative, with only few topics. Another who varied was E. G. D., who was very talkative, resentful in tone, importunate when first in hospital; later became taciturn and quite unwilling to discuss anything but the state of his bowels; he would shout loudly when obliged to take his food.

As to the remaining fifteen patients in the series, the amount and form of their talk, as apart from its content, seemed average. Some talked little to their fellows, but freely to the physician, others the reverse; but without a closer knowledge of their former talking habits than could be obtained from any history, it was not justifiable to suppose any change ascribable to the illness.

It is evident that to suppose depressed patients to be uniformly sparing of speech is incorrect, that a mood of resentment may be associated with much talk—the tirade, the catalogue of wrongs—as well as with little—the sullen silence or the bitter rejoinder.

The bewildered and the resigned tend to say little, the agitated to say much, but it is no constant association. Importunity is found with much talk and with little, chiefly with the former. There is no mood that always goes with more or less talk. There may be nothing in the form of a depressive's scanty talk, of one kind, to distinguish it from the scanty talk of a well-preserved, suspicious paranoid schizophrenic; in both there may be pauses, hesitation, evasion, breaking off, brevity; the conclusion must rest on other observations—of content and general behaviour. Scanty talk may be only when a painful subject is being discussed. There is almost always in depressive patients a reiterative tendency, a preoccupation with a few topics. It is necessary to consider the previous habit carefully when deciding if the illness has brought any change in output or manner of talk.

RETARDATION

Slowing of thought and action has long been recognized as an important feature of depressive states. Zichen wrote in 1896: 'Nowadays, by the term melancholia, we mean a psychosis whose chief symptoms are: (1) A primary sad change of mood. (2) A primary slowing of ideation or inhibition of thought.'

Bleuler similarly writes that the basic symptoms are depressive mood, slowing of the mental stream and of the centrifugal functions of willing and acting. All writers agree as to the importance of it, but few define it or its manifestations, leaving such phrases as 'psychomotor retardation' or 'inhibition' to speak for themselves. It is proposed, therefore, to examine the features which may be included under the heading 'Retardation' or 'Inhibition', and then to discuss them in the light of the literature on the subject.

There is first the subjective experience of it, the patient's description. It is with regard to difficulties in thinking that these are most often obtained.

Thinking

In the majority there was a bare statement: 'I can't concentrate.' 'I can't think much at all.' 'I cannot fix my mind on things.' 'I can't think very well.' 'My mind does not act properly.' 'I can't put my mind on anything.' 'I can't collect my thoughts.' In addition, a number of patients gave more detailed descriptions of how their thinking was affected. A constant press of thought is the main characteristic.

F. H. said: 'My mind goes like a kaleidoscope. All my life comes in my head. My brain never stops. It goes like an engine.' F. N. said: 'I can't think of things. I can't concentrate. My thoughts run on; it's so hard to control them.' R. S.: 'I can't follow anybody explaining. I can't remember names. I can't concentrate on anything. I feel as if I want to get everything over in an instant . . . my wretched mind keeps on making me think terrible things. . . . These thoughts, I can't get my mind on anything else. . . . I can't make out what's driven me to think such silly things, they're so real. . . . It's not right always to be in a track of thought that you can't stop. . . . I can't seem to think about anything but myself.' M. T. complained that her thoughts would not stop: 'My head, it's all gone funny. It keeps on singing. Songs keep running through my head.' Whatever she looked at, she had to describe in words in her own mind. Whatever people said to her, she had to repeat in her head. I. M. said: 'My brain is always working. I can't stop thinking of myself. . . . I feel dense. . . . I get a pain in my head whenever I try to do anything.' E. N.: 'When I put my mind on anything it seems as if I can't do it. It hurts when I put my mind on anything.' E. J. said: 'Thoughts keep coming up and worrying me from the past. I couldn't leave it.' W. G. said: 'I keep thinking too much of myself. My mind is so hard, trying to struggle on the present, like.' M. L. said: 'I feel I have strained my head and my nerves. . . . A kind of thickness in my head. . . . I can't remember what I have read or where I have laid things.' (Similar complaints of inability to remember trivial things, either past happenings or injunctions to be fulfilled, were very common, generally reported as 'my memory is so bad'. As these, however, are rather descriptions of happenings than of subjective experience, they are not included here.) E. B., describing herself as muddled, said: 'My mind sort of wanders; my thoughts keep going all the time.' Complaints of bewilderment, perplexity, feeling muddled, confused, were obtained from 27 patients.

The influence of bromides or other drugs could be excluded in all these cases. If one makes allowance for the patients in whom information as to subjective experience was not obtained because of relative inaccessibility, or not inquired after particularly, there remain very few patients who did not speak of some kind of disturbance of their thinking. It is important that not a single patient of the whole 61 said spontaneously that his thoughts seemed to be slower or fewer; on the contrary, many complained of over-activity—of a constant surge of thoughts. The examination of the thought disorder is left for consideration, in connexion with the literature, below.

Action

The subjective data here are complicated, in that the patient's description is seldom only of his inclinations or feeling, but is usually interwoven with his account of his behaviour. A. G., for example, said: 'I sit and moon all day. I go mooning about. I do nothing all day, but think about my father.' No attempt has been made, therefore, to consider separately the patient's account of his feelings with regard to activity, his account of his actual activity and his relatives' account of it. Often alterations in this regard had been the first symptom of the illness, becoming less obtrusive as agitation, delusions, self-reproach, etc., filled the foreground of the picture; without direct and, in this connexion, necessarily leading questions, a statement by the patient of her present inclinations to activity could not be obtained. Further, the conditions of hospital life are artificial; the patient lies in bed during the worst part of his illness, and little more is required of him than to eat, be cleanly, and do a little work, no harder than he seems equal to—raffia weaving, straw plaiting, knitting, etc., according to sex, inclination and adequacy. There is, therefore, during the period the illness is most severe, small chance of estimating the patient's capacity for work, unless it is grossly reduced. So, excluding for the moment observations on activity made while in hospital, the presence of fatigue or anergia has been decided from the patient's statements, and the reports of relatives as to conduct before admission to hospital. It was present, using these criteria, in all but 2 of the 61 patients. The two who neither said they had felt disinclined for or unequal to work nor had it said of them by their relatives, were L. C. and H. C. As to the latter, it may be mentioned that both his own account and that given by his father laid emphasis on his having, in a previous attack, been unable to get on with his work, and in the present attack it is recorded that 'he feels he cannot go out and face his work again; he still lacks confidence'—presumably evidence of a feeling of inadequacy. L. C. was said to have 'let everything go; neglected her appearance'.

This almost invariable symptom appears in self-description as 'tired', 'worn-out', 'easily exhausted', 'listless', 'too weak to move', 'everything seems too much for me', 'I feel run-down; everything is too much of an effort', 'I seem to have no strength', 'I don't seem to have any will-power, I can't do things', 'I feel I just want to let everything go', 'My children seemed too much trouble', 'I felt I wanted a rest, I couldn't do my work', 'I felt I wasn't equal to my work, everybody seemed to be getting in front of me'. E. N. said: 'I couldn't work properly; I took no interest in it.' The desire for utter rest was strong in some, for example, A. E. N., who said; 'If I could only go to sleep, I shouldn't have to trouble any more. I feel I'd like to lie down and pass away.' At the same time she desired to work, tried to work and said: 'I did not exercise my will-power. I neglected the house' (as she had done). There was similar conflict of inclination in M. H., who said: 'The work didn't satisfy me the same. Everything used to irritate me. I felt if I gave up work, I didn't want to lay in bed because if I did I wouldn't want to get up no more.' R. S., who felt he wanted to get everything over in an instant, at the same time felt he wanted to stay in bed all day—felt he could hardly walk. R. H. took to his bed two days after the beginning of his illness, and would not get up. G. M. got in a muddle with her housework; started many things, but did not finish them: 'At times I feel absolutely done for, as though I can't move.' The accounts by the relatives abound in statements about neglect of the children, the meals, personal cleanliness and tidiness; the patient has been sent home from work for inefficiency, has tried to help, but proved a hindrance, has become less energetic, given to sitting idle or to unproductive and restless moving about.

For reasons already given, the patient's ordinary or spontaneous activity is little guide in hospital, because there are few requirements and many restrictions in this regard. Attention has, therefore, been given rather to the extent to which patients who showed or professed incapacity would respond to stimulation, in the form of suggestions, encouragement, or a definite insistence that some task should be completed. In other words, this part of the investigation is concerned with the relation of what the patient could do, if urged, to what he felt or said he could do; it covered the response to 'occupational therapy' (activity in the sense of movements applied to a task), and to a set of simple tests of memory, grasp and calculation (more specifically mental effort, directed to a task).

(*a*) Taking the first, it may be said in general that the incapacity is greater in the patient's report than it appears in his behaviour. This is a common clinical observation, and is borne out by investigations conducted at the Maudsley Hospital, in which tests of perception were given to depressed patients. The patients protested that they could not possibly do the tests, but the psychologist, a pupil of Professor Spearman, found that their actual performance was in many cases the same as that of normal persons.

Any sharp distinction in this respect is impossible; there is no even approximately accurate method of assessing it. From personal observations and the reports of nurses, occupational workers and supervisors of drill and games, the following relationships have been concluded: 29 patients could do much more than one would have expected if one had taken their statements and expectation as guide. This group covers most of those who were less obviously ill, without delusions, for example, clearly well in touch with their environment, but not by any means only these or all of them. Fifteen others showed a disproportion between performance and feeling of adequacy, but less definitely than the first group.

The final group in whom no such disproportion could be recognized during the period in hospital consisted of 11 cases. These patients were either agitated, stuporose or semi-stuporose; some of them were often wanting to do some work, such as sweeping; others made no statement as to how they felt, and there was, therefore, no means of determining the relation to their performance;

they had mostly, according to the history, continued to work at the beginning of their illness although feeling unequal to it; many of them had been at work until a short time before admission. One of them, A. H., during a brief and partial intermission in her illness, spontaneously sketched some neighbouring buildings (she was an architect), and wrote a number of fairly well-composed letters. In another, L. W., one had the impression that resentment and sullenness were closely related to her inactivity, but similar behaviour had been conspicuous while she was at home, and cannot be accounted for adequately by relating it to her resentful mood. In short, among this last group there was no disproportion, because they carried out no tasks until they improved, or made no statement about their feeling of inadequacy. Observations made during the period of improvement have not been included; it is sufficient to say that generally the patient has become more active before he reports any falling off in the severity of his feeling of inadequacy, which may be the last symptom, often referred to in the patient's statements as 'lack of confidence'. It is only with complete recovery that his expectation runs equal to his performance; if he be on the way to mania or hypomania, it outruns it.

(*b*) The tests employed here consisted of questions as to orientation in time, space and identity, questions appropriate to the patient's apparent social and intellectual level, to determine his grasp of general information (whatever variations were introduced, all patients were asked to name the present and last three Kings, the Prime Minister and Chancellor of the Exchequer, the capital of the larger European countries, and to give the date of the declaration of war and of the armistice; the other questions varied greatly); calculations, including the subtraction of serial sevens from 100, scored according to time taken and number of errors, and tests of rote-memory (repetition of numbers forward and also backward), together with repetition, after reading, of the cowboy, gilded boy, and bee and pigeon stories, recollection of a name told to the patient, and the events of his own life, recent and remote (checked against other sources of information). It was found possible to apply all these tests to the majority of the patients. The tests were mostly given on admission. It is not pretended that they are tests of intellectual capacity alone, nor, of course, of capacity to think; they have been regarded in this connexion only as evidence of the patient's power to attend to, and conclude, a task requiring some intellectual effort, to be measured against his assertion of difficulty in thus concentrating his mind. It must also be said that with them, as clinically employed, there can be little question of precise measurement; the patient varies from day to day and from morning to evening, and he varies according to whether he is put through the gamut of tests at one sitting or at several; and in evaluating the tests, even such easily measurable ones as the subtraction of sevens from 100, the previous talent and occupation of the patient make comparison, e.g., as between a charwoman and a bank-clerk, impossible. So an illusory precision has not been aimed at.

It was not possible to do the tests on 5 patients.

The tests were done very well by 10 patients: among these only M. B., E. W. D.,

M. L. and A. N. had complained of difficulty in concentrating, but E. B. and R. S. had said they were muddled. The group is most varied in its general clinical features.

These tests were done fairly well by 23 patients. Of these, in 14 cases, there had been a complaint of difficulty in thinking. In all the 23 patients of the group the tests were done less well than one would expect of such a person when in good health, though the mistakes and omissions were, on the whole, trifling. Most of them could be corrected by the patient himself. Whether the defects were commensurate with the patient's professions of incapacity, in the 14 who had expressed such feelings, it was mostly impossible to decide, but a number of them professed an incapacity at starting which was not borne out when they did the test. This group, like the last, is clinically heterogeneous.

The tests were badly done by 15 patients. The errors and omissions were gross. All of these but four had said that they had difficulty in fixing their minds on a task. Among them are the most dissimilar conditions, from the most obviously 'psychotic' to the predominantly 'neurotic'. To attempt to differentiate them according to the degree to which they responded to stimulation, as Lange and others would, is not possible, for L. C., H. C. and B. S. were able to correct their mistakes, when urged, and to recall apparently forgotten things, just as strikingly as R. J. or G. M., while A. C. was very little influenced by such stimulation, abiding by her declaration, 'Oh, I couldn't do that, Doctor; it's too hard.'

Various points in assessing these tests in this connexion must be mentioned. As in the giving of the Binet-Simon tests, for example, or in any such artificial situations, one has to consider the interest of the patient in the task, and the various factors spoken of together as 'attention'. Using the language in which the situations have been recorded in the clinical notes, one can say that inattention and preoccupation have seemed responsible for most of the patient's deficiencies in dealing with the tests. The patient's gaze wanders, he falls into a brown study, he gives indefinite answers without rousing himself or looking at the questioner, he asks for the question to be repeated or gives an answer to the previous question, he passes from subtracting sevens to subtracting sixes or fives or tens, and then recalls himself, becomes temporarily alert and sometimes discomfited; he says 'Eh' or 'What's that' without looking up, or repeats the question mechanically. In brief, he is paying no heed, one concludes, and he is preoccupied. Inattention, though, does not always seem due to preoccupation. In some patients, for example A. C., it is associated with a restless or idle looking round the room and reference to irrelevant matters, which, though met in the hypomanic, is also common, in ordinary life, among the stupid or lazy-minded. Some of the mistakes due to inattention are gross, e.g., in the 100–7 tests, A. E. N. said that 7 from 86 left 81, 7 from 47 left 41 and so on, perseverating. E. W. would skip over a score, saying that 7 from 93 left 76, and so on. She (E. W.) also illustrates the necessity for considering a great number of observations and tests; thus, she repeated the stories almost word for word, likewise numbers forward and backward, but her account of recent events contained many gaps and incorrect details (e.g., of her admission to hospital through the out-patient department), and her calculations were badly done.

This great variability in response to different tests was present to some extent in almost all cases. M. S. kept mixing herself into some of the tests, supposing them to have some bearing on her, e.g., 'I am the dog' (cowboy story), but with this overcome, her responses became even. R. D. reported: 'When I try to work at these tests, this dizziness comes over me.' G. S. refused at first to try the tests; 'I can't, I haven't concentrated for a long time,' and interspersed her answers with similar assertions. Similarly, G. M., R. J. and S. R. and others.

Another factor is anxiety. The patient becomes perturbed, fears that some penalty will befall him if he answers badly, tries to be quick about it, asks repeatedly if he has done well, is disconcerted by such failures as he is aware of, and does much better when accustomed to the examiner or reassured about the purpose of the examination.

Finally, a decision was come to in each case at the time of examination and during treatment as to the presence of retardation, by which was meant definite evidence in the patient's behaviour of a slowing of his activities; it may be taken as representing a general impression rather than a conclusion based on the examination of special points. The cases in which retardation was recorded as present are: 19 in all. An examination of these shows that emphasis was being laid on slowness of movement and occasionally of talk, or, on evidence of inhibition, as recognized in speech broken off before completion. Some precise tests in 'retarded' patients failed to show any motor retardation in the performance of a simple task (pulling a grooved bar a short fixed distance).

In considering the literature on the subject, it is as well to see what Kraepelin and Bleuler say. The former wrote: 'The exact counterpart to flight of ideas seems to be the inhibition of thought which we see in a varying degree almost everywhere in depression and in some stuporose mixed states and related forms of excitement. The patients often feel a very distressing inability to call up the ideas they require. It seems that the individual ideas develop slowly, and only under strong stimulation. Consequently an impression does not spontaneously and readily arouse a crowd of associations which call only for a choice between them. Association, when it does occur, is in accordance with the ideational contents. Usually nothing at all occurs to the patient, and he has to make a special effort of will to continue his line of thought. Therefore, thinking is laborious and slow, there is unreadiness in answering simple questions, lack of comprehension, poverty of ideas' (*p. 1198*). And later: 'Here and there the ideas which continually force their way forward against the patient's will look exactly like obsessions' (*p. 1199*). Bleuler, strongly influenced by association psychology, discusses the distinction between obstruction (Sperrung) and inhibition (Hemmung), and holds that in the inhibited melancholic the retardation of thought and movement is always recognizable, it cannot be suddenly overcome, and is not limited. As to the relation between the depression and the inhibition of thought, where Ziehen had said that they were both primary in melancholia, with reciprocal influence, Bleuler remarks that the disturbance of affect represents merely the most conspicuous symptom of a general transformation of the psyche, in which the intellectual disturbances seem concomitant manifestations of the affective change. Earlier German writers had occupied themselves with the relation of 'Denkhemmung' to 'Ideenflucht'; thus J. Schroeder pointed out how both could be present in the one patient, and thought that 'The cropping up of new ideas and their repressive effect on those that persist contributes just as much to the feeling that one has not one's ideas at one's disposal, as does the persistence and the slow fading of ideas'. It was also pointed out in this connexion that Kraepelin had included '*Denkhemmung*' as a disorder of the 'Einbildungskraft', 'Ideenflucht' as one of the 'Gedankengang'. Pferrsdorf pointed out how in some cases there is a definite 'Localization of the inhibition or retardation to definite groups of ideas and affective reactions'. Wilmanns regarded the feeling of intrapsychic inhibition as characteristic of melancholia with its anxious and attentive self-observation, and compared it with the feelings of insufficiency of the patient with dementia praecox. The careful examination of the problem by Wilmanns and his colleagues has recently been adverted to by Gruhle in the passage: 'Blocking seems pathognomonic for schizophrenia, but unfortunately the same cannot be said for retardation in depressive psychosis. I remember how we in Heidelberg, when between 1908 and 1912 we were so busy with manic-depressive psychosis, were firmly convinced that true retardation (and especially its subjective reflection) was a characteristic of this affective disorder. Further experience has destroyed this hope, and since then I have found the best description of subjective 'retardation' in a description of his own state written by a schizophrenic, who has since completely deteriorated.' With this conclusion I am in agreement, and in early as well as late schizophrenic patients have found the same description of feelings of inadequacy and the same anomalies of behaviour in this formal respect. Another recent writer, von Domarus, in an analysis of the thinking of depressive and manic patients, concludes: 'That it must be regarded as misleading, to say the least, to talk of a specific manic depressive mode of thought.'

Deron writes: 'In depressive states the mental slowness and paralysis are apparent even to superficial clinical examination; there is here slowness of adaptation, of comprehension and assimilation, and the cause of this seems to be the difficulty in calling up ideas and the blotting-out of images.' If one examines the writings of C. Schneider and K. Beringer on schizophrenic thinking, one is struck by the applicability of some of the features described to the thought disorders shown in the patients here; this is especially true of the 'incapacity to command the stream of thought' and 'diminished span of the intentional arc'. It is, of course, not to be assumed that all the features of disturbed thinking in schizophrenics may also be found in depressive patients. It may seem superfluous to devote much consideration to the disorder of formal thinking, but no less an authority than Wernicke has attributed to the retardation of thought a predominant significance in melancholia; he has derived all the rest of the symptoms from the 'intrapsychic hypofunction'. Jahreiss, more recently, has suggested two elements in the thought-disorder, one having its roots in primitive changes, a 'vital' factor, in the sense of K. Schneider's 'vital depression', and characterized by general inhibition and slowing of thought; the other secondary to the depression, influenced by the emotional value of a small range of images or 'complexes'. Bumke inclines to a similar opinion. Detailed considerations of the depressive thought-disorder in relation to its form, apart from questions of content, are not to be found in English writers except MacCurdy, with whose views, presently to be dealt with, Henderson and Gillespie are in agreement. Stoddart says that 'retardation of the flow of ideas may arise as the result of partial paralysis of the cortical neurons' in melancholia. Craig and Beaton talk the language of association-psychology: 'The associative processes may be so sluggish that no logical thought can be performed, simply because all cohesion is lost in the intervals of forming the elemental associations.'

What emerges from an examination of the 61 cases here considered is that difficulty in thinking, not slowness of thought, is the characteristic feature; if the thinking is directed to an end, the carrying out of a particular intellectual task, e.g., grasping and answering a question, deciding on a course of action or doing a problem, then that end is either not attained, or only after a long period and with great effort; what the patient appreciates is the difficulty in thinking; what strikes the observer is the slowness in performing the operation. Where the thinking is free, not directed to a conscious end, its characteristic is in many cases not slowness, but great rapidity; the patient complains of the press of thoughts, 'going like an engine', and whether these thoughts are the same ones recurring or fresh ones is irrelevant to the question of the quickness of their succession; it may be said that the thoughts throng, but their ordered direction towards a conclusion is interfered with. To enter here into the careful analysis of the process of thought, with its complicated literature, is inappropriate; it may be said, however, that, in general, the impairment of the process in depression affects the material, the ideas or images least and the intentional act most. It is scarcely necessary nowadays to point out the inadequacy of the views concerned solely with ease or difficulty of association.

If inhibition had not physiological and neurological as well as psychoanalytical implications, it would be a better word than retardation to apply to the thought-disorder. Retardation is descriptive of one manifestion of it, which is not always in evidence.

Is the thought-disorder secondary, of the same sort as the difficulty we experience during 'normal' depression? MacCurdy thinks it is. 'The other phenomena we have analysed were seen to be related to deficient psychic energy. The retardation seems quite plainly to be a direct expression of this. It, too, is frequently present in everyday life. We all know the effort it requires to think or move actively, particularly if we are called to duties that seem onerous. . . . Every acute introspectionist knows that his intelligence is keen when it is engaged in solving a welcome problem, but that distasteful mental exercises are laboured. From this we can gain a hint as to the aetiology of retardation—that painful thoughts are slow. Routine examinations of depressives show the same phenomena; when the patient is questioned about neutral matters, such as facts of orientation, the answers may be prompt enough, but when personal troubles are touched on, the retardation appears promptly. . . . When any personal topic produces such an interference with thought, the reaction has developed to a definitely psychotic degree. In the deepest depressions retardation is so extensive as to affect all thinking and even bodily movements. But at no point is there a change in its nature; it simply becomes more frequent, more inclusive. . . . We shall see later that by viewing retardation from this angle it becomes a simple matter to explain the nature of psychological processes in depression.' A simple matter, as he says, but too simple to account for the facts. There may be in the so-called 'manic stupor' great 'retardation' with a cheerful mood, or, what has been shown in the detailed examination of cases above, there may be severe mood-depression with little evidence of 'retardation' of thought, certainly not of general psychomotor activity; in some patients there was stupor or semi-stupor, but not proportionate depression; others were excited, 'over-active'. In normal psychology one finds similar interference with thought and action from other emotional states, such as fear and bashfulness, so that it cannot be regarded as peculiar to depression. Furthermore, the same interference, in all its essential and recognizable characters, may be found in definitely schizophrenic patients, not particularly depressed. It is probably more in accordance with the evidence to suppose that there may be (1) interference with thought because of an unpleasant mood-tone; (2) interference due to preoccupation with certain topics, 'complex-determined', affect-laden, from which it is difficult to divert the stream of thought; and (3) a general disturbance due to profound, 'vital' changes in the organism, affecting the whole of integrated psycho-biological activity, including thought as one element.

As to activity, excluding agitation, one finds similar interference with the completion of a task, with subjective experience of the difficulty, either anticipatory or during performance. MacCurdy has given the same facile explanation for the difficulty in thinking, and says that 'the patient feels the conflict, or rather feels the paralysis resulting from the deadlock reached between expression and repression'. Benon regards this 'retardation' in action as entirely secondary to the depression of melancholia: 'This asthenia is characterized by slowing of mental activity, with difficulty of recollection and general lessening of muscular power; it is determined by the intensity and persistence of the emotional distress. . . . The fundamental fact, to be defined clinically, is the appearance of asthenic phenomena which are secondary to the emotional distress'. This secondary asthenia of melancholia he distinguishes sharply and with emphasis from the primary asthenia of periodical depression: 'In true melancholia, in which there may be pronounced asthenia, one sees the asthenia get a footing and grow; it is a secondary asthenia, proportionate, like all the asthenias of sadness and grief, to the depth and duration of the emotional disturbance. In melancholic depression, however, besides the asthenia being primary and setting in at the very beginning of the illness, it persists with pretty much the same strength throughout the attack.' He is obliged to do some very confusing juggling with 'les dysthénies post-mélancoliques' in order to make the facts consonant with his theory.

Pierre Janet, in his paper on 'fear of action as an essential element in the sentiment of melancholia', insists that the feeling of inadequacy is essentially a fear of action, a flight from action, a checking regulation which stops one action, seeks to replace it by another, an opposite action, and in so doing causes failure of action; the essential psychological fact is always action; thought is but a reduced reproduction of it; a feeling of exhaustion, therefore, causes irregularities and interruptions to which the organism reacts with failure. fear of action: the exhaustion has occurred because these melancholic patients are psychologically weaklings, who show also the physiological signs of exhaustion, especially of the functions of the central nervous system. It becomes clear from Janet's illustrative cases, however, that a number of different clinical conditions, including obsessive states and psychopathic personality, are in question. Moreover, it must be considered that in the melancholic it is less the fear of action than the conviction of inadequacy not only in anticipation, but also during effective performance. If one accepts Janet's explanation, one is left with no more than a ready tendency to exhaustion as the primary phenomenon, and no hint as to the relation of this to the other features of melancholia save that in his final paragraph he suggests, more in a homiletic than in any precise psychological strain, that sadness contains fear of action, and should therefore not be cultivated by individuals or nations,

Bostroem examines depressive inhibition of action to see what disorder of will such patients display; the chief disorder, if the inhibition is not primary, lies in 'decision', the true volitional act; difficulties may also occur in the motivation. In examining this opinion, one recalls the investigations of Spearman's associates, Webb and Aveling: the latter concludes on experimental grounds that the volitional act, by which we decide, is in essence effortless, and is to be distinguished from a conation of which it may be the cause; a conation is an experienced act, bodily or mental, of doing, i.e., striving or effort. If this be so, no impairment of the volitional act can be held immediately responsible for the difficulty and feeling of inadequacy and effort in the depressed.

From the cases in this series, one concludes that the feeling of inadequacy is more important than the performance, though less measurable, because it may be found when there is no corresponding difficulty in action evident, such as may later develop, and because it is less influenced by former habits of work, thoroughness, persistence in completion of tasks, application to a single task, output—in other words, it is less modified by the previous personality; moreover, it is evident that some were desirous of rest or averse from action, and so neglected their work or were ineffectual; others started many jobs, became muddled and completed nothing. No single explanation offers itself to cover all, though the end was the same—inadequate activity. Inadequacy is present in every patient, either demonstrably or as a feeling.

It is impossible to distinguish clinical groups according to the degree of response to stimulation, in other words, the disproportion between the patient's feelings of inadequacy and the actual performance (obviously it is always some stimulus that drives to action, and the intensity of stimulation will depend more on the significance of the stimulating force for the patient than on its mere quality). Further, there is nothing to distinguish this disorder of action from the feeling of weariness prominent in 'neurasthenia'; if neurasthenia is to be distinguished from states of depression, it must be on other grounds than the character of the weariness and incapacity for action; no such features in neurasthenia, as are put forward by writers like Benon, are tenable, since they apply also to patients in whom the psychosis 'melancholia' could be diagnosed beyond doubt. Considerations of the nature of the volitional disorder lie outside the scope of this clinical study; subjective experience of a defect of will often receives, at any rate, verbal form in the patient's account. The actual slowing of movements appears less characteristic than an incapacity to complete a task; in mild examples only complicated tasks offer difficulty; here, as with the thought disorder, slowness is only one form in which the essential difficulty may manifest itself. The formal thought-disorder may be largely responsible for the disorder of action, since the nature of the task or the necessary steps for its completion may not be clearly grasped and held during performances. Preoccupation also may lead to bad performance of a task, or the presence of delusions, as where some awful consequence or significance is ascribed to the action.

STUPOR

This extreme form of inhibited action needs special consideration. So close is the connexion of stupor with retardation that Ziehen's definition of it was aprosexia, inhibition of thinking and immobility. Bleuler, on the other hand, speaking of a stupor as a state where 'one does not observe any, or very slight expressions of will', is disinclined to apply the term to severe melancholic inhibition. For most writers, however, certainly for English ones, the term is purely descriptive: 'The subject's activity is reduced to a minimum. . . . In the lesser degrees of stupor, the patient may sometimes be partially roused for a moment or two to pay some attention to, or even to answer, simple questions.' In this purely descriptive sense, taking stupor as a term to cover states of complete or almost complete immobility, with an essential failure to react to external stimuli, five patients were found to show stupor at some stage of their illness. Stupor not quite so definite was found in six patients; these showed what is sometimes called semi-stupor.

It must be stated clearly, however, that in not a single case was there complete immobility and apparent failure to respond to external stimuli, such as one sees in catatonic stupor. Some of these patients were for a time absolutely mute, had to be fed by hand or through a tube, but they were not, except on isolated single occasions, incontinent of faeces or urine, nor did they at any time show a complete failure to respond to their surroundings, even though the response was minimal. Drug-produced conditions are, of course, excluded. In looking through the case-records of those, not included in this series, who had been regarded at some time as depressive, and who had been quite stuporose, one found in each of the cases evidence of schizophrenia (which had been sufficiently strong to exclude the case from the present study). In this connexion it is noteworthy that Bleuler wrote that 'melancholia attonita, as it was formerly called, is usually a catatonia, with or without depression'. Particular attention has been paid in the clinical observation of the patients in this series to any features that would bear out Hoch's conclusions about benign stupor; but neither apathy nor preoccupation with death were discovered; and the consideration of Hoch's and MacCurdy's views is therefore needless. The conclusions of Strecker are more in accordance with the findings: 'Stupor of retarded depression. Befogged consciousness, motor inactivity, scanty ideational productivity. There is not emotional apathy, but often acute mental suffering.'

Since complete pure melancholic stupor has been so often described, one is loath to consider it a dubious diagnosis; it is sufficient to quote Lange, who gives a description of it, and adds: 'Really severe forms of this sort rarely occur.'

AGITATION

Agitation has to be considered as the outward motor expression of a mental unrest, which may, however, also be expressed only in words. Whether there shall be extreme restlessness or apparent stupor is in many cases a question of how much concomitant inhibition there is, for the motor restlessness, which is usually meant in psychiatry when agitation is spoken of, may be regarded from 'normal' experience as the expression of inner tension and unrest; and it is customary to distinguish the restlessness of mania and of agitated depression from the hyperkinetic states of catatonic schizophrenia by its psychological comprehensibility—as in Wernicke's definition of the latter, 'weder neurologisch erklärbar noch psychologisch verständlich' ('neither neurologically explicable nor psychologically understandable').

Sixteen patients who at some time showed great motor restlessness were the ones who kept getting out of bed, wandering about, wringing their hands, erking their limbs or trunk, trying to get out of the continuous bath, picking at their faces, pulling off their bandages and so on. They were of varying ages, it will be seen; and in some there was concomitant 'retardation', or bewilderment. Some also passed through a stage of partial stupor.

Others in whom actual motor unrest was not strikingly evident, but who complained of inner unrest, were numerous. A typical example of these was R. S., who, in addition to his feelings of weariness and desire for peace, said: 'I get in such a terrible state; it's the thinking. . . . I'm in such a state that I can't keep still; I don't know where to get; I can't get a moment's peace of mind. . . . I feel all of a stew.' Yet he stayed quietly in bed and did not betray his agitation in his behaviour. S. R. equally composed and quiet in her superficial demeanour at most times, complained, 'I don't seem as if I can rest.' During an interview she would rub her hands together, just as others twisted and untwisted their fingers, rubbed their faces, fingered their lower lip. Others said: 'I want to be up and doing; I feel I want something with action in it.' 'I feel I can't keep still; I keep going outside without any clear purpose.' 'I feel frantic.' 'I always want to be somewhere else.' An important aspect of the agitation is that it often is expressed in the form of wanting to go home wanting to be somewhere else, and in the treatment of these as voluntary patients the symptom becomes very important, since it may result in an application for discharge. Agitation of this kind, appearing as an expression of 'morbid dissatisfaction with the surroundings', may result in the interruption of treatment over and over again. In others, the agitation is expressed in the form of a desire to work, though the capacity is lacking: 'I want to work; I want to be away from my thoughts.' The inner unrest is the constant thing, the motor unrest is variable, the rationalizations are often transparent. Into this group of moderately agitated persons, without pronounced motor restlessness, fall 16 cases: An occasional wandering down the corridor, fidgety or restless behaviour in bed or when sitting in a chair, and rubbing or picking, were the chief motor features of agitation in them.

A milder group, in whom the symptoms were predominantly though not exclusively subjective, includes 25 cases.

Among the 61 patients were 16 who had been of a worrying, fretful, fidgety or over-anxious disposition prior to their illness of whom 7 showed much motor restlessness in their illness. It may be, however, that the prominence of this symptom of the illness influenced the reports given about the patient's previous personality by the relatives and others. These patients belong to the group of 'selbstunsichere Psychopathen', anankasts, of whom Schneider has written. The relation to obsessive and anxiety features, *sensu strictiori*, is discussed below.

MANIC FEATURES

It is appropriate at this point to consider the question of the so-called 'mixed forms', in which it was supposed that manic and depressive features were found together. This view of Kraepelin's has been examined by many psychiatrists, and the occurrence of motor unrest and agitation in depressive patients has frequently been commented on in this connexion. MacCurdy puts the view of American psychiatrists clearly in his book; with his general argument, his plea for the recognition of types of reaction, there is now general agreement among English-speaking psychiatrists. But he is too easy; he says, for example, that in Kraepelin's description 'depressive mania' there is nothing that would not cover cases of involutional melancholia in which free associations are prominent; he gives no explanation of why or how this could occur. 'Depression with flight of ideas' he takes to be 'an inaccurate and incomplete description of what we call perplexity states'. In agitated or excited depression the patient, says MacCurdy, 'has not abandoned himself to free association, his delusions are not so urgent as to absorb his whole attention, but, at the same time, he is not fighting to maintain his sanity. Like many involution cases, he has given up the struggle, and finds it easier to use his intelligence in defending his false views wittily than in spurring on his insight'. The difficulties are too great to be thus lightly disposed of; and in such speculations and explanations there is the methodological vice, so often castigated by Jaspers, of supposing that a comprehensible relationship is a causal relationship—in other words, that to understand a phenomenon is to explain it. Without entering into the general controversy about mixed states, it may be pointed out that the difficulty lies in deciding what are the essential features of a manic or a depressive illness; if over-activity, flight of ideas, volubility, are manic features, then it must be agreed that they can occur in conjunction with a depressive mood, and are not then invariably transition phases; that they occur most commonly as such is clear in this series, but there are also patients, as has been seen in the sections on talk and retardation, who exhibit these features alongside characteristic depressive ones, without passing into a characteristic manic phase. Among 61 cases, mixed features of this sort do not occur so often that one can draw conclusions from them other than this: that features which are commonly associated with one condition, mania, in which they are striking, can also be found in another, melancholia, if the details of the mental state be examined carefully.

DELUSIONS

So far it is the form of the disorder of thought and behaviour that has been considered; it is necessary also to examine its content and direction. In the most general way it may be said that it is the purpose of thought and behaviour to bring a person into relation with his environment, to recognize meanings and to effect changes. In this sense, Kahn has considered delusions according to the disorder of reference, *Ichbeziehung* and *Beziehung* generally, and of *Bedeutung*, which covers the ascription of meaning and symbolization. But in this one recognizes the difficulties if one would classify the delusions of the melancholic according to it; it is evidently more readily applicable to the delusions of the schizophrenic; possibly only a pragmatic objection, but for the purposes of description and investigation important. Jaspers has divided delusions into two classes—delusional ideas and true delusions, the former being secondary, and comprehensible as arising out of an affective state or other experiences, whereas true delusions are primary and not thus comprehensible. In this, Grühle follows him. Into the details of the controversies about delusion, in which the French and Germans have been conspicuous, it is not appropriate to enter here. It has seemed better to attempt no such distinction as between predominant ideas, preconceptions, delusional ideas and delusions, but to take all incorrigible or persistent false beliefs of morbid genesis, and to group them according to whether they contain false judgments about one's self (of sin and fault), about one's possessions (of poverty and ruin), about the possibility of recovery (of hopelessness), about others (of being despised, punished, persecuted, and of causing them harm). Bodily preoccupations include hypochondriacal delusions, and are therefore also considered in this connexion. It is superfluous to say that the content is closely dependent on the patient's pre-psychotic personality and experience.

Delusions about poverty and ruin were found in only 7 patients. They said that they had no money or that they would be ruined or lose their jobs; all of them were engaged in business except one.

Twenty-five patients voiced a conviction that they would never get well. It is probable that many other patients expressed the view at some time, but that it was not recorded, as from personal recollection there are several of the 61, not included in the above list, who had said that they felt hopeless or would not get well when, at the ordinary ward round, one asked them how they were. The above represent those in whom the conviction was strong, and was uttered spontaneously or frequently. Its relation to hypochondria is noteworthy.

Hypochondriacal preoccupations or delusions were found in 25 patients. There has been so much dispute about hypochondria that it is well to make it clear what is here meant. These patients were all unduly concerned about changes in their bodies; some feared that there might be such change, others were sure of it, but this was partly, at any rate, a question of verbal form given to the preoccupation; the essential features were that it was clearly morbid and centred on the body. So close is the attention which depressed patients pay to their experiences (as Wilmanns and others have emphasized) in the matter of difficulties of thinking and action, that it is not surprising when they give undue significance (*Bedeutungswahn*) to the various bodily sensations which can be experienced even in the 'normal' state if sufficient attention be paid to them. The question of whether these feelings are or are not accompanied by anxiety appears irrelevant, so far as their presence is concerned, and confusing. Gillespie has insisted on such a differentiation which seems quite arbitrary: 'Overt anxiety is no part of a purely hypochondriacal state of mind in the view adopted in this paper. One of the essentials of the hypochondria concept, if it is to be useful at all, is that hypochondria shall be differentiated from anxious preoccupation by the absence of anxiety or similar affects in the former. . . . The affect in hypochondriacal preoccupation is better described as a type of interest, not of a fearful kind. . . . Closely connected with the affective attitude is the reality value for the patient of his hypochondriacal notions. It may be said of the merely anxious patient that he fears but does not believe that he suffers from the malady which he professes to apprehend, and that, in fact, he chooses something to worry about which he knows in his heart to be a perfectly safe topic upon which he can always get dogmatic reassurance. On the other hand, for the hypochondriac the fancied ailment is real. He has a conviction, and not a fear, of disease—it may be simply of malfunction, or it may be of morbid structural alteration.' This is an unwarranted distinction, unless one is prepared so far to limit the meaning of the term 'hypochondria' as to exclude from it all the anxious bodily preoccupations of the depressive state. Gillespie's case-histories lend themselves to diagnostic criticism, but it is sufficient to say here that his definition of hypochondria is unacceptable.

Examining the patients in detail, one finds frequent reference to the bowels. M. A. was convinced that her bowels were not opened. J. G. said: 'The bowels, of course, are gone all wrong.' R. S. said: 'The food just wedges in me; I eat and eat. . . . Began five months ago, this stomach trouble; something turned the stomach over. I can't digest anything. . . . My bowels aren't working properly. I only pass a little.' E. G. D. said: 'I'm all blocked up inside; I can't open my bowels. . . . I haven't got any bowels. . . . The stool doesn't come from my bowels.' He absolutely refused to eat, had to be tube-fed and used to roar loudly during the feeding; he complained frequently of pain in his stomach. He also said he couldn't pass any urine and did not for two days; he had to be catheterized for several days. Only 3 patients in this series were tube-fed in the Maudsley Hospital in one instance only on one occasion. Many others were on the brink of tube-feeding frequently, but just missed needing it. J. C. struggled violently during the feeding, and always vomited most of the feed immediately after it had been given. A few patients were at one stage of their illness voracious eaters, e.g., H. C. and E. B. E. G. D. would eat plenty when he was drowsy with somnifaine. Another, who had delusions about her bowels, though not nihilistic ones, was A. F.; she had complained of pain in her rectum after a pelvic operation; while under treatment here she complained of bearing-down pain in the abdomen, rumbling, frequent desire to pass urine, burning sensations in her forehead (where she had a prominent, pigmented mole), said (incorrectly) that she was having diarrhoea, that her pains were excruciating, that she would sooner be dead; she became convinced that the lower part of her backbone had become displaced by a fall she had, and that there was a disfiguring eruption on her face; she asked frequently whether it was not true she had cancer, and also asserted she must have the plague. E. B. had a most florid arabesque of hypochondriac delusions, the description of which, taken down verbatim, at one time covered many pages. They concerned the whole of her alimentary tract, especially her mouth and gullet; her body felt dry inside—her bones felt alive with worms—her body had become closed up—she had insects breeding in her inside—she was rotting. In the details of all this, the influence of a recent traumatic episode and of crude sexual preoccupations was traceable. C. W. believed she was rotting away, mortifying from venereal disease. So did I. W. and E. R. F., who also thought that her sexual parts swelled up so as to become noticeable to passers-by, and E. J. F., who actually had gonorrhoea; she felt a lump in her throat, was afraid food would choke her, and thought she had worms in her inside, especially in her throat. M. C. felt she was wasting away in her left side, and eructated swallowed air with noisy persistence; she said also that her head was closing up. A. H. said he had spinal syphilis, and he was always on the watch for fresh symptoms, testing his pupillary reaction in light in the mirror and so on (he had been a nurse in the National Hospital, Queen Square). R. D. thought he had tuberculosis (a scoutmaster who committed paederasty with him had tuberculosis); he worried also because he thought he had had a 'stroke'—a sudden blank feeling across his forehead. G. S. said: 'All my inside is stiff. . . . Pains start in my eyes, go to my stomach.' E. P. had the feeling of a dead weight in the lower part of her body; she felt she could not walk or breathe, she was choking; she also often inspected and displayed her hands, saying that they were no longer human hands, but a canary's claws. In her the particular form in which the delusions were clothed was comprehensible from her recent experiences. J. C. said that her heart was bad, that she had pains all over; she declared that she could not walk or breathe or eat; she was sure she was dying. L. L. C. said her abdomen was swollen and painful—'awful feelings in my stomach. I can't get it out of my head there was a baby coming; there's something left'; she thought she might have a cancer.

These were the patients in whom concern about their bodies and their health was a prominent feature. Others in whom it was less so, and who bore the stamp rather of anxiety and preoccupation than of delusion, were A. G., F. H., who said, 'There's something inside my chest gnawing. It's so heavy, this despondency. I can't breathe through it. It's choking me'; D. C., who said her head felt it was being pushed out; M. C., who wanted to know if everything was satisfactory in the physical examination—blood, etc.—and complained of pains in her head, pains in her chest, etc.; G. M., who was much exercised over spots before her eyes, in spite of frequent explanations of their nature, and who was convinced there was something in her ear (though there was not); L. W., who had peculiar cold feelings in her head, and thought that some pimples on her face were indicative of some bad disease; J. M., who had pains in various parts of her body, which she worried about constantly; and E. W. D., who worried about his hernia and his temperature, said he wasn't fit to get up and that he had rheumatism.

There is in these cases a wide range, from fussy, old-womanish valetudinarianism to gross and grotesque delusions. To differentiate them according to the accompanying affect would be misleading. There are gradations from 'as if' constructions—'I feel as if my head were bursting'—through verbal forms, not essentially different—'my head is bursting'—and anxiety expressions—'I've got such a weight in my chest, I can't breathe, I'm choking'—to definite delusions—'I can't eat, I'm all stopped up.' It is therefore equally difficult to distinguish between them on grounds of degree of conviction. The degree to which the 'sentiment of the real' is lost has been urged by French writers, and even so long ago as 1857 Witmaack wrote with gusto: 'Severe hypochondriacs can estrange themselves more and more from the reality of their bodies, until at least they pass beyond all possibility of re-awakening and the soul buries itself well-nigh irredeemably in the murky depths of misanthropy.' But estimations of the strength of the sentiment of the real are apt to turn into questions of metaphysics, and are not in place here, any more than the old controversies about 'hypochondria cum materia' (cf. Pick). Bleuler differentiates the hypochondriacal delusions of depression from the hypochondriacal catathymic delusions by the attitude of the patient—in the former fearful of the future, the latter concerned about the present, demanding relief. It is by no means a satisfactory distinction; it does not apply in the cases here given. His other view, however, that a depressive fundamental mood is necessary for the development of all really delusional hypochondriacal ideas ('holothyme Wahnbildungen'), is in accordance with the findings here.

The view of these phenomena which seems most applicable to the data here presented, is that there is an interaction of depressive or anxious affective states with more or less diffuse somatic sensations. Changes in the vegetative nervous system, coenaesthetic disturbances, especially of the alimentary tract, are frequent concomitants of such mood disorders; attention is directed to them, and their significance worked on in the manner of delusional formations of any kind. Pathoplastic influences may readily be traced in the patient's previous, especially recent, experience; sexual factors are prominent, as in many of the cases just cited.

It is an observation which cannot but force itself even on the casual observer, that there is a close connexion between hypochondriacal delusions and those feelings of bodily change which are called depersonalization phenomena, or 'somatic hallucinations'. One might properly consider them here, but their connexion with anxiety, compulsive and other neurotic features, and with feelings of unreality, is so close that they are considered in that context below. Schilder and other psycho-analytic writers have laid much stress on this connexion; the general psycho-analytical view on hypochondria is discussed by Carp, who considers that there is a concentration of libido on the body-ego (the part of the psycho-physical personality that is somatically experienced), which is so great as to cause a total withdrawal of libido from the part of the personality that is psychically experienced, and so there are depersonalization feelings. Whether such a construction is as illuminating as it is ingenious may be doubted. He concludes also that there is a 'genitalization' of the body in these hypochondriacal experiences.

The difficulty of considering separately any group of phenomena is seen also in the relation of hypochondriacal delusions to thought-disorder. A patient may say, 'My head feels empty; I haven't got any thoughts; there's nothing at the back of my head; it is hollow,' and one has difficulty in deciding whether this is a vivid description of difficulty in thinking, with verbal elaboration, or a hypochondriacal delusion. The difference is not essential, but chiefly a difficulty of formal classification; it serves, however, to indicate the relationship between the two, or rather the similarity. In both there is disproportion between the patient's estimate of the function concerned and the observer's conclusion as to the degree of functional derangement, from examination of behaviour. It is in one case the most highly organized of all the psycho-biological integrations—thought—that is the function under examination, and in the other a lower level, vegetative or reflex; but the patient's false judgment and exaggeration of the degree of functional impairment is found in both. One recalls Raecke's insistence that the essential feature of hypochondria is 'it changed feeling of self, whether it affects to a greater extent somatic or the psychic aspect of personality'.

Something must be said of the 'délire des negations'. As Cotard, after whom the syndrome is usually called, first described it, the ideas of negation bore either on the physical domain—no heart, no stomach, no brain—or on the psychical—no thoughts, no feelings, no will; they may be turned outwards—no reality, no life, no doctors, no flowers, no justice, no God. He confused it with hypochondriacal delusions occurring in the paranoid; mainly, however, he associated with these hypochondriacal ideas melancholic anxiety, conviction of immortality, ideas of damnation or possession, and impulse to suicide. As Toulouse has pointed out in his careful study, the characteristic feature is the systematization, extension and predominance of the nihilistic hypochondriacal system, overwhelming other melancholic ideas. Toulouse and others have examined the psychopathology of these ideas; here it is only necessary to point out that they may be quite absent from the agitated melancholia of the involution period and present in young people; that the more complete the negation of bodily contents, the poorer the prognosis. Where there is complete negation, to call it a syndrome is not justified; there are, for example, gradations from unjustified worry about the bowels, as in many otherwise healthy people, to complete denial of any abdominal viscera; the association with anxiety in the melancholic patient is striking; the less the accompanying anxiety, the worse the prognosis. To delusions of enormity the same conclusions apply; both they and the ideas of negation were exemplified in E. B., who said she had swallowed the whole world, changed the world at the same time, as she believed that she would never die or rest, and could not be killed, that her bowels were stopped up, and had not been opened at all for eight weeks.

There was a definite and overt sexual colouring to the delusions and preoccupations in a number of the patients. In many these bore a relation to recent happenings—masturbation, illicit intercourse, homosexuality, incest. R. S. was afraid of impotence; D. C. said that she wanted to be loved. There may be also mentioned M. H. and E. P. and A. M. P., who believed their babies would be monsters, as did L. L. C. and D. N. and A. H., whose behaviour was erratic in different ways, and A. C. who kept her legs tightly adducted during physical examination, so that it was difficult to test the knee-jerks, motor power, etc. There were 8 others in whom the sexual colouring was not so overt.

It is necessary to make brief reference to a variety of false belief or apprehensions concerned with sleep. A striking example of this was G. M., she worried constantly about not having sufficient sleep; it was her chief and at times her only complaint; she asserted she had not slept for weeks, though most careful special observation by different people on many different nights established that she had slept soundly the whole night through; nothing convinced her, however, and this was a quite unshakable delusion. In others in whom such a conviction was a prominent symptom there was not only conviction that they had not slept the preceding night, but also that they would not sleep that night (expressed either as a fear—anxiety—or a certainty) unless one gave them some sleeping-draught. Some of them slept well without any drugs, others on small doses or medinal (2½ gr.) of sodium bicarbonate. It need scarcely be pointed out that the majority of depressive patients actually have disordered sleep, or that dread of sleeping and of anxiety-dreams or sexual dreams may be an important factor in the insomnia of the melancholic. In this group, however, there is an assertion of sleeplessness which is not in accordance with fact—a variety of '*delire de negation*'.

SELF-REPROACH, SELF-ACCUSATION

These are among the most striking of melancholic symptoms. It was prominent and persistent in 27 cases. The particular wording varied according to the patient's education and *milieu*, and was in some bare and brief, in others florid, with Biblical vigour and richness. In this regard, as with hypochondriacal ideas, it is hard to distinguish between the simple affirming of a conviction of exceeding moral or bodily degradation and the hyperbole of others, not feeling so much, but fertile of language—language frequently reminiscent of Job or the Psalmist: 'I am a worm and no man; a reproach of men, and despised of the people. All they that see me laugh me to scorn; they shoot out the lip, they shake the head. . . . I am poured out like water, and all my bones are out of joint; my heart is like wax; it is melted in the midst of my bowels. My strength is dried up like a potsherd; and my tongue cleaveth to my jaws; and thou hast brought me into the dust of death.'

It has been said that whereas in hypochondriacal delusions there is an egocentric-egoistic attitude, in self-reproach it is egocentric-altruistic: in the former I have something bad, in the latter I do something bad; not I but my neighbours are in danger, through me. Any such opposition, however, is unjustified, for both these attitudes may be found together, as in patients who declare they are rotting away from the plague or venereal disease, and that they have wickedly infected others with it. The accusations against themselves are always on the moral score: they have failed in their duty to God or to themselves or to other men.

'I've been false to the Almighty, possessed by the Devil' (especially common among Catholics). 'It's all my fault; I didn't exercise my will-power'. 'I neglected myself; I let myself go.' 'I've been wicked; I didn't do enough for my sister.' 'I've committed the unpardonable sin.' 'I'm a lost soul; I've given myself to the Devil.' 'I've been selfish.' 'I'm an immoral pervert, the worst in the world; I'm an absolute cad, not fit to be seen.' 'I'm in mortal sin.' 'I've let everybody down.' 'I neglected the house.' 'I've wrecked the home; I'm a wretch.' 'I've betrayed my trust.' 'I've no consideration for others.'

Some patients have only a general vague feeling of everything being wrong, e.g., M. S., who said, 'I seem to do everything at the wrong moment. . . . It's all the wrong way round'. Of such are the patients who wander about, looking perplexed and ejaculating tearfully or in agitation, 'It's all wrong; everything's gone wrong'. The relation of this to disturbance of consciousness, perplexity, Ratlosigkeit, suggests itself; this is considered below in connexion with the appearance of unreality and other changes in the environment. The patient just referred to, M. S., also said she was lazy and that she was always doing something wrong.

Other patients refer their wrong-doing to the past, giving chapter and verse and falsifying only in the attribution of evil motives to themselves or magnifying the part they played in bringing about evil; occasionally a patient gives an entirely false account of misdeeds, e.g., A. H., who said she had purposely burnt down a house, and L. C. who said she had plotted to bring about her husband's death by consumption. In nearly all, however, there is rather misrepresentation of actual happenings, however trivial, than invention. There is also an exaggeration of personal responsibility that is not to be distinguished in kind, but only in degree, from the *hubris*, the almost glorifying aggrandizement of those who declare themselves the chief sinners, Devils incarnate: 'There never was anybody in the world as wicked as me.' 'I'm the only case in the hospital that isn't genuine.' It is another aspect of the tendency towards the extreme seen already in the delusions of negation and enormity. In many of the patients, recent happenings regarded as traumatic or precipitating gave their form to the delusions, as in E. B., H. C., who declared that he had married for lust only, E. P., who said she had wilfully stifled her twin babies in the womb, and others. Whether in these it was only the temporal relation between the incident and the onset of illness, and the relation of the incident to the content of the delusions, which made one regard the happening as having aetiological significance is a pertinent question to be considered in connexion with 'reactive depressions' and other such divisions.

Many patients reproach themselves for 'impure thoughts'; having had compulsive thinking with overt sexual trends and the unpleasant affect that accompanied the obsessions, they may go continually to confession, (e.g. one who had had obscene thoughts at communion, and had been to various confessors until they refused to see her again), or otherwise seek to purge themselves of their iniquity, as they feel it; I. W. wanted to give herself up to the police. The involutions of the delusion may be intricate; thus, G. S. mentioned no definite fault she had been guilty of, but was sure she would never be pardoned; she said it was 'just something dreadful', and when pressed said she had given people a false impression: 'If I hadn't said all those things about myself, people wouldn't have thought I was ill'; her fault, in short, lay in malingering through uttering delusions. Similarly, M. R. said she was here under false pretences.

Not all the forms of self-accusation come under the rubric of delusions. The patient's self-reproach may have good grounds: 'I am a troublesome patient; I worry the nurses.' 'I think too much of myself and not enough of other people.' 'I neglected the house.' 'I am a wash-out. . . . I'm selfish. . . . I'm certain I'm disliked wherever I go.' These statements, stripped of their moral implications, were correct enough. H. C. said: 'Now I'm seeing myself as I really am. I'm in a position now that there's no getting out of. I've got to face the reality and be a man and carry on. It's what I'd like to do, but I haven't got the guts to do it. I've got a sort of general fear of life. It seems to me to be in line with all the previous breakdowns. I haven't got the moral backbone that I was kidding myself I had. I feel I've committed the unpardonable sin, and yet my beliefs are rather loose now.' These cannot be called delusions—'I feel I've committed'—and he appraises his character and position justly, if severely, but in thus singling out the worse aspects and suppressing those which would balance or even outweigh them, there is the harsh and pessimistic attitude which is the essential feature. (M. B. in addition to saying she had been lazy and 'had slacked', said she could now see things plainly as they really were, not as pleasant illusions.)

M. L. said: 'I have fallen below my ideals. . . . I ought to make a clean breast. . . . I'm afraid to say what comes in my head because I feel in my bones it may be a mistake. . . . There is something wrong in my life which I must put right. . . . I have committed the unpardonable sin—the closed mind.' Here, just as with M. S., there is a vague sense of wrong, in addition to such definite peccadilloes and alleged wrongdoing as she told of, from wandering away at the age of two to defrauding the London County Council through her teaching scholarship. In her, however, there were none of the other features, suggesting a disturbance of consciousness, seen in M. S., and in many of her self-critical remarks the criticism was sound.

The behaviour that carried her beliefs into actions was, however, sufficient evidence that those beliefs, even though correct, were of a morbid quality; she wanted to rectify or acknowledge her peccadilloes, though they had happened many years before, and the persons concerned were at a loss to know what it was she was avowing, having themselves forgotten the matter.

There were 18 other patients in whom self-reproach occurred, but without prominence or persistence. Most of these reproached themselves for having neglected their babies or their homes, with having been lazy, or with not having made sufficient effort (cf. E. A., who said, 'I ought to struggle against this feeling'). I. M. said: 'This has come as a punishment,' thus introducing the same idea of retribution as L. A. H., who said that having spoken unkindly about her stepmother, she was having to suffer now, and added, 'What's the use of me in this state? What good am I to my husband?' (self-depreciation rather than self-reproach). D. P. and M. T. said, 'I know I have done wrong', alluding to their sexual experiences, but they did not show any lively remorse, though occasionally they wept when speaking of these happenings. R. D. and E. W. recalled peccadilloes, the former also saying about the homosexual experiences, 'I must take the blame myself.' E. N. said: 'I feel at times as if I've committed a crime'—the same words as she used when expressing her attitude towards coitus. E. H. troubled like E. J. with compulsive sexual thoughts, said her thoughts were disgusting, but asked if she was wicked, she replied: 'No, I'm not.' M. H. said: 'It's my fault because I oughtn't to have worried like I did.... It's my fault; if I'd had glasses it would all have been different.' Male patients were sure they had made mistakes in their work; some of them had, but in the others it was another form of recognition of difficulty in carrying out tasks. A. G. believed he had made mistakes, though he had not, and also said: 'You think I'm a dirty beast, I expect; in some ways I am. . . . I have acted as a coward and a cad towards the girl.' E. R., having told about her sexual activities, said: 'I don't suppose there's another character like that in the whole hospital. I'm ashamed. I'm a degraded woman.'

The self-reproach of a great number of these patients centred on their sexual behaviour. Masturbation, among the male patients chiefly, and pre- or extra-marital intercourse among the women, are the chief topics, together with homosexuality and other perversities or anomalies. They are considered together with the other details of sexual activity.

The patients in whom there was no self-reproach discovered, or scarcely any, were 16 in number. One of these had declared herself, at home, to be a wicked woman and a fraud, but denied it here, and said, 'I've never done anything I regret.'

As to the genesis of such ideas, apart from psycho-analytical speculations, it may be found in the disproportion between what is accomplished and what is desired or aimed at, which may be regarded as the root of all dissatisfaction. Religious and ethical ideas have always been prominent in human societies, and it is unnecessary to lay the burden on our present culture as Bumke does: 'The added feeling of responsibility with which modern civilization burdens us, brings so close the idea of personal blame that any prolonged depressive change of mood readily makes play with it. Over-valued ideas thus gain ground in the mind, and countless neurotics are accompanied through life by a feeling of inadequacy, a touch of bad conscience. But if the depression and anxiety grow worse, an invincible conviction crystallizes out, and the dubious belief becomes a delusion.' With the latter part of this, and its refusal to distinguish absolutely between feelings of insufficiency, wavering ideas, definite delusions, retrospective ones and those coloured by anxiety, the present writer is in agreement.

There is an aspect of these ideas which needs special consideration. Some of the patients believe that their conduct influences others detrimentally in an unusual way.

In schizophrenia, ideas of influence and passivity feelings are common, their direction being from another person to the patient; his thoughts and actions are influenced from without. In melancholic delusions here under consideration the influencing of thought and behaviour is also evident, but in the opposite sense: the patient is responsible; it is the others who are influenced. On the one hand, there are affinities with grandiose delusions: 'I affect others,' 'I work upon them by some (mysterious) power' (cf. 'omnipotence of thought'), and on the other hand with paranoid beliefs, as just seen.

In a number of these patients the belief has to do with eating: six believed that through their eating, other patients had to starve; thus, M. S. said: 'I know that staying in bed and eating all that food is wrong; it does harm to the others . . . they're getting thinner and thinner.' She also said: 'When I stay in bed, it upsets the others; they are all restless when I am in bed. . . . I'm making people ill. . . . I made all the mess in the hospital.' Similarly, E. P. said she must not eat because it stopped the others from doing so. 'I oughtn't to have come here, to this place. You know those ladies that act funny in the ward; they do the same things that I used to do; it seems to me they're gone like that since I came here. . . . Everybody here has to imitate what I do.' H. C. also said that she put the sun out. E. R. F. said: 'If I don't eat my food, something's going to happen; somebody's going to be killed.' Sixteen other patients expressed ideas of this sort, though not connected with food. J. G. said: 'But for me none of these dreadful cases would be here. Many more followed me, and not suitable cases. . . . I gave the other patients bad breath. . . . I'm upsetting the whole hospital.' This grandiose strain is also plain in A. G. and in A. H., who declared: 'All the others are being punished on my account; I am responsible for the whole hospital,' and who denied any authority to the sister of the ward, saying always: 'I am responsible for everything here.' Likewise, E. W., who maintained that she harmed others, influenced them for evil, and that it would 'hasten the Fourth Coming if I died'. The sacrifice or Messiah notion is here evident. E. B. said that others have to think her thoughts and imitate her actions: 'I injure everybody now.' E. H. said: 'I worry everybody that comes near me. . . . I have no proof, it's an atmosphere.' C. W. said: 'People are going rotten like me. . . . Everybody's mouth goes sore like mine.' Others who declared that they had made all the patients ill and were responsible for all the trouble in the hospital were L. C., W. G. and G. S. Other forms of it were seen in M. C., who thought all her family and her employer would go to Hell solely on her account. E. J. F., who believed the other patient's hair had gone grey as hers had done, and E. A., who thought her son had altered as a result of her trimming his hair.

It will be evident that most of these patients were agitated and bewildered, and that there are two elements—a projection of the patient's behaviour and emotion on to others, and a setting up of a false relation to account for their real or seeming behaviour; the grandiose aspect of the belief is connected with the extreme of self-reproach and humility, as in the delusions of enormity and negation already discussed.

Paranoid beliefs in melancholia are readily explained as the correlate of the idea of sinfulness: 'I'm worthless; others know it; they treat me accordingly, they put slights on me, they persecute me.' But this is to make the matter very simple, simpler than the data permit. Adequate though this 'comprehensible relation' may be to account for many cases, there are others where it falls short. It will be well to give the data first, and then discuss the psychopathology. Ideas of reference or of persecution were found in a majority of the patients. They ranged from a mere impression of contempt, jeering, avoidance or hostility on the part of others to a conviction of being poisoned, followed about, shot at, tormented, etc.

Thus, M. H. thought people stared at her when she went out; she felt inferior to other people. R. J. disliked going out of doors because she thought she looked different and people noticed it. E. W. D. and M. L. were suspicious, A. H. was disinclined to face anybody, M. T. thought people showed signs of noticing an unpleasant smell about her, and E. H. believed people stared at her, were aware of her 'disgusting' thoughts and gave meaning sniffs: 'I notice people laughing when I am there; I am on the alert for it.' These are the milder forms. H. D. H. felt all the patients knew about her incest and treated her accordingly. M. R. thought everyone disliked her. E. P.: 'A girl here looked at me as if it's me made her like that.' E. R.: 'You look at me, Doctor, as if to say, "I know all about you"; I don't suppose there's another character like mine in the whole hospital.' A. P. thought people talked about her, and so she 'cut' them in the street. E. R. F. said that she was followed about by people to punish her, and that people wanted her to confess, but she didn't know what. A. F.: 'The nurses and patients whisper about me, and stare at me; you all despise me.' S. R. likewise, 'People seem to be looking at me lately; they talk about me', and F. N. who was sure everybody knew about him, that he masturbated: 'I thought everyone was looking at me; the patients here avoid me, they despise me.' M. B. said nobody wanted her here. W. G.: 'I have the impression somebody's waiting for my bed. The people want me out of it. They hint.' He believed he was spied on and ridiculed. A. H. said that her sister's letters were from an impostor: 'Our place at Ridgecroft has been usurped. . . . The other patients dislike me, hate me for some uncleanness.' H. C.: 'The others talk about me; they blame me, put slights on me. They think I'm the Devil. . . . You pass me by as if I wasn't human. . . . They think I bewitched the food. People are afraid of me. . . . Everyone looks at me.' C. W.: 'People shrink from me; the others don't want me.' M. S. said everybody thought her lazy and talked about her, called her 'Death' and 'pig' and didn't want to have anything to do with her. E. J. F. thought people were after her, talking about her, laughing at her; everything was against her: 'People think I'm no good. . . . People are afraid of me, they point at me.' I. W. said everybody knew what she had done; she felt everybody hated her; people looked disgusted, they knew her thoughts; other patients were put in the ward to annoy her, an article in *Punch* was written about her, her food was tampered with to harm her, and the tea burnt her throat; later she thought this had been done to spoil her sense of smell and so save her from the unpleasant body-odour she gave off; she eavesdropped, said the people next door were always listening, and that political parties were conspiring with her employers. E. G. D. likewise had a mixture of ideas of reference and paranoid ideas; he thought the other patients disliked him, and also declared that he was bathed with lysol, that he was 'doped' to stop up his bowels (he had been receiving somnifaine injections shortly before he said this); he had at the beginning of his illness felt that everyone at work was getting in front of him, had become very suspicious and took offence easily. L. A. H. said people watched her, followed her, thought her lazy; people believed she had poisoned someone; she also said that her own food was poisoned and that there was a plot in which everybody was concerned; people stared at her, laughed, made songs about her, detectives were after her. A. G. said people suspected him of poisoning his father; he was shunned, detectives were after him, the doctors were making inquiries about him at the bank, the doctors and nurses talked about him. M. C. said people laughed at her, and were in league against her, there was a woman in the ward set to spy on her; she was suspicious, thought the doctors and nurses knew more than they would say, and she constantly read meaning into harmless remarks, making them sinister. D. N. said men in the garden watched her, detectives followed her everywhere: 'People all know about me, but they can't really, it's my feelings.' L. C. thought people wanted to hang her for having plotted her husband's death. D. J. thought 'everybody was a C.I.D. man'. M. C. thought people wanted to kill her. E. B. thought 'they were all after me', and she had phantasies of doing harm to others in various ways; she felt everyone was looking at her because she looked 'funny'. R. D. thought people were all against him. A. C. said she was being watched by patients on the lawn below. A. N. thought that strangers in the street were saying he was blind or deaf and dumb; they looked at him strangely; one girl laughed at him and said, 'You're dumb'; the rumour had spread that he was deaf, blind or dumb (in consequence he had not gone out of the house for weeks). B. S. said people were trying to hurt her; E. W. said in her grandiose way that others represented her, the sick people in the ward were representing her death, that there were articles in the newspaper about her, that the courts were busy about her forthcoming trial by the Archbishop of Canterbury and Bernard Shaw, that everybody was laughing at her, it was all a hoax. J. G. believed all her curses were put in the newspapers, and everyone knew of the exceeding evil in her, and that the police were about the hospital, seeking her. M. A. said people accused her of immorality and of starving her child. G. S. said: 'Everyone thinks I'm a wicked woman,' and when she was under the influence of opium she said she was being given drugs to damage her irretrievably, and finally, R. H., who held not persons, but God and fate, responsible, saying, 'Life is so damnably cruel', railing against society in general and providence.

This concludes a list of paranoid delusions, attitudes and feelings, the detailed repetition of which seems justified by the omission of any reference to such phenomena in melancholia, in standard English textbooks, like 'Henderson and Gillespie' and 'Craig and Beaton'.

All these patients felt or believed that they were discriminated against. If the explanation briefly alluded to above were correct, one would find, as one often does, an attitude, not of resentment, but of resignation: 'I deserve it.' Thus, Séglas said in 1892: 'The persecutory ideas found in deluded melancholics are not true ideas of persecution. Their foundation is not pride, but the peculiar humility of the melancholic; they bear the stamp of that peculiar quality of resignation which is their own; for the patient finds his persecution justified by his unworthiness, and notwithstanding the "persecution" label we attach to his delusions, he remains first and foremost a self-accuser.' Ballet, speaking at the same time, put it more concisely: 'They are victims, but guilty victims, not as ordinary persecuted patients, innocent victims.' This, then, is a definite criterion; how does it apply to these patients? There were

17 patients who thought they were getting their deserts, who did not exculpate themselves or make a grievance of the way people treated them. It is necessary to qualify the statement with regard to some of them. Resentment was shown in their words or behaviour: thus, M. C. occasionally struck the nurses. H. C. occasionally said to the doctor: 'Get about your business.' E. B. threw things on the floor and at the nurses occasionally, and said they were insulting her. J. G. wrote to her brother: 'You will be surprised to hear that Wednesday I said Damn all the doctors and nurses and the whole world, Heaven, Hell, Christ Jesus and the Holy Ghost. A few days previous I said Let the King die.' E. J. F. said that people knocked against her bed deliberately (and after apparent recovery she became litigious and quarrelsome). E. P., though she said 'I'm punished for some wrong', was resentful at being in hospital (and has become more so, as well as quarrelsome with her relatives and neighbours since discharge). M. R. said: 'Inwardly I was annoyed with my sister for being ill when she should be looking after me.' In some of these cases the evident resentment was only occasional, in others a recollection, possibly falsified in the recalling.

Another group, while conceding their sinfulness or wrongdoing, mentioned persecutions or discrimination against them for which they could not account, and which they did not regard as the punishment or result of their wrong-doing. A. C., who thought men watched her, became definitely paranoid with the shift from depression to mania, but during her depressive period she was surly and aggressive, especially to the nurses; the only fault she avowed was neglect of her baby, and she did not attach much importance to that. W. G. made many complaints against the workmen who were hammering; he said that he was given medicine to harm him, and demanded to know what was being done to his mother; his manner was aggressive and hostile. E. H. was variable in her attitude; asked if she thought she was wicked, she replied: 'No, I'm not. People think my thoughts are nasty. So they are. Oh no, they're not. It's my consciousness.' F. N. was resentful towards the people at his office, who, he said, 'pestered' him; he became quarrelsome during his period of subsequent hypomania. A. M. P. resented people's supposed attitude to her sufficiently to 'cut' their acquaintance, and she was seen, after her confinement, shaking her baby and hitting it on the head; also, she said angrily to her husband, apropos of her pregnancy, 'See what a fine position you've got me into'. E. R., while bearing supposed looks of contempt with resignation, was resentful at being questioned about her sexual life, and very resentful towards a neighbour who tormented and abused her. B. S., who confessed to no other wrong-doing than leaving her home uncared for, believed people were trying to shoot her. I. W. was angry because her 'food was different', and said, 'Nobody cares here what I get'; she was also resentful over the supposed articles in *Punch*, and the questioning during examination of her mental state.

There was also a group of patients who made outspoken protests against the way others treated them or in defence of their innocence. A. N. and M. A.

denied that there was any ground for people behaving as they did toward them. S. R. asked: 'What have I got to blame myself for?' though occasionally she said she had neglected her children and was dirty. M. C. said: 'I wonder if you think it's my fault,' herself denying that it was thus to be accounted for. L. A. H. was forever loudly proclaiming her innocence and her wrongs: 'I've never done anything wrong. I've always been honest with my husband,' although she also said she was being made to suffer for having said unkind things about her stepmother; her whole manner was angry and resentful; she would toss her head and her eyes would flash with indignation. A. G., while blaming himself harshly for his behaviour towards a girl, denied vehemently the accusations which he said people made about his having poisoned his father: 'There is no truth in it whatever; he died a natural death'; once, when he was questioned about eating, he looked very fierce and angry for a few moments and asked the purpose of the question. E. G. D. admitted no faults; he said his illness was the result of his treatment here; he resented most of what was done for him. D. N. was able to write in the same letter: 'I know I have been a very, very wicked girl, over mostly groundless worry, but not entirely, but, if I may say so, you do not know what I have suffered, and rightly suffered. . . . I know in my heart of hearts I am worthy of it, and you would never regret helping me. . . . It will bring the greatest happiness to a home of sorrow, entirely caused by me. . . . I have been truly a funny girl, but never intended to be wicked in my life. . . . Everyone has the greatest faith in me. So it really shows that I could not have been so bad before in any case.' And again, in an interview, she said: 'Everything is my fault. I know after I went out I was followed about by detectives. And you'd think when I went into a shop I was going to steal something. . . . I was a simple good kid when I started. I've willed my life away. . . . I don't want to go to prison. You mustn't blame my mum and dad. It's that rotten office that's done everything. I know everybody thinks it's groundless. In that rotten office there's one man who did it all.' She often said, in direct contradiction of statements made shortly before, that she was really a good girl, that she was sure she hadn't deserved all this; as her health improved, self-reproach disappeared, and the desire to prove her innocence became the chief subject of her talk; she was full of resentment against the woman who had accused her of misconduct. G. S. and A. H., while under the influence of drugs, uttered similar protestations. A. H. said: 'I am not really a Bolshevik. . . . I have not been violated.' And G. S. said frequently, when drowsy with somnifaine: 'I didn't do it.' On one such occasion she said, over and over: 'I don't want to kill you, Doctor.' As a rule her replies were fretfully aggressive. A. H. occasionally fought with the nurses and even struck them; and finally, R. H., for all his self-denunciation ('I'm a filthy coward'), blamed his circumstances and life in general rather than himself, and was bitter in his denunciations of society and God; towards other people he was irritable.

In order to conclude the list of patients who showed resentment (though in these without particular relation to paranoid ideas), 10 further patients must be mentioned. In L. C. C., F. H. and L. W. the resentment was against the hospital, and has persisted since recovery. In A. C. and R. D. it was against the patient's husband, in E. W. D. against his wife. In D. P. it was against some nurses and one doctor, in M. T. and M. L. it was against me. In D. C. it was against her relatives, who told her it was her own fault; she was querulous and made complaints against the nurses, and she also said: 'It isn't fair; I have done nothing to deserve all this, and nobody will listen to my troubles.'

Starting from delusions of persecution, one has come to a consideration of the patient's attitude to his environment. In connexion with the patient's talk, importunity has been mentioned, and in another connexion his response to encouragement or stimulation. If one is to consider the patient as he is in his setting and not as an isolated individual, his relation to the surroundings must be prominent. There are still several such relations or attitudes to be considered; here it is appropriate only to point out that humility and resignation are by no means the only attitude the melancholic patient takes up, but that resentment and hostility may exist alongside these, or may even dominate the picture. The attitude may show itself in various forms, but is to be detected in a majority of patients, either diffuse and vague or sharply directed. Resignation is certainly the commonest attitude towards the persecutory ideas, but it is not by any means the invariable one. It may be said that it is an admixture of other forms or reaction-types, which produces in some patients a resentful attitude towards the supposed discrimination, but where so small a number out of 61 patients are quite free from such features, one is more inclined to regard it as part of the depressive type of reaction. One may seek its signs in the previous personality of the patient or in the essential nature of the melancholic reaction. Psycho-analytic writers have followed the latter road, and have emphasized the hostility and hate of the melancholic patient, only ostensibly directed against himself. If the previous personality of the patients be considered, one seeks for the sensitive, the self-conscious and the querulous. These and other features of the personality are discussed later.

Among writers there is considerable diversity of opinion about the paranoid beliefs and feelings of the depressives. Stoddart, for example, says: 'There is another class of melancholiacs . . . who ascribe their condition to interference by other people. These interpret their inability to do things as due, not to their own weakness, but to an increased resistance in their environment. . . . In this way they develop delusions of persecution, they believe that other people are against them, even that there are worldwide conspiracies to do them harm.' Bleuler, on the other hand, insists: 'Delusions of persecution do not belong to the depressive forms of delusion. The delusion of deserved punishment must not be classed with that of the unjust persecution. The former comes from a general depression, the delusion of persecution is a catathymic symptom which grows from a single emotionally toned idea. Every depressive delusion is a symptom of potentially transient condition, but the delusion of persecution mostly belongs to chronic diseases.' He admits the occurrence of *Beziehungswahn* in melancholia, but apparently only in the sense of guilt: 'In the form of delusions of reference they sometimes attach new ideas to what goes on about them. It is their fault that the other patients are sick, that one had died . . . everyone talks about them; in this world and the next they must be punished. . . . In a milder melancholia the feeling may appear now and then that things are not so bad as all that; an expected punishment may appear unjust. In other cases also there may sometimes appear, in the endlessly complicated workings of the human psyche, a real idea of persecution, e.g., even in healthy people—but to melancholia belongs only the depressive delusions. . . .' Bumke takes up a position midway between these: 'Paranoid notions are not over-common, at least if we exclude certain suspicious twists which depressed people not infrequently give to things. Sad people are normally inclined at times to withdraw from the world and to regard every harmless look, every well-meant question as an intrusion. Similarly depressive patients occasionally believe people want to make fun of their pain, feed on their misfortunes, and humiliate them; people fail to greet them and avoid them, cannot be bothered with them in their business or home. . . . In severe cases there may thus develop illusionary misinterpretations and delusions. People are thought to be making pointed allusions, putting their heads together; they break off their conversation or stand up when the patient comes in; there is a policeman outside, the public prosecutor is making inquiries. If anxiety still further beclouds judgment, then the institution is thought to be a gaol, letters are forged, a scaffold is being run up for them; occasionally in convalescence melancholics have ideas that are really closer to those in paranoia. . . . If these are combined with definite melancholic features, then we have either a manic-depressive mixed state or else the exclusive or predominant influence of an organic lesion. Most often we see a paranoid colouring to the depression in some of the climacteric forms.' And also: 'If a dejected patient complains about every little disturbance by his fellow patients, it is at most a manic-depressive mixed state, but certainly not a pure melancholia.' And finally, Lange, in his recent monograph, says: 'Ideas of persecution play a part only insofar as they are the expression of depreciatory ideas. There is never in them a hostile tendency towards the environment. . . . The persecutions are regarded as well deserved, or insufficiently severe punishment' (p. 82). But elsewhere, discussing a typical form, he writes (p. 163): 'Fleeting paranoid phenomena are often met with at least in fairly well-marked periodic disorders, manias as well as melancholias, and they are rarely quite absent in cyclothymia.' He goes on to emphasize the frequency of these symptoms in the mixed state, where the melancholic phase is changing to a manic one or the reverse—a point first raised by Specht—and he discusses the influence of time of life and of personality in determining the paranoid colouring of the circular psychoses. The general question of the relation of the manic-depressive psychoses to paranoia and paranoid states, which Lange next considers, is not appropriate here. It is sufficient to point out that scarcely any writers recognize the occurrence of paranoid ideas, with resentment or protestations of innocence, as a common feature of depressive states. The examination of these 61 patients, however has shown it to be frequent. It may be said that in some of them the diagnosis is questionable, and the patients should be regarded not as primarily depressive, but as paranoid, with concomitant and secondary depression. The reason for denying that these were depressive would be the occurrence of the definite paranoid features; on other grounds their recognition as affective psychoses with depressive colouring appears justified. A. N. and E. H. might be regarded as examples of 'sensitiver Beziehungswahn', as described by Kretschmer; indeed, many of the patients might without difficulty be included under this head, 'It is always through an affective influence on the patient's awareness of meanings that the change to a delusional attitude is effected.' It does not invalidate their inclusion here that they may be thus denominated; if one were to exclude them from the depressive group on that account, one might as well exclude hypochondriacs for showing that type of reaction, or the anxious patients, or the compulsive. It is noteworthy that, in discussing such cases, no less an authority than Kehrer writes: 'In the great majority of cases of sensitive delusions of reference and of erotic and other more reactive delusional states, we can see that the experience that is alleged to have given rise to the illness consisted in some kind of failure with consequent self-reproach.' He is concerned with the peculiar psychological development to which this experience is the last straw, but it is clear from what he says that self-reproach is by no means incompatible with the development of 'sensitiver Beziehungswahn'. The connexion, indeed, may be regarded as an essential part of the sensitive reactions, as in France. Nathan, for example, writes: 'Kretschmer's patients, like the classical paranoiac, believe themselves to be spied upon or exposed to public hate, but unlike the paranoiac, who is sure of his right and his worth, they are humble, remorseful, abashed . . . they consider their persecution justified . . . it will be seen that these patients in the most clear-cut cases are akin to the psychasthenics and melancholics; but others are closer to the paranoiac.' Into the questions of classification and terminology it is not necessary to enter here; it is sufficient to have shown aggression and resentment to be compatible and often associated with the commonly recognized features of the depressive type of reaction.

In any attempt to categorize the various phenomena of mental disorder, one is confronted with the difficulty of deciding how some symptoms are to be regarded—a patient says he is afraid, he will go mad or be tortured; he looks terrified; is this to be considered as a variety of delusion or as an affective state? Bumke considers that *Angst* (usually, but not quite correctly, translated as 'anxiety') plays the chief part in the formation of delusions in melancholia. It may, moreover, be 'free floating', without definite delusions. The affective state, therefore, will be considered separately; here only an enumeration of the patients with preoccupations, predominant ideas or delusions of a pronounced apprehensive cast will be given.

There were 24 such cases. Of these, 8 said they were afraid they would go mad;

several of them were afraid they would die. E. J. would not go about alone, and said she was terrified of something undefined. R. S. feared insanity or, rather, certification: 'I picture terrible things, that I shall go to an asylum. Another terrible thought is that I've got to let myself die. . . . I'm in terror that I can't hang on. I feel as if I'm going to collapse.' F. H. said: 'I feel the walls will come in on me. . . . I don't know what's going to happen.' M. C., H. C., R. D. and L. A. H. expressed lively fears for the welfare of their relatives. M. C. pictured her whole family crushed beneath falling walls, run over in the street, carried off by pneumonia (besides her private fears of being herself sent to an asylum or mutilated). L. A. H. was very concerned for the welfare of her husband and son, as well as sure that she would herself die and be supplanted as wife by a girl she and her husband knew. R. D. was most apprehensive, on account of his father and the rest of his family, lest the peccant scout-master should attack them. H. C. was painfully and vividly anxious about the welfare of her family, especially her daughter.

If Bleuler's statement is to be accepted, 'katathymic anxiety referring to a particular member of the family, present in normal and abnormal individuals, is as a rule the expression of a repressed wish that this member should be dead'. These patients, then, were unconscious extirpators. As anxiety is so often stressed in connexion with the melancholia of the involutional period, it is as well to state that it was as severe and unremitting in three pre-involutional patients as in any of those at the climacteric or past it.

ATTITUDE TO ENVIRONMENT

Importunity, resentment, suspicion or hostility, the taking of responsibility for the doings of others and humility have already been considered as well as the response to stimulation and encouragement. There remain such difficult things as attitude towards reassurance and general response to a change in the total situation. The latter is so vague as to be impossible of determination; one can say no more than that the patient is aware of what is going on around him, is disturbed by it in varying degree, depending in part on his condition and in part on the nature of the change; one can state the response (speech or action) and state the stimulus (change in surroundings), but to assess their adequacy, except where the disproportion is extreme in either direction, is very difficult in practice. It was attempted in each of the 61 patients; and, though there were extreme cases at either end, to make sharp divisions or gradations proved impossible with the available data. It is of some importance, because many writers have insisted on the diagnostic value of such observations; none of them have given the exact data on which they based their conclusion as to reactivity; they give only their general impressions, much as people do about body-build. Thus, Gillespie points out that 'a comprehensive account would note especially how his condition varied from day to day under the various external stimuli of general environment and treatment, and the internal stimuli of the topics of preoccupation. The psychiatric observer has not usually asked himself what were the specific responses to such factors, and how the latter have seemed to influence the general condition. . . . It seemed, therefore, that a more minute examination of the behaviour from hour to hour and from day to day while under observation and stimulation of various kinds might be of some use, prognostically and therapeutically, in further differentiating clinical conditions. . . .' These admirable intentions are clearly difficult of fulfilment. When Gillespie passes on to the fourteen cases of his 'reactive' group, however, he gives the criteria in more detail, and their very restricted range of applicability and dubiousness of interpretation becomes evident. The patient's responsiveness to influences, he writes, was 'exhibited in relation to a variety of factors: (1) The apparently precipitating causes of an external nature. . . . (2) Changes in the environment during the course of the illness, e.g., the period following the entry into hospital, when the patient was commonly better for a time; changes in the personnel of the environment (departure of other patients to whom they had become attached); visits of relatives and visits home; the receipt of bad news; changes even in the weather (restriction of outdoor recreations); economically compelling circumstances occurring in the course of the illness. (3) Change in the internal environment: (*a*) conscious rumination of a pessimistic kind, (*b*) altered coeanaesthesis. . . . (4) Therapeutic attempts . . .' This is much less than 'minute examination of the behaviour from hour to hour', but if one considers (2) and (4)—and by 'therapeutic attempts' one understands chiefly explanation, persuasion and reassurance—then one sees the wide possible divergence in response to the various factors. A patient may be uninfluenced by reassurance on a delusional topic, yet show a great response to changes in the behaviour or personality of her nurses, to visits from her relatives, and so on. The responsiveness to stimuli of such different kinds and coming from such different people—doctors, nurses, relations, other patients—can no more be recognizable in the lump and susceptible of classification in depressed people than in healthy ones. It has already been seen here how resentment is directed towards a single person or a small group, and is seldom a general or indiscriminate response, i.e., attitude.

It has seemed better to consider the response to the physician's attempts at reassurance, and, separately, the extent to which the patient's bearing during interviews, at ward rounds, and in the garden betokened a readiness to adapt herself to her surroundings in the way of smiling when jested with, answering when spoken to, and so on. There is no need to point out that in all this the severity of the mood-change or the degree of conviction with which the belief is held is the most important factor, though not explicitly considered.

As to reassurance, it seemed to make no difference, or scarcely any, to the patient's conviction in 29 cases. Some of these paid heed to what one said, others did not, but it was all the same; it made no evident impression. In 11 cases there was an apparent effect of reassurance, which wore off soon after, and the beliefs were again obtruded unchanged. As to the remaining patients, they either had no conspicuous false beliefs or varied in their response. As to the response to treatment over a period, it would be absurd to evaluate it in terms of reactivity where so little is known of the factors that determine recovery and there is small opportunity of control observations. Accessibility to reassurance, the more immediate observation, is a resultant of the two factors: strength of conviction, and confidence in the physician, or, as it is commonly termed, strength of the transference. The latter may also be estimated by the frequency with which the patient seeks private interviews, his general demeanour, etc. Those who showed dependence on the physician or attachment to him were 10 in number. Those who had resentment or antagonism towards the physician ('negative transference') have been enumerated elsewhere. The 'transference' factor appears far less important, in this matter of reassurance, than the strength of conviction.

As to the patient's readiness to adapt himself to his surroundings, one must first consider the patient's awareness of them and interest in them, e.g., a 'stuporose' patient or an agitated one. Twenty-four patients seemed to show almost average or normal adaptation to their surroundings in the very restricted range of observation available—it seemed profitless to collect data from nurses, occupation workers, etc., on so very vague a question. Some, e.g., D. P., took strong personal likes and dislikes, and acted accordingly. Other patients, not included in the above list, showed a very definite response to situations at times, e.g., E. G. would at times smash a window, if she was not allowed to see her visitors; she would resent a curt answer, and if one smiled and made jesting remarks she would on occasion smile back; the same was true of J. G. and M. B. and others not far removed from stupor or greatly agitated. E. B. said once: 'When I speak to anyone I feel better.' Others would complain of the other patients disturbing their sleep or annoying them by complaints, e.g., F. H. Many of the patients were worse after visits, but this was in some cases a response to a painful and emotional happening, closely connected with the causes of the patient's illness or the subject of delusions, e.g., a visit from a lover with whom there had been sexual relations, now a matter for self-reproach; in others it might be regarded as a response to the general bustle and disturbance of routine on visiting afternoon, with its reminders of ordinary life; these are reactions of different kinds, but both occurring after visits. Observations of this kind were not made on all the patients, and no conclusions can therefore be given; in some cases they were contrary to expectation; for example, M. T. had a visit, not only from the foster-brother who had had sexual relations with her, but also from his fiancée on the same day, yet it had no perceptible effect on her; H. C. and M. C. were especially agitated after their relatives had left, picturing the accidents that might befall them on the way home. This whole question of response to environment, so broadly considered, is confused. Lange, whom Gillespie has followed, can write, 'Depression depends, even in its course, on the precipitating cause; it recovers when the conflict is resolved; it is readily influenced by change of surroundings, conversation, alleviation of oppressive circumstances', and 'a change of mood that comes from without, that is determined by some experience, and is constantly open to modification by outside happenings, in contrast to the affective state in melancholia, which cannot be thus influenced', but he is describing lump observations and conclusions, made on some extreme cases and applied to others more forcibly than naturally. Such observations, with more adequate differentiation, would be of great value in determining a number of points in treatment. It was thought also that patients who left hospital, still ill, against advice, and who recovered quickly after they went home, e.g., B. S., would be found to have been very quick to respond to changes in their environment, even small ones, but it did not turn out to be so; and a series of such cases has had to be investigated along other lines to determine the factors which would have permitted a forecast of this course. A precise *ad hoc* study of response to certain situations would assist towards recognizing which features of hospital life were beneficial and which the reverse, but in the cases here reported such data have not been recorded in sufficient detail. Lange and also Gillespie speak of the patient's reacting to situations, whether for good or ill, and of the patient's improvement if appropriate measures are taken, e.g., changes made. Thus, improvement through change of *milieu* is a criterion as much as imperturbability when faced with real calamity: 'Whatever the issue of the matters in question, they do not affect the course of the illness. The most painful happenings, occurring during the psychosis (e.g., death of an only son by hanging), do not lead to an aggravation of the malady.' Gillespie, who reports in his Case 2, chosen as a typical example of 'reactive depression', how the patient received bad news, 'the news of his wife's death the next day was followed by a feeling of relief that his wife's sufferings were ended', yet writes that 'of all the single criteria employed, it is probable that reactivity in the sense of this paper is the one of greatest practical value. The importance of a survey of the entire history is shown in the manner in which a reactivity, which may not be apparent to the psychotherapist in his daily encounters with the case, becomes evident when the whole condition is looked at in retrospect.' Not all investigators are so readily satisfied.

FEELINGS OF UNREALITY, DEPERSONALIZATION

It is common in text-books of psychiatry to find a descriptive explanatory passage such as this: 'There is a total loss of feeling—the patient complaining bitterly of the lack of any emotion whatsoever, including a loss of affective response to those whom he formerly loved. As our appreciation of reality depends so much on our ability to "feel ourselves into" the activities of other people (or, more technically, to project our feelings as well as our perceptions), patients suffering from emotional deficit of this kind frequently complain that everything seems unreal to them. This feeling of unreality may be distressing in itself and may even be the chief complaint.' . . . 'In unreality ideas everything is expressed as seeming different—the streets and houses look unusual, the patient wonders whether his friends are the same people as they were or whether indeed they exist at all; he feels differently in himself, and may wonder whether he himself exists' (Henderson and Gillespie). This is a mixture of clinical description and of psychopathology, the latter much influenced by MacCurdy: 'The feeling of the reality attaching to any idea is proportionate to our emotional interest in it. Loss of the feeling of reality is, then, only a manifestation of loss of interest which is, in turn, related to the loss of energy and stimulus susceptibility.' If one accepted this view, it would be sound and convenient to consider as essentially one symptom loss of affective response (loss of interest, incapacity for taking pleasure) and feelings of unreality, including the unreality of one's own body (depersonalization). Such an equation, based on a particular conception of their nature and relations, seems unjustified and likely to ignore some important differences. For this reason, separate observations have been made as to the occurrence of each of the three in the sixty-one patients here reviewed.

Thirteen patients actually complained that they no longer took interest in things or got pleasure from them. E. A. said: 'I've lost all vitality, I've lost all interest.' H. D. H.: 'I can't enjoy anything; there's no love in my heart.' M. H.: 'I can't enjoy flowers now.' E. J.: 'I felt I couldn't take an interest in anything.' A. N.: 'I lost interest in all the things I was interested in.' R. S.: 'I can see nothing beautiful in anything. I used to love flowers; now I don't see much in them.' L. W.: 'I've lost interest in everything.' C. W.: 'Material things don't change but I don't enjoy them.' (In answer to a direct question, if things looked different.)

Patients who palpably took little or no interest in their surroundings or who were reported by their relatives as having been listless and taken no interest are not included in the above list, unless they also complained of their loss of interest or inability to enjoy. It must, however, be remembered that these patients were mostly city-dwellers; in a clinic such as that at Heidelberg, where most of the patients are peasants from the Palatinate, or Baden, one is amazed at the frequency with which depressive patients mention this failure to enjoy the sight of their fields, the sky and the trees and the flowers as one of the most distressing of their symptoms, a deprivation most keenly felt. Of course, a loss of affection for relatives would be a symptom coming under the same heading (though more complicated), not dependent on any such accidents of locality, upbringing and habit as the enjoyment of nature may be. Of the patients just enumerated six never complained of feelings of unreality or depersonalization. There is the possibility of there being in some no more than a verbal difference between expressions of loss of interest and inability to enjoy and the feelings of unreality; when a patient says, 'Everything looks as black as black can be,' or 'Everything seems empty and dull and dead, and I don't care about anything,' or 'There's no love in me, my heart's dead', it is difficult to decide how much of objective reality there is in the words or how much metaphor. There are, however, cases where no such confusion is possible and where the complaint of the loss of affective response is unambiguous, as is the reported impression of unreality.

Nineteen patients reported changes in themselves (depersonalization). There is a close relation between hypochondria and depersonalization feelings. E. B. said: 'I feel all different, hard in my body. I feel I'm a horse. I feel like a corpse. I feel like wood.' L. C. said: 'I'm quite unable to feel natural. My stomach feels very strange, and my breasts feel strange' (there was no question of lack of affective response in this patient; she wrote most affectionate letters to her husband, and spoke with enthusiasm of 'this lovely day', 'How delightful to see God's sky'). E. G. D. said: 'I'm not a man, I'm only a trunk.' E. R. F. said: 'I have no feeling at all in me' (the double usage of 'feeling' for sensation and affective state makes this a little equivocal). E. P. felt that her body was dead from the waist down, her hands and feet felt different. C. W. said: 'My body is all dead, no feeling in it. I feel all dead. My body went all wrong—funny' (in E. B., also, the change had come on quite suddenly, in a moment). Among the others in this group there were varying expressions of the change experienced: A. C. said she had no feeling, she didn't know whether she was hungry or not, she had lost all sexual feeling (there were patients who had lost all sexual feeling who did not report any changes in their body or outside in the way of unreality). H. C. said: 'I feel as if I'm dead, as if I'm breathing backwards.' D. N. likewise included 'wrongness' ideas: 'I've done wrong, and my body's different; it's working the wrong way.' G. S. said: 'I am losing my personality. I do things mechanically . . . my inside is stiff.' I. W. felt she was not lying in bed, but floating in space (? vestibular hallucination). M. S. said: 'I have no soul, I have killed myself.' F. H.: 'My hands and legs don't belong to me. My voice isn't mine. I'm changed.' G. M.: 'I don't seem to have that same feeling I did, whatever I have to do. Everything seems different. Instead of being full of life, I have a sort of dead feeling. I feel so queer now.' M. H.: 'Nothing seems the same; I don't feel the same; I don't seem as if I've got any sense at all for lots of things. I'll never be the same. If I have a baby it will be abnormal' (she had had a Caesarian section nine years before). R. D.: 'I don't really feel myself now.' D. C.: 'I have a dreadful feeling I'm not real. I don't feel real; it's not I that's talking. I'm acting all the time' (here the fraud, deception idea seems to be involved whether as cause, concomitant or effect of the unreality feeling; more commonly it is the others who are acting, cf. I. W. and M. C. and A. H., as described below). A. H. doubted her own identity: 'I used to be Miss Annie H. I desire most urgently to be identified.'

Twenty-one patients reported changes in their environment (grouped under the general heading of 'feelings of unreality', but not always described in terms of reality or 'aliveness'). M. S. said that the people in the street were machines; they had no souls (she said the same of herself). G. M. that everything she touched was different, everything seemed changed. I. M. and D. C. also said everything seemed changed and unreal. Several, observing some change, thought they were being tricked; thus A. H. denied the identity of her sister, declared that she was in a strange ward in a strange hospital, that her sister's letters were actually from an impostor. M. C., after sending in great haste for a priest to make confession, declared that he was only a bogus priest when he came; she denied that this was a hospital, and said: 'Queer people, queer things here. People seem to come and go in a flash like.' I. W. also denied that this was a hospital or that the physician was what he purported to be: 'Everybody's acting,' she said. C. W. and W. G. thought their relatives looked changed (the latter wanted to know what had been done to his mother to make her look so unreal). E. B. said things seemed different to her. H. D. H.: 'Things have seemed unreal to me for a long time. It's as if I'm in a dream. I've lost my grip on reality.' E. W.: 'It seemed real. I don't know what's real and what's not.' L. W. said things looked mysterious, and nothing was real.

Many of the patients said that it was almost impossible to describe what the change was; they could see things quite clearly, and yet it seemed as if there were a veil or a mist interposed between them and the object; it lacked brightness and life somehow. M. H. thought the fault lay with her eyesight, but most patients recognized it as something other than mere vision. E. P. and F. H. reported actual colour changes (? question of saturation); the former said, 'It all looks pitch black, yet it's daylight,' and on another occasion, 'It seems white and foggy,' while the latter said, 'I can't see things; the street. Everything's black and miserable.' S. R. said: 'It seems dark. It is dirty. At home we live in dirt'; she also said that she felt her baby, after she had weaned it, did not belong to her. There were many others who reported changes in their relatives or changes in their ability to recall their relatives' images (the two can scarcely be separated). Thus M. H. said: 'Everything seems unreal. I can't remember my friends with pleasure after they've gone.' A. F. denied the identity of her relatives, including her son; she said everything was unreal; that they and her old life were all a dream. F. N. said: 'My own people seem complete strangers. After they had gone, it all seemed as if it had happened a very long time ago.' (The connexion with the experience of time was clear in this and in several other cases. Erwin Straus has pointed out the disparity between 'world-time' and 'subjective time', experiential time, in depressive states, but his conclusions are more readily applied to such phenomena as unreality than to the problems of differential diagnosis, to which he would extend them. The consideration of the experience of time in depressive states has formed part of a special study (*Proc. Roy. Soc. Med.*, March 1932), but the number of patients among these 61 in whom available data were collected was too small for the matter to be gone into here.) E. A. in each attack has felt that her son was unreal, or that his hair was unreal, associated with fears of harm coming to him. B. S. said: 'I've been away from my children so long. I can't think they're alive now. My babies are dead.' An unusual change was reported by D. P. who said: 'Everybody's voice seems far away.'

Clearly the emphasis must be laid on a change in the environment, which may be interpreted as unreality, mystery, death, acting, imposture, soullessness; it is not only a question of unreality. It has connexions with the affective state, with the state of consciousness (bewilderment, muddle, impression of mystery and confusion, dream-like state), with memory, ability to recall images with vividness, experience of time, individual relationship (e.g., to son, E. A.), and perhaps also with actual perception. Which of these are causal relationships is difficult to see. The literature on the subject is mostly speculative, and influenced by psycho-analytical theory or by the French doctrine about 'l'application au réel du psychisme'.

MacCurdy's views are, briefly, that in depressive conditions there is a 'locking of unconscious processes in infantile, anti-social motivations. These must be repressed. So thorough is the repression that it inhibits interest in the environment. The affect engendered—that of incapacity, heaviness, sluggishness—is rationalized mainly in projection on to the idea of self. In so far as it is projected on to the environment, the latter seems to be dull and inert. That is, it feels unreal.' But MacCurdy is aware that there are patients to whom this will not apply, in whom there is no 'retardation'. To explain these he compares their state with that of epileptics. The 'dominant sexual motivations' are so intermingled with the social that 'instinct-processes of the latter order' are repressed with them, but the group of 'ego-instincts' escape and these 'can motivate all kinds of adaptations that express expedience and can be achieved by intellectual effort'. He also remarks that 'when we have emotional contact with anything . . . we are identifying ourselves with it. When this identification takes place, the thing feels "real"; before that it is phantasmal, shadowy.' And he goes on, *à propos* of the mystical experience, to say that, if an excessive feeling of reality develops in connexion with thoughts or perceptions, these experiences are 'real in the very sense that the world around is real'. This is a wide field for speculation; but about the 'feeling of reality' he is more precise, in distinguishing it from the 'sense of reality'; 'the latter disappears only when such a profound introversion of interest and attention takes place that intelligence itself is affected. This introversion is the foundation of functional insanity'. 'The depressed patient suddenly thinks that his soul is lost, while the schizophrenic imagines that the world is destroyed. Both these ideas are dramatizations, as it were, of a sudden loss of interest or emotional contact with the environment.' This is only an incomplete account of MacCurdy's views which have exercised much influence on American and English psychiatrists. The difficulties of his explanation are, however, sufficiently evident. There is an affect of sudden incapacity which is projected; there is a withdrawal of interest or libido; these are parts of the same explanation of unreality in retarded depression; in non-retarded 'unreality depression' it is an escape of 'instincts' which can achieve adequate activity by intellectual effort; and there must be identification with things before they are felt as real—surely this is unwarranted stretching of the meaning of 'identification'?—who identifies himself with a petrified tree?—and it is through intellectual disturbance that a feeling of unreality changes to a sense or conviction of unreality (which is essentially the process of delusion formation, involving degrees of conviction), and the process is essentially the same in the schizophrenic's 'end of the world' experience and the depressive's conviction of having lost his soul. It is impossible, and perhaps misleading, to examine so complicated a system as MacCurdy's except at length, and that is not possible here. In recognizing that the 'unreality' experience may occur in other states than those of retarded depression, he is obliged either to give up his view that it is the correlate of withdrawal of emotional interest, or so to adapt this view that it becomes applicable to states where there is no sufficient evidence of such withdrawal.

Wilmanns was one of the first to point out the characteristics of depersonalization in cyclothymic depressive states. Esquirol had given a perfect description of it in the words of one of his own patients. Juliusburger included it as a manifestation of his 'pseudo-melancholia' and there was much controversy between him and Heilbronner, which made it clear that depersonalization could occur outside manic-depressive pictures. Schilder was forced to the same conclusion, as anyone must be who studies the mental state carefully—perfect descriptions of depersonalization surpassing those reported in the cases of this series have been collected from obsessional and schizophrenic patients here in the hospital—but in Schilder's conclusions about its relative infrequency in melancholics he seems to be misled by the volubility and eagerness with which many non-melancholic psychopathic patients recount their unreality experiences, whereas the melancholic seldom makes much moan about this symptom; it is necessary often to ask him 'How do things look to you? How do you feel in yourself!' or even 'Does your body feel all right?' In some cases it is only when there is a swing to mania impending that the unreality feelings are brought up and reported to have been present for some time, though not complained of. From personal observations one would judge depersonalization and objective unreality feelings to be especially common among the obsessional inquiring doubters, those who are compelled to think constantly about the why and wherefore of everything, the origin of life and the metaphysical bases of knowledge. The literature of the subject since Schilder has been concerned more with the interpretation of the symptom in terms of libido and cathexis than in giving it its place and significance in clinical states. To this Lange is an exception. It is his conclusion that the unreality phenomena are not part and parcel of the fundamental disorder of circular insanity, but are effects of other, independent predispositions: 'We may only suppose that there is here a pathological intensification of possibilities of reaction that are generally available, their appearance in these cases being facilitated by the melancholic disturbance. A corresponding view must be adopted in regard to the not uncommon observation that a cyclothymic depression sets in with features of another type of reaction such as the obsessional'. With this view one is in agreement, though without excluding other influences than pre-formed disposition. As K. Schneider has shown, and indeed as common experience would lead one to expect, an apparent change in the objects of the environment may come about in disturbances of consciousness, or more strictly in limitation of field of awareness, as well as in affective changes, so far as such constructions and distinctions can be made with profit. Malamud, much influenced by Schilder and by *Gestalt* psychology, has examined three cases, and concluded that reality is a relative experience, dependent on the balancing between standard subjective values and standard objective stimuli. To this general conclusion there can be no objection, though his elaborate identification of the outside world with the ego-ideals seems a conjectural structure—more of an oblation on 'dynamic' altars than a help to understanding. For depersonalization to occur, there must, according to Rickman, be partial withdrawal of object and egocathexis —a pathological condition of the ego which responds to a loss of cathexis as to a narcissistic injury, and a relative hypercathexis of unconscious phantasies.

Birnbaum, accepting as purely conceptual, rather than essentially explanatory, the psychodynamic mechanisms of a splitting-off of affective elements from special functions, especially the self complex, rejects psychogenetic interpretations in the sense of a flight from reality or a flight from the ego. Rosenfeld insists on the integration of the total personality, acting on the environment constantly and only conceivable in relation to the environment, as it is presented in Stern's psychology; it is the loss of this totality-function hat is concerned in feelings of unreality. He quotes Oesterreich, who thinks there is a disorder of the affective accompaniments of perception-processes—really only a translation into psychological terms of what the patient is telling us—and Löwy, who considers the fundamental phenomenon to be a loss of the 'Actionsgefühle' which accompany all activity, possibly itself the expression of a lowering of psychic lability or of psychic states of energy. To these chiefly transliterating 'explanations' Rosenfeld adds his view that the 'delusional mood' (*Wahnstimmung* or *Wahnbewusstheit*) is a change of the consciousness of self, such as is especially common in acute stages of mental disorder and usually accompanied by strong affect; there is a feeling of fundamental change; where this occurs suddenly, the patient may turn away from the environment, and there occur illusionary falsification and transformation with loss of interest. Mayer-Gross deduces unreality from a discrepancy between actual sensory sharpening of excitability on the one hand, and an incapacity to allow this improved function to become an 'impression' through the 'sensory movement' (an explanation closely associated with his and Stein's views on perception), and he points out the difficulty of accounting for the frequent occurrence of unreality feelings in states of exhaustion, in fever, etc., if one accepts the current views which lay the chief emphasis on the content of the thing experienced and regard content as the directive factor in the datum of reality. He also, in reference to Janet, points how common the experience is, in 'psychasthenics', people of a particularly sensitive discriminative temper, easily stimulated by small happenings. Janet had laid emphasis on the disturbance of the 'fonction du réel' leading to what he has denominated 'le sentiment du vide'. His views were dependent on his theory of the nature of perception. For French writers perception is a practical act; to recognize an object is, in Bergson's phrase, to know how to make use of it; perception gives us an image of reality only in the measure of our desires or needs; the most important part of perception comes from ourselves. It will be seen that from the clinical problem of unreality one is led to the larger question of perception, with its pathological aspects in illusions and hallucinations and its close connexions with the state of consciousness and the affective state. The artificial separation of elements of psychic life, pathological or not, is constantly defied by the data, and the assertion of causal dependence is often only a statement of a temporal relation, not constant or total or precise. It is not only that unreality appears elsewhere than in depressive states; it is not only that it is part of a general relation of the personality to the environment; it is also a token of the essential likeness between clinical states, generally regarded as either opposed or dissimilar. There is, for example, a good description, in Deron's monograph, of the illusions, errors of interpretation, false recognitions and other disturbances of perception in manic states; the greater part of it might well serve as a description of the disorders of like kind recorded as having occurred among these sixty-one depressed people.

DISORDERS OF PERCEPTION

To these Kraepelin devoted four pages of his description of depressive states. The majority of writers have considered that true hallucinations may occur;

but Delmas says that, unless complicated by confusion, delusional melancholia is not accompanied by hallucinations, though occasionally 'Vivid mental pictures may be mistaken for hallucinations'. Séglas thinks that true hallucinations do occur. Before quoting other writers on the point, the findings in these patients may be given:

There were disorders of perception, apart from unreality and depersonalization feelings or false somatic interpretations, in 21 cases. In none of these patients, except M. C., was there any question of drugs being responsible. M. C. was receiving a mixture which contained hyoscyamus. In 5 they were only auditory; some of the patients heard the screaming of babies, which may have been misinterpretation of similar sounds coming from other wards; M. C. heard indistinct moanings; R. D. heard noises like bells and chickens, as well as voices, of his parents and the scoutmaster; he said: 'It's very hard to explain; I don't think it's my Dada's voice . . . it's just what I think Dada is saying; he doesn't say anything.' He was unable to say exactly what it was that he heard. Another example of *Gedankenlautwerden* is A. N., who thought he heard people say, 'He never talks to anyone when he sees all this, so he must be dumb'; this is less hallucination than misinterpretation in a special direction. Similarly H. C. thought she heard the gramophone say that she was the Devil. A. F. and M. S. likewise misinterpreted what one said to them, construing it in the sense of blame or contumely; the latter, for example, thought that the nurses called her 'pig', and she overheard the physician speaking of her in disparaging terms. A. G. heard talk about hangings and executions and references to stables and his father. (He was ashamed of his father, who had been a jobmaster.)

Visual hallucinations were mentioned by several patients; they always had occurred at night, and it was difficult to ascertain from the patient's account whether they had been dreams, visions while definitely awake, or hypnagogic hallucinations; the last seemed the most likely in all of them. Their indefiniteness and the readiness with which the patient forgot the details were characteristic of hypnagogic hallucinations. The patients who reported them were J. G., D. N. and E. W. In E. N., however, and A. P., they were not so regarded, but in the former as anxiety dreams and in the latter as definite anxiety hallucinations, possibly with toxic causation; E. N. has continued to have them, and A. P. to remember those she had. A. P. had them for four days after her confinement; she was being strangled, the rack was prepared for her, the stake was put up, her funeral passed before her, an old man and a baby laughed at her, saying, 'They have taken knives and forks out of her stomach.' E. N. said: 'Directly I shut my eyes, it's all red and I'm standing like on water; just as if giddy, that's the sensation. Terrible things. One night it woke me up; seemed to say to me, "Take some poison"; it woke me up' (dreams probably). D. N. gave a description of the Devil as she had seen him, but added, 'I've imagined him.' J. G. said: 'I saw faces all through the night. I'm always seeing faces; everything I look at; all various faces; animals and men and all the rest. I fix my eye on something and it turns into an animal, mostly monkeys. I don't actually see it.' The last sentence is illuminating.

There is another group of patients who have hallucinations in more than one sensory sphere; it would probably be more correct to say 'false perceptions' than hallucinations. In E. B. they were visual, auditory, cutaneous, bodily, olfactory, gustatory and vestibular; they were fantastic, often vague and muddled, and where they were elaborated it was largely in conformity with her attitude towards her painful sexual experience, as disclosed in delusions; her description of her sensations, as taken down from her lips, covered many pages. E. P. had visual, auditory, somatic and olfactory hallucinations; she heard her own voice also, when she was not speaking. I. W. heard voices talking about her; her food tasted peculiar, she saw horrible faces at night; she believed she emitted a foul odour: 'I can smell it, and I can see the expression on people's faces.' C. W. had similar olfactory hallucinations, and felt insects crawling under her skin. E. J. F. said she could smell a bad odour from her body; the water tasted 'funny', she heard voices saying, 'Come home.' E. R. F. had horrible visions of being buried alive, and heard voices reproaching her and talking about her. E. G. D. had auditory hallucinations at the beginning of his illness, heard bangs and other noises which he believed were to annoy him, and later asserted that he gave off a vile smell which he could notice himself. M. C. declared that she saw a crucifix turn away from her, and also that she heard the Devil say, 'Ah, ah' near her.

There are three possibilities: a disorder of consciousness, akin to delirium, with hallucinations; a misinterpretation in the sense of prevailing trends of pre-occupation (illusions); a true psychogenic hallucination, complex-determined. Which of these is found, or are all of them? To consider only the content of the error of perception, the things seen or heard, the kind of smell and so on, is to escape the main problem of genesis and nature. Hypnagogic hallucinations and misinterpretations of things seen and heard are not difficult to account for; there remain such patients as E. B. and E. P. and J. W. and A. N., to take extreme cases. Either their hallucinations are to be explained as one of the direct manifestations of the anxiety-affect or of depression, or as manifestations of disturbed consciousness, secondary to toxic or affective changes. The whole problem of hallucination is so intimately bound up with this small special aspect that any comprehensive survey of the point at issue is impossible. Recent French writers have considered that the essential feature of true hallucinations is their independence, the impossibility of tracing their derivation, since they are manifestations of pathological automatism. German writers tend to regard true hallucinations as primary experiences, essentially physiogenic. Bleuler, discussing the hallucinations in schizophrenia, says, 'They keep this character (of being the consequence of a state of irritation in the nervous system), in so far as they increase and diminish with the exacerbations of the disorder, apart from delusional requirements. But for the most part they are worked upon by psychic requirements changed and adapted to the delusional ideas. The more elementary the sensations, the more they are of physiogenic origin.' But on the other hand, hallucinations (of chiefly paranoid colouring) occur as psychogenic phenomena in prison psychoses, and after earthquakes and other great catastrophes (Birnbaum); they lack vividness. It does not seem that any of the patients in this series who had true hallucinations can be included in this group of persons with psychogenic hallucinations and clear consciousness. In all who appeared to have genuine hallucinations there was concomitant evidence of perplexity and disturbance of consciousness (not severe, except in A. P. and E. B.). It is, of course, possible for affective states to result in a disturbance of consciousness with hallucinations (cf. Rosenfeld), and in such cases the characteristics are those described by Mayer-Gross in his 'oneiroid states'. These characteristics were evident in all those with true hallucinations in this series, except for 3 patients. E. G. D.'s auditory hallucinations were of that 'elemental kind' referred to by Bleuler as characteristically physiogenic; they disappeared within a short time and did not return, but were replaced by bodily feelings of a peculiar kind and olfactory hallucinations of a dubious genuineness (? inferences from delusional misinterpretation, elaborated), and he was found to have had active maxillary sinusitis at this time; in B. J. the hallucinatory experience was transitory, and appeared associated with periods of cardiac failure or inefficiency; in A. M. P. the hallucinatory experiences were vivid, not dream-like, and were remembered long after; they also cleared up within four days, following childbirth. In these three patients, the hallucinations were physiogenic, occurring in a confusional state of toxic origin in E. G. D., cardiogenic in B. J., and toxic-exhaustive in A. M. P.

It has not seemed desirable to consider as somatic hallucinations either headache or pains in various parts of the body, or odd internal sensations or depersonalization phenomena, though Kraepelin does so. They are here considered each in a different connexion. It has not been necessary to emphasize the dependence of the content of the hallucination on the mood and beliefs of the patient; this is evident from the records. The relation has been analysed in much detail by Schroeder. Reference must also be made to Cramer's famous views on hallucinations in affective states, especially melancholia, in which 'Gedankenlautwerden' was referred to changes in muscle-sense perception.

SUICIDE

All writers lay stress on the risk of suicide; few give indications that will guide one in assessing the risk. In this hospital the precautions against suicide are not extreme; in order not to sterilize the environment, some opportunity is inevitably left for the patient to attempt suicide. It is clear that in such circumstances one must use judgment in deciding the degree of risk, which patient may be in the less carefully observed wards, which may be permitted to walk about the hospital, which must be under more adequate observation and which under constant surveillance. The important factors in deciding this are the patient's statements about his intentions in this respect, the depth of his depression or agitation, his statements about whether he finds life worth living, and his previous record in the respect of suicidal attempts. The last is usually the least important; many patients are admitted to hospital after trying to commit suicide, are nursed in an open ward, but make no further attempts. It must be admitted that these criteria occasionally fail, as much on the negative as on the positive side; those whom one regarded as determined on suicide make no attempts, in hospital at any rate, and those whom one judged safe, do. There are certainly other factors.

Laignel-Lavastine has drawn attention to the necessity for remembering that suicide can occur after ripe reflection, for perfectly reasonable motives—he adduces the case of Admiral Ito. The reasons may be practical, e.g., incurable disease, dishonour, ruin, or theoretical, as in the case of Paul Lafargue. If one considers the state and the beliefs of many depressed patients, one's wonder is not that they should attempt suicide, but that some of them do not. Gestures, when they are made, are usually regarded as play-acting; the patients who take elaborate steps or announce their intentions freely are regarded as hysterical, seekers after sympathy or attention, criers of 'Wolf' overmuch, notoriety-mongers, infirm of purpose; many such succeed in killing themselves, which is the main point, but it is dismissed as a mistake they made, an error of judgment in staging the performance, a too thorough dramatic effort, an excess of zeal, inadvertently lethal. Such distinctions are often little more than casuistical niceties. D. C., for example, threatened suicide frequently, kept throwing the window open and leaning out, asking about various poisons, and otherwise openly suggesting her intentions; she sucked some tablets of creosote and lysol, and when found she volunteered the advice that white of egg and milk were the best antitodes for corrosive poisoning; she made small cuts on her wrists with scissors, wrote letters saying that she had thoughts of flinging herself from the window of a railway carriage; yet she finally put the bolster in her bed, so as to make it appear that she was still sleeping, and walked out into the sea very early in the morning and was drowned. E. T. was disregarded by her family because she threatened so often and did not carry it out, but her final attempt had every feature of determination and mortal effect. It is not to be denied that there are patients who have phantasies of suicide, much as children do, in which their central rôle, the remorse of their persecutors and those who misunderstood them, the dramatic event, are the chief features, but from them one cannot conclude that suicide, determined and effective, may not occur. A patient of this sort was E. W. who sent souvenirs, flowers, forget-me-nots to her friends, and contemplated with anticipatory enjoyment her post-mortem importance, an object of pity to archbishops and judges; F. N. wrote farewell letters and went to the electric railway, found himself less ready for death than he had thought, and went home again and gave his father the farewell letter; but there have been a number of depressed patients in this hospital, not included in this series, who were regarded after just such behaviour as being unlikely to make a serious attempt at suicide, who have cut their throats dangerously or otherwise shown the error of the assumption.

Twenty-six patients attempted suicide during the course of their present illness. Patients who talked about suicide but made no attempts are not included, nor those who wanted to starve themselves. The attempts were desperate or almost successful in 12. In the remainder the attempts were feeble, abortive things or dubious; the inadequacy of the attempt seemed in most of them to be due to the muddled state of the patient, not permitting of effective plans and action; there were none in whom it seemed to be primarily a demonstration. Turning back from the full accomplishment of so irrevocable an action also played its part. There were such anomalies as A. F., who repeatedly asked to be put out of her misery and would supplicate for poison, yet had made only a poor attempt (taking an overdose of medinal) though she had had opportunity. Of course allowance must be made for individual repugnance to available methods; many would poison themselves, for example, who would shrink from cutting their throats.

Drowning, burning, poison and gas are the common forms in this series—the patients are mostly women. J. G., besides trying to burn herself, tried to bash her head on the iron pillars and the stone; L. A. H. threw herself from a window; M. R. dropped heavy weights on her head and stepped on live wires; I. W. tried to swallow half a crown; E. E. T. swallowed a nail; R. S. and B. S. tried strangulation. G. M. showed a change. Her first suicidal attempt was described by her as follows: 'I began to think of doing away with myself; life wasn't worth living; I wasn't doing my duty. At last I told myself I'd be better off dead, and so I took camphorated chloroform and twenty tablets of aspirin. I wrote my husband three letters; I told him to look after the baby; I said I couldn't carry on. I picked the baby up after I took it, and I walked round the kitchen and did some work; then I got queer and my sister came in and found me, and I lost consciousness.' Later she had apparently recovered from her depressive illness, and was about to be discharged from hospital when she arranged at the week-end a suicide pact with another patient; they both took enormous quantities of aspirin and the other woman died; the patient's behaviour had given no inkling of her intention to her husband, who left her an hour before the attempt was made. After this she made three more attempts at suicide, and was finally certified and admitted to a county mental hospital, because she 'could not be alone; she had an overwhelming desire to kill herself, and could not control it'. An awful feeling with intense depression would come on suddenly and she would feel this impulse. In hospital she was bright and happy because she felt safe. This attitude, suggestive of a compulsive quality about the suicidal inclination, was seen also in A. H., who went to a police station, asking to be protected against himself, and in I. M.

To make a clear distinction between obsessions to commit suicide and the suicidal inclinations of the melancholic is not practicable, for many of the latter keep their promises to report any strong suicidal inclination, or do so spontaneously, though they have not promised; this would suggest that there is still a general discomfort at the inclination, or a resistance to it, and that the patient seeks the assistance of the physician in overcoming or thwarting the tendency; and in many the suicidal inclinations are not wholly explicable from the patient's state. 'Something seems to tell me to do it' many patients say, rather than 'I want to do it'. R. S., who had tried to hang himself, said: 'My wretched mind keeps on making me think terrible thoughts, that I want to be dead. . . . A terrible thought that keeps on in my mind is that I've got to let myself die. . . . I'm in terror that I can't hang on.' To determine whether the inclinations referred to are 'obsessive' or 'melancholic' would be difficult.

Neither from the patient's state of depression nor his beliefs, nor the concomitant behaviour and expression when he talks about any suicidal intentions he may have, can it be determined with considerable probability whether he will make effective attempts at suicide. There are some who invoke another factor, 'the death-instinct'. Into the historical development of psychoanalytic theory concerning the death-instincts this is not the place to enter; Freud has written, in *The Ego and the Id*, that in melancholia, 'what is now holding sway in the super-ego is, as it were, a pure culture of death instinct'. That this may be held to account for suicidal attempts is a further conclusion. Several have examined this view. Blacker, rejecting specific death instincts, concludes that 'the instinctual frustrations that characterize severe endopsychic conflicts . . . express themselves somehow as aggressiveness. Guided by cultural influences absent in the animal world (which influences, I think, are well epitomized in the conception of introjection) the aggressiveness can be directed upon the self and take form as active suicidal wishes.' He regards deaths by active suicide as 'exceptional and harmful miscarriages arising in abnormal circumstances, of biologically useful instincts'. It seems necessary to invoke some factor, not clear in the state of the patient or even implicit in it, to account for suicide; to proceed on the assumption that it is a logical reaction to the utterly intolerable situation of the patient is to account for only some of the cases of suicide, certainly not to account for those who, in equally intolerable circumstances, make no attempt at suicide. One must assume either an urge to death, not secondary to the depression, but rather released by it, and sufficient to overcome the urge of life (which is, broadly put, the psychoanalytical theory), or else an urge to life which is so much stronger in some than in others that it prevents them from taking the only possible way of immediate escape from a sea of troubles where others do take it. This latter view, which finds the difference between individuals in this respect to be a difference in make-up, in instinctual endowment, is not far removed from the view of Morselli, who wrote, 'We believe that if it were possible to know exactly the physiological temperament of all self-destroyers, and, above all, the hereditary transmission, direct or indirect, of the morbid germs, we should be able to trace back the fatal determination of their last act to its true and efficient cause.' He considered suicide was one way by which the weak were eliminated from society: 'It is a weak character who is destroyed in the struggle for life when it is a question of suicide.' There is the problem, in concrete terms, of why M. E. B. never made the slightest attempt to harm herself, while E. E. T. killed herself. In neither was there much self-reproach; both were weary of life, which had become stale and unprofitable; both had relatives who wished them to live; both believed they would never be any happier; there was nothing, save the earlier suicidal attempts of E. E. T., to indicate how differently they would behave in this respect; one assumes a tenacity to life, but this is no explanation and no help in assessing the likelihood in any case. By what other standards can such a quality be measured? It is a question closely associated with the whole problem of reaction to illness, recovery from illness, not susceptible of present solution here, or perhaps elsewhere. It may finally be suggested that the tendency to suicide is less closely connected with self-reproach than the psycho-analytical school are inclined to suppose.

ATTITUDE TO ILLNESS

It is customary to speak of the patient's insight into his illness, and great importance is by some attached to it, e.g., Yellowlees has referred to 'the final and subtle touchstone, namely the presence of insight in the neuroses and its absence in the psychoses. The psychotic, however mild his illness, had not insight'. This is an extreme, almost extravagant assertion, but others speak in the same sweeping way about 'insight'. As long ago as the 'eighties, Pick suggested that in the patient's awareness of illness there were two features; a feeling of illness and an insight into the nature of the illness. Heilbronner, twenty years later, made a further distinction; the patient may be aware of a change in himself, he may be aware that it is morbid, he may be aware that it is not so much bodily as mental: insight is present 'where the patient not only feels that a change has taken place and is aware of a morbid reduction of his psychic functions, but is also able to take a critical attitude towards the individual symptoms, and especially to recognize as morbid symptoms which do not lead immediately to a subjectively experienced somatic disorder or lowering of mental capacities, i.e., where his attitude to his own illness is as objective as that of an ordinary layman to the illness of another'. This is a just, if over-schematic, distinction, and one reached here independently, on examination of the grounds on which an opinion on insight had been based in each of these sixty-one cases. To limit insight, on the one hand, to recognition of non-reality of delusions and hallucinations, or, on the other, to recognition of illness, is inadequate; to blend them, confusing.

Twenty patients declared, many of them protested, that they were not ill, that there was no need whatever for them to be in hospital. Nine patients believed that they had physical ailments, but not mental or nervous ones. The patients who said they were ill but did not discuss the nature of the illness or analyse it were 18 in number. Fourteen considered they had some mental or nervous disorder. The attitude towards individual symptoms will be considered separately.

There is much practical importance in this matter. Patients will be willing to come to a hospital for treatment if they believe they are ill, but they will not stay if they believe they have some physical ailment which is not receiving the attention, surgical or otherwise, which they consider necessary. Even in a purely voluntary hospital, it will be seen from the above lists that there may be many people who deny that they are ill at all, as well as others who maintain that there is nothing about them that calls for treatment in a psychiatric or neurological hospital. Even allowing for those who come and remain because of pressure from their relatives, etc., it is clear that patients may protest they are not ill mentally, and yet have enough perception of their disordered state to recognize the desirability or benefit of their being in a quiet place, nursed, cared for and medically supervised, if not actively treated by interference. The patient's willingness, in most cases, to give an account of his life and his illness, suggest a recognition of the possibility of medical help. It is therefore not right to conclude from the patient's statements that he is quite sure he is not ill; furthermore, many such patients vary in their statements on this point, e.g., E. H. said, 'I'm not ill; my nerves are very strong; it's not nerves,' but also 'Perhaps I'm a little mad; hadn't I better be put in an asylum'; A. E. N. said, 'There isn't really anything the matter with me,' but also 'I wonder if I shall get all right again'; E. R. said, 'I'm not ill; I just had this nervous breakdown'; B. S. said, 'I imagined things,' but also 'I didn't come here as a patient'; B. S. said at one time, 'I'm not ill at all, there's nothing wrong with me,' at another time 'I must be daft'; similarly B. J. Where patients observe themselves so carefully as does the melancholic, there is at any rate a recognition of a changed state, as expressed in complaints of difficulty of thinking, etc.; the difficulty arises where the appreciation of this change is given a definite form, as by the hypochondriacs, who believe they have a physical ailment *per se*, and not merely as outcome of their mental illness; and the apprehensive, who insist that they are going mad, less a judgment than a fear, almost a delusion, though formally an appreciation of mental illness; and the moral who translate the change, not into terms of health, well or ill, but into terms of good and evil: 'It's not illness but sin or perhaps possession' (E. J.). Some patients, who deny they are ill, yet show a clear appreciation of their own character in its trends and failures, e.g., H. C. or M. B., who said, 'I'm not ill; I can see things plainly, as they really are', yet she was also aware that there was a change in herself, which was to be deplored. One is driven to consider what people mean when they say they are ill; for most, illness is a change imposed from without, the hand of God or accident, whereas a change in the direction of depression, boredom or restlessness is a failure of their will or, at all events, chiefly an internal happening; but common to both is the perception of a change in oneself which is unpleasant; the difference lies in the interpretation of how it has come about, and secondarily in its ascription to definite organs or essentially to changes in tissue structure. 'It's not illness, but I'm afraid I'll lose my reason,' said E. J.

Many of these patients use the 'as if' constructions, e.g., H. C., who said 'I feel as if . . .'; 'I wouldn't have these fancies if . . .'; M. S., who said, 'It must be imagination. I feel as if I'm causing all the trouble. I don't really think I poisoned the others'; H. D. H. said at first, 'I am going mad', and then said, 'I am quite healthy and well, but I'll go mad if . . .' This idea of going mad was sometimes expressed as a delusion with vigour and coloured by the 'I'm a fraud' attitude, e.g., J. G. said, 'My brain's a bit off; the whole truth is the brain is all right but the nerves aren't. I haven't any control over it. I feigned I was mad. . . . It's an imaginative complaint, hysteria.' Similarly M. B. and M. R. who said, 'I'm not genuine, I'm a fraud; I'm not ill at all; I've just pretended. I've ruined my brain by turning things over and over.' W. G. said, 'I am mad, I can't control myself'; M. H. denied that she was ill, but said she was not 'all there'. R. H. said, 'My head's gone wrong, but I'm sane enough to talk of it. I ought to be killed like a mad dog.' F. N. said, 'I'm not really ill; it's just a weight on my mind.'

As to the attitude to particular symptoms, there were no patients who insisted on the objective reality of their auditory or visual hallucinations (which were vague), though they would act on them occasionally, going out to see where the noise came from or the wailing, and so on; unpleasant olfactory experiences they were convinced of, in many cases, as of 'somatic hallucinations', hypochondriacal bodily feelings. In many, as already remarked, the 'as if' construction was used. As for delusions, spontaneous utterances and the response to objections and reassurance are the chief criteria, together with the degree to which the patient acts on his beliefs. The response to reassurance has already been discussed, as has also the degree of conviction. But response to reassurance and degree of conviction do not always go hand in hand with insight; the patient may regard his false beliefs as morbid phenomena and yet be quite certain of their truth—a logical contradiction, but not an impossible one psychologically—e.g., E. A. was quite sure her son was changed, yet she would add reflectively, and as if by way of a concession, 'The alteration is really in myself.' D. N. said, 'Detectives follow me; people know all about me; but they can't really, it's my feelings.' Into discussions of belief and intelligence, so often introduced into this problem (cf. Heilbronner), it is not appropriate to enter here. It is necessary to call attention to the comparative infrequency with which these patients conceal their beliefs; concealment implies among other things a recognition of how others regard the beliefs, a knowledge that by ordinary standards the beliefs are false, and may lead to dissimulation during improvement and convalescence, such as has been written about especially in the German literature. Among these patients it was well seen in A. N., who declared with indifferent success that he thought it had all been imagination, and may have been operative in G. M., who seemed well, but went and attempted suicide (cf. Bostroem).

The matter is summed up by Lange, who, speaking of depressive states, remarks: 'Even in mild cases there is often a strong feeling of illness, and in later attacks many patients with periodic melancholia regard their symptoms with complete insight. A more or less obscure awareness of illness is rarely absent even in severe melancholia; indeed, it can coexist with pronounced delusions; in that case, however, it nearly always refers to the bodily state only, while the possibility of there being any mental disorder is repudiated.' This is better than Stoddart's assertion that 'all who suffer from insane delusions lack insight . . . ; we find insight most characteristically in cases of intermittent and periodic insanity, other states associated with depression . . . provided always that the patient has no delusions'; or Strecker and Ebaugh's 'there is usually some degree of insight during the illness, though as a rule it is quite faulty', which may mean anything; or Yellowlees' dictum, already quoted, which cannot be true.

CHIEF COMPLAINT

The subjective experience of the patient is not always deducible from his behaviour; he may, like R. S., lie quite still and be tormented by inner unrest. There may, furthermore, be many features of his condition, which seem to him of minor importance, though they bulk largely in observations upon him.

It is only occasionally that one finds the 'intellectualization à outrance', as Minkowski has called it, in which the patient observes himself with detachment and severely scrutinizing criticism, and even that is weighted on the side of condemnation. It has seemed desirable therefore to consider which are the symptoms that chiefly trouble the patient or of which he is most aware; necessarily a 'cross-section' of the mental state at a given moment, a static way of considering it as opposed to the dynamic flow of phenomena changing and reacting, as portrayed in other parts of this study; but it is only in this way that one can learn what is the patient's hierarchy of values, often very different from that of the physician.

The patient's spontaneous description of his symptoms, or his replies to the question, 'What do you feel the matter with you?' or 'Why have you come into hospital? What do you feel wrong with you?' or 'What seems to be the chief trouble?' form the material from which the following has been taken. The observations were made generally during the first week in hospital.

Feeling muddled, puzzled, dazed, dizzy was the complaint of 10 patients; inability to think properly or to concentrate was complained of in 5 cases; press of thoughts in 2; feeling tired, fed-up, weary, listless in 6; 5 felt run down; 2 felt tense and restless; 7 felt worried; 6 complained that things seemed unreal; 7 were distressed about their wickedness, 3 about sleeplessness, 3 about irritability, 4 about their peculiar bodily sensations. In 4 cases it was the harm they might do to others that worried them chiefly; dirt caused great concern to 2; 3 complained of everybody looking at them. Three were chiefly concerned about their going mad, 2 about the illness killing them. Two patients said only that they were terrified; they did not know of what; another two were distressed because they had dissimulated illness and had misled people; two because they had neglected their homes; one because she had been inefficient. Two said their chief trouble was worry about their souls; one loss of religious feeling, confidence in God; another loss of self-control; another hopelessness; another inability to 'get out of myself'; another moodiness; another a feeling of weight on her head; another, 'I've got something on my mind I can't get rid of'; another the floating of specks before her eyes all the time; another her inability to leave off crying. Noises either outside or in their heads were the chief complaints in 3.

If one compares these complaints with the general clinical features in the same patients, or even with the account of subjective experiences which could be elicited from them by further questioning, it will be seen how different is the value and relative importance attached to symptoms by patients from that which one would often expect. Something must be allowed for the patient's conception of what it is one desires to hear about from him; but the infrequency of complaints about bodily ills would suggest that this is not a considerable factor in determining which symptoms he reports. The nature of the patient's preoccupation, his self-criticism, the relative distress symptoms cause him, and his attitude towards his illness, will be other factors.

FOOD AND WEIGHT

The refusal of food is one of the prominent features of any depressive state. It is familiar in ordinary life, and is a regular accompaniment of sadness, frustration or indeed any unpleasant affect. In morbid depression it ranges from a mild disinclination to an absolute refusal. It may be indirectly or directly responsible for the patient's death, and is by some writers regarded as an expression of a wish for death—in other words, as a persistent and prolonged suicidal attempt. Psycho-analytic writers find in it fruitful material for investigation and speculation. Bio-chemists see it as evidence of profound metabolic disturbance. It may be the manifestation of obscure vegetative changes, or of highly elaborated delusional beliefs. It may change quickly, and the formerly anorexic, obstinately aphagic patient becomes a ravenous gobbler of double portions, a snatcher of remnants and the meals of others; the change may occur whenever the patient is under the influence of a narcotic drug. These are vagaries, however; depressive states are almost invariably characterized during the greater part of their course by disinclination for food. The alleged willingness of the patient to take the food, if it is left by his bedside and nobody is watching, has not been seen in these patients. Every legitimate device was adopted to induce them to eat spontaneously, but only constant immediate persistence on every occasion was effective. Some, hard pressed, resort to subterfuges, e.g., J. C., who would promise to drink her milk or egg and milk, but would quietly pour it away when no one was looking, or who would pretend to sip, letting it run down her chest, or not making any swallowing movements, or tilting the glass any higher. In all these patients the tendency is for the weight to be lost, and this is the only sufficient criterion of whether the patient is having sufficient food. In some, however, this criterion fails. Kraepelin and many others have pointed out that a steady fall in weight may occur even when the patient is receiving sufficient food, and some of these patients defy all attempts to arrest their progressive emaciation. There were 7 patients in this series whose weight fell, although they were unquestionably receiving food of which the caloric value was in excess of their requirements. In all the others the loss of weight was no more than might have been accounted for by their reduced intake. One does not lightly undertake the tube-feeding of a patient, for its psychological effect may be wholly bad, and its main end frustrated by the patient's determined efforts to vomit; several of the patients in this series therefore showed a considerable loss of weight, but in none was a steady or rapid fall allowed to go on; in most cases by means of persuasion and insistence (in one case following a single tube-feed—L. W.) it was possible to maintain the patient's general nutrition.

SLEEP AND APPRECIATION OF TIME

As disorders of these functions were the subject of a special investigation in which some of these patients have been included, it is not proposed to discuss them here (see *Proc. Roy. Soc. Med.*, March 1932).

FLUCTUATIONS

Diurnal variations, in the nature of improvement towards evening, are usually stressed as characteristic of true melancholia. Lange, for example, speaks of them as invariable ('bemerkenswerterweise ausnahmslos'). The number of patients who showed this variety of diurnal fluctuation was 11. It is not a symptom to which at the time the physician or the nurses paid particular attention; it is therefore only in cases where the evening improvement was striking and constant that there is a record of it, either in the medical or the nurses' notes; it was never directly inquired after. In I. W. it is recorded that her levitation-feeling as though she floated in the air, would pass off as the day went on; E. E. T. had peculiar sensations in her head only in the morning. A. H. said 'I get clearer in my mind in the afternoon and evening; in the night hours I get very despondent. I am awfully depressed in the mornings. I feel a bit happier in the evenings.' Yet later on, when he was a patient in a mental hospital, it is recorded that exactly the reverse was the case. H. C. said that he always felt worst in the small hours, as most people do.

This matter of daily variation received much attention in the early days. If one was dealing with a periodic illness, might there not be other evidences of periodicity? For example, during the course of the day? Melancholics, it was concluded from various experiments by Kraepelin and others, show, as compared with healthy people, in the afternoon a greater increase of ability to calculate, of muscular strength, and of grasp, with qualitative improvement in tests of choosing. Lange goes on to make the matter one of diagnostic importance, and describes as common what is, on the whole, rather rare: 'Daily fluctuations are extraordinarily frequent, and in this form are found only in circular cases. In the majority depression and retardation are most evident in the morning, often especially so following a good night. As the day goes on the depression and retardation lessen, even in severe cases. The patients want to get up, they occupy themselves a little and can more easily be got to talk and even laugh. The reverse diurnal fluctuation is very rare. In his earlier article he says that if, in psychogenic depression, there are phenomena suggesting daily fluctuations, then it is a question of that slow and painful waking-up and getting going in the morning that is characteristic of psychopaths. But if one regards the cases given above, and applies the customary criteria for distinguishing 'true melancholics' from 'psychoneurotic depression'—a fallacious exercise—one finds a predominance of the latter among them; all exhibited features which Lange and others would regard as psychopathic and psychogenic, or, as many would say, using all the possible combinations of the Greek words, neurasthenic or psychasthenic. On this point one is in complete agreement with Gillespie, who says: 'Diurnal variation of mood (and consequently of activity), although common in the autonomous group, was not peculiar to it, and was found in the reactive group as well.' Riddoch has said: 'The neurasthenic has periods, which often appear almost fortuitously, in which he feels "almost himself". These are more common in the afternoon, and with the psychotic it may be so too; but in his case the depression only "lifts" to some extent.' Of course, one may have brief periods of depression lasting a few hours and then clearing up, and recurring later, or they may last a few days (cf. M. T., in whom the depressive attacks coincided with her menstrual periods); such cases are described by Paskind; but in the cases here reported the change was regular, occurring every day. The patients in whom daily variations were observed occurring sporadically are considered in connexion with the features of personality. There were other patients, who showed variations in their state from day to day, or lasting for only a few hours, and apparently independent of any change in their circumstances.

CHANGE IN CLINICAL FEATURES

The detailed summary of sequences in the clinical picture of each patient it would be tedious to recapitulate; it may be said in general that variations either from day to day, or within a few days, are common; actual relapses after apparently complete recovery are rare; the initial symptoms are oftenest a feeling of inadequacy, sleeplessness and slight bodily complaints, especially headache (a proportion of the patients have previously been treated for bodily ailments by the general practitioners and hospital out-patient physicians, who have referred them to this hospital); the changes from 'retarded' depression to agitation or 'stupor' are seldom sudden, though a change of ward may sometimes be associated with a sudden aggravation of severity in the clinical picture, as where a patient who appears likely to attempt suicide is transferred from a private room to the 'acute ward'. The sequence of clinical states, however, is anything but uniform, and the same may be said of the duration of the various phases; one would need a very much larger number of cases before one could apply any statistical criteria.

In 1 case sudden changes occurred after visits from his wife; in another case at the time of her periods. To consider the changes in content of delusions would not serve any purpose. One remarkable change worth recording is that from refusal of food to voracity, such as was observed in 3 cases, neither in these cases, nor in others in whom it has been observed, does it seem to be associated with any other notable change, or to have any unfavourable prognostic significance; it may last only a week or two or be continued for months. Dependent as one is on history, it is very difficult to obtain satisfactory information about the initial symptoms; there is often discrepancy between the respective statements of the family doctor, the patient and the relatives; and from so small a series of cases, statistically considered, it does not appear justifiable to draw any conclusions on this point. As to the suddenness or gradual nature of the onset, there are similar difficulties; so far as one could ascertain the following were the relations: sudden or fairly sudden onset in 19 cases, in the rest, gradual. In saying that the onset was sudden, however, no more is implied than that definite symptoms of illness appeared within a short time, where previously the patient had appeared well; in the majority of these with 'sudden' onset there had been painful rumination, 'worry', for some time previously; or they had been dissatisfied with their environment or aware of an inner perturbation, more a background to their daily activity than a part of it.

There were a number of patients who were not well when they left hospital, but who recovered at home. They are considered below in connexion with the outcome of the illness.

SCHIZOPHRENIC FEATURES

The extent to which schizophrenic features are found in depressive conditions, and their form, will necessarily depend on the requirements for making the diagnosis of the depressive state, and the features regarded as essentially schizophrenic. There is, of course, a depressive variety of schizophrenia, but it is not in this purely descriptive sense that the term 'depressive state' and 'depressive reaction' has been used here. One can learn little more from an analysis of the schizophrenic features in depressive states than one's own diagnostic criteria. It may be said that nowadays the characteristics of schizophrenia are well defined; in a sense it is so; as a total reaction it can be recognized with as much certainty as many an illness with a known (structural or chemical) pathological picture; but when the reaction is as clear and sweeping as this, one no longer describes the condition in which it occurs as a 'depressive state', but rather as a schizophrenic one, with depressive colouring (and none such have been included here). The recognition of isolated symptoms as schizophrenic, however, is quite another matter. There are no pathognomonic signs, no unequivocal marks of the schizophrenic symptom. Even where the whole picture is schizophrenic, much difference may occur in the judgment of good observers; for example, at the Boston Psychopathic Hospital the percentage of patients diagnosed schizophrenic has diminished by one-third (from 43% to 28%) in a decade, and the discrepancy of diagnosis of schizophrenia in the same patient between the Boston Psychopathic Hospital and the State Hospital to which the patient had been transferred increased by 15% in the same period. There are two ways open in assessing a given symptom or even group of symptoms—one may say 'It is my impression that this is schizophrenic; it conforms to my previous experience and judgment'—essentially an intuitive diagnosis—or one may appeal to the rather formal lists of schizophrenic primary symptoms, as given by Bleuler and by Gruhle and Mayer-Gross. Secondary symptoms, the results of pathoplastic influences, are clearly of little significance. But if one accepts Bleuler's or Gruhle's formulations one accepts, it may be said, the implication that these primary symptoms are the evidence of a structural change, the 'process'. This is not necessarily an objection. These primary symptoms are, in essence, the irreducible, not further explicable, features supposed to be the fundamental, ultimate manifestations of schizophrenia; those of Bleuler, of course, are not exactly the same as those of Gruhle, nor arrived at along the same line of thought, but in both they are the result of a searching clinical and psychological analysis. The American formulations are looser (cf. Campbell), though agreeing in clinical essentials with those of the German writers. The British view, essentially clinical (cf. Mapother), tends to lay stress on the bizarre quality of behaviour and thought. This is no place for a discussion of these complicated issues or for an expression of personal judgment. It may be said, however, that the chief criteria here employed were first, disorders of thought or of conduct into which it was impossible for the observer to enter except by an intellectual process, rather than from understanding through comparable experience; and second, a severe disturbance of the relationship between person and surroundings, especially persistent self-reference. Hallucinations, though regarded by all writers as primary schizophrenic phenomena, have not yet received consideration, since they may, of course, occur in other than schizophrenic phenomena, and it is not appropriate to enter into the differential diagnosis between schizophrenic hallucinations and others.

Twenty-three patients were thought to show schizophrenic characteristics. Of these seven were included because of their ideas of reference. Thus M. S., in repeating the cowboy story said that she was the dog; it was meant for her; L. A. H. thought people made signs in the street, that 'PRTY' on a bag of flour was a sign to indicate her death, and that the word 'Charmian' in a song referred to her. A. G. said: 'There's a lot of suggestion here in words and gestures; people made signs. . . . The idea was put in my head when I came here.' M. C. saw signs in everything; her wedding ring was changed, for example, and that meant she could never go home. There were many others with ideas of reference (*Eigenbeziehung*), either already quoted in connexion with delusions or included in the larger group of schizophrenic symptoms, now to be described.

E. B. grimaced occasionally; she said her eyes influenced other people and hurt them; she was making the world; she had swallowed everything; she seemed to be drinking her own urine, she felt; her thoughts were being read; she was in Hell; there were electric shocks running through her; she was half man and half woman; these symptoms were not obtrusive, and appeared only incidentally, amid characteristic melancholic utterances. A. C. during the transition from melancholia to mania felt as though suckling animals were moving about inside her (and had many well-defined auditory hallucinations). H. C. covered her eyes because by looking at the sun she could put it out; her behaviour in suddenly banging doors, etc., was at times very odd, considering the total situation. E. G. D. believed that food exuded through his skin and caused a foul smell; R. D. with his bewilderment, anxiety and auditory hallucinations was considered at a clinical meeting to be schizophrenic, but the diagnosis was revised, as also in the case of E. P., who had said her hands were canary's claws, and who thought the behaviour of the other patients was a sign to her. E. W. thought that the illness of the others, paragraphs in the paper, the doctor's visits, were all staged to teach her some lesson; she imputed curious mystical qualities to the number 7. A. F. had bizarre beliefs about her body, and declared that there was an eruption on her face in spite of all evidence to the contrary; likewise E. R. F. W. G. once pulled all his bedding out into the middle of the floor and later said that he did so because 'something seems to come over me that whatsername way'; 'my mind is so hard'; he showed occasional sudden variations of mood, laughing without evident cause on a few occasions; he said there was to be a war between England and America, because his mother was English and his grandmother American; he saw references to himself in the papers. A. H. was at times blindly negativistic; she would smile at one in the midst of her agitation. A. H. said that the seed (semen) represented the Holy Spirit in man, and voiced other somewhat mystical religio-sexual notions (largely the product of ill-digested reading, it seemed, in accordance with certain trends). B. S. said there were some pulling her one way, some pulling another. C. W. expressed bizarre beliefs about her body having rotted away. I. W. persisted in believing that there were jokes put in *Punch* especially on her account.

It is recognized that to wrench symptoms from their setting in the above fashion, to quote isolated utterances and single actions, is to make it impossible for the reader to form his own opinion about the value of the phenomena and their significance. But it would be going too far afield if one did otherwise. As in Greenacre's paper, no more has been attempted than to deal with the schizophrenic content, leaving the dynamic aspects of the symptoms alone. With her collection of schizophrenic features, though not entirely with her grouping, the above observations agree, viz., distortions and misinterpretations of actual occurrences, influence and passivity feelings, hallucinations, gross distortions of body sense and body appreciation, incongruous behaviour occurring either episodically or not in keeping with or apparently motivated by the prevailing affect. Greenacre, however, has included rather more as schizophrenic than has been done here. It need hardly be said that the question schizophrenic or manic-depressive is not one that can be considered important either from a prognostic or therapeutic point of view, unless much else be taken into account.

The literature on this subject is very large, and concerned with problems of constitution, inheritance, and clinical differentiation, into which one cannot enter here. It is sufficient to say that, as may be seen in the above records, schizophrenic features are by no means infrequent in depressive states, and their occurrence is usually to be accounted for if one examines the family history, the previous personality and the general trends prevailing during the illness (especially in the hypochondriacal patients).

ANXIETY

The relation of anxiety to depression is intimate. 'Among the varieties of depression,' say Bleuler, 'anxiety occupies a particular place'. Mapother remarks similarly: 'When depression is well marked its exact form varies greatly, grief finding causes for unhappiness in the past, fear which seeks them in the future, and a simple sense of wretchedness about the present, seem the primary types. The melancholic is, of course, apt to experience all these varieties of depression.' Delmas, to take a distinguished French writer, declares: 'The melancholic delusional state rests on anxiety because anxiety always exists in some degree when there is a delusional state, and as anxiety is the painful emotional state concerned with harm to come, melancholic delusions are always directed towards the future even when the melancholic seems to have them about the past.' And Lange, following Kraepelin, says:

'Very often, oftener indeed than one would gather from the spontaneous utterances of the patient, there is anxiety in some form or other. Sometimes it is only a mild occasional feeling of indefinable vague anxiety, but often a general profound anxiety is the very nucleus of all other unpleasant feelings.'

The purpose of collecting this weight of authoritative opinion from various schools is to establish—what is barely indicated in current British textbooks—that anxiety is a common and probably integral part of the depressive reaction, and to permit of a consideration of the nature of anxiety, at the purely descriptive level (for the discussion of its psycho-pathology is far too large a matter to enter into here).

The words of psychiatry are often unjust stewards, sorry guardians of meaning, workers of deception. 'Delirium' is something very different in English from the French '*délire*', the '*amentia*' of Meynert from the 'amentia' of Tredgold, yet one occasionally encounters the mistranslation. One suspects something of the same sort with regard to anxiety. In the older British text-books of psychiatry anxiety as a technical term does not occur, e.g., in Craig's textbook of 1905 one finds frequent reference to 'morbid fears', but only casual use of the word 'anxious' or 'anxiety', whereas in the edition of 1926 there is a chapter on anxiety-states, in which the word is used to denominate an affect and to characterize a syndrome. What has produced the change? One surmises that it was the influence of the Germans, especially the psycho-analytical writers in that tongue. But the German word '*Angst*' is not so easily to be rendered into English as 'anxiety'. A German patient will naturally use the word 'Angst' to describe his state where an English patient would say he was scared or worried or frightened, or that he felt something terrible was going to happen. It is uncommon for a patient to use the word 'anxiety' spontaneously as a description of his condition, unless he has been under the care of a psychotherapist and has learnt his language. This would be no objection to the technical use of the term, if it were not that in German 'Angst' covers a much wider field than 'anxiety' in either literary, colloquial or ordinary medical English. The distinction between anxiety and fear, psychiatrically, must consist in the presence and reality of the thing apprehended; in ordinary English 'frightened' or 'afraid' can, of course, be used where the object of the fear is quite uncertain, e.g., 'I feel afraid of what's going to happen next'. The German position with regard to the two words 'Angst' and 'Furcht' is clearly laid down in Schulte's paper. But there is no such clarity about the use of the words in English, except among the psycho-analysts, who have adopted the German significations exactly (cf. Rickman No. 14 (1), general remarks). Craig and Beaton, for example, say 'anxiety is a state of expectancy dominated by fear. Psychologically it is the acutely displeasing feeling tone which accompanies a threat to the well-being or self-regard' (the latter part possibly adapted from Hoche's assertion in 1910, 'Anxiety represents the subjective side of the threatened tendency to self-affirmation'). Gillespie and Henderson define it: 'Anxiety as a technical term is a fear of danger, usually from within, e.g., impending physical illness. It may occur either as a continued state of fear or (more commonly) in episodic attacks. . . . Apprehension is usually confined to the fear of external danger.' But later on in their text-book they write: 'The commonest conscious emotional symptom is "fear" in the special form of distressful apprehension usually designated "anxiety" '; and again, 'anxiety states . . . with the external focus of the anxiety varying'. The confusion as to the precise meaning of the word has led to much misconception; and it is therefore of some importance to examine it before going on to consider the occurrence of the state it connotes. 'Anxiety' is used in this paper as indicating an unpleasant (affective) state with expectation, but not certainty, of something unpleasant happening. In this sense anxiety will be seen to be a common symptom in depressive states; under the heading 'Agitation' the forms in which it is associated with disorder of motor activity, restlessness, have been considered, and the patients who showed apprehension enumerated. There remain for consideration the patients in whom the anxiety manifested itself in attacks, with the characteristic physical concomitants—sweating, tremulousness, palpitation, tachycardia, etc. There were 7 patients who had 'anxiety attacks'. In addition, 2 patients were particularly troubled by anxiety-dreams, E. N. and A. M. P. R. R. S. complained that 'his stomach turned over' and that he sweated and felt he was going to collapse; 'it's fear', but his state was constant rather than episodic. In B. J. it was hard to know how far his diseased heart was responsible for his attacks of dyspnœa, sweating, palpitation, and fear of imminent death. The association of anxiety with substernal tension ('Präcordialangst') is stressed by many writers on depression, but the symptom was less often reported by the patient than, say, Lange's or Benon's accounts would lead one to expect. The former goes so far as to agree with Westermann that this feeling of oppression in the breast (often referred to the heart) is part of the feeling of sadness—may even be independent of anxiety: 'Westermann affirms this with regard to the sadness of endogenous depression. Doubtless he is right in this, but I can often find no proper differences between the sadness and the anxiety of the melancholic. That peculiar feeling of oppression in the chest, so suggestive of slight cardiac symptoms, but not necessarily experienced as anxiety at all.' Since reading this assertion of Lange's, it has been my custom to question every depressed patient seen for the first time in the out-patient department as to the presence of any such feelings of discomfort in the chest, but in only a small number has a description of them or of other feelings of pressure or weight been obtained. This is surprising, since Paskind has found such sensations to be common in a group of patients similar in many respects to those whom one sees in the out-patient department.

It is unnecessary to say that the bodily concomitants of an 'anxiety attack' are equally to be observed in the more prolonged anxiety states which have been described in connexion with 'agitation' and 'apprehension'. But there the symptoms do not come on with such dramatic suddenness, and are often not so striking, as in the 'anxiety attack'. The bodily features are as much parts of the anxiety reaction as are the mental, and in making the distinction one is doing violence to the facts for the sake of convenience of thought (one of Vaihinger's 'as if' constructions, so plentifully used in the descriptive examination of symptoms, 'psychological entities' and other products of artificial division). Clearly the whole organism participates in the reaction, and the James-Lange theory need not detain one.

The attacks in some of the patients enumerated above occurred in response to a painful situation. Thus A. C. had an attack of anxiety whenever an injection was made: on one occasion an injection of ergotamine was responsible, and on another occasion one of omnopon. It happened that M. B. was lying in the bed opposite when A. C. had one of these attacks, in which she became very pale; M. B. thereupon had a severe anxiety attack herself, in which she trembled violently, sweated, felt most apprehensive, and had a rapid pulse; she had another attack of the same kind that evening. M. C. had an attack when venepuncture was performed; R. D. during an interview in which he was being questioned about his earlier life. E. P. had had an attack shortly before her baby was born.

Anxiety is, of course, a normal psychological experience; it is, however, present in these patients (all who showed anxiety whether in attacks or as a lasting state) in excessive strength and without any occasion that would ordinarily be adequate. An injection, for example, cannot be regarded as an adequate occasion for the manifestation of severe anxiety. Anxiety is not the prerogative or the characteristic feature of any psychosis or neurosis: it is more prominent in some than in others; it may be less associated with other signs of mental disorder, or may be clearly related to a certain type of personality; it may be more frequently found in people at the climacteric who are facing finality and completion away from growth and hope; but to call conditions of one kind 'anxiety-neuroses' and of another kind 'anxiety-psychoses' because anxiety bulks largely in the manifestation is a matter of nosological convenience, not of essential nature and distinction. If one is making one's differentiation on pathogenetic grounds, into which questions of 'mechanism' enter, one is still accounting for the symptom anxiety whereever it may appear and not setting it up as an independent type of reaction; much as with depersonalization, one must take into account the concomitant manifestations of the organism's response before one can evaluate the symptom 'anxiety' in its total setting. This is a matter which will come up again when the relations of depressive states to other types of reaction is considered. One may, however, quote here Birnbaum: 'Clinical experience does not yet permit the setting-up of the reactive anxiety-syndromes as a psychogenetically unitary group, unless one accepts schematically the relatively rigid psycho-analytic explanations which are predominantly sexual. . . . For the present it is only on causal grounds that one can differentiate these psychogenic anxiety-states from organic ones. One cannot here so conclusively carry out a phenomenological differentiation of the kind attempted by Schneider in respect of psychogenic depressions, which would distinguish between those at the level of the psychic vital feelings and those at the level of the somatic.'

'NEUROTIC' SYMPTOMS

The records were gone through and a note made of the presence of any 'neurotic' symptoms, other than those of compulsion and anxiety. It is easier to carry out such a search than to give the precise grounds for the decision as to which symptoms are 'neurotic'. The concept is a loose one, and its use can be justified here only on the ground that many writers have insisted on a distinction between 'true melancholia' and 'psychoneurotic depression'; it has therefore become necessary to consider what features commonly occurring in 'psychoneuroses' were present in these patients to lend colour to such a differentiation. Buzzard, deploring the neglect of textbooks to pay due regard to the 'features which distinguish neurotic from psychotic forms of depression', referred to the 'motley of neurasthenic symptoms'; motley was the jester's wear, and if it be not straining the metaphor, one might say that here the motley of the garb is no more variable and bewildering than the names and identity of what it covers; 'neurasthenia', 'neurosis', 'psychoneurosis', 'psychasthenia', 'constitutional nervousness', here is a medley of names emblematic of the hodge-podge of symptoms in which they are bodied forth.

The chief features which have been subsumed here under this head are 'aches and pains', descriptions of indeterminate bodily discomforts, not obviously delusional or hypochondriacal; symptoms of a 'conversion' type, such as vomiting or headache, when confronted with an unwelcome situation; histrionic behaviour or melodramatic exaggerated talk; an attitude of dependence, attachment or otherwise 'reaching out'; wandering away to avoid difficulties; feelings that the eyes are fixed and staring, etc. It is emphasized that features of anxiety and compulsion are discussed elsewhere. Some of the symptoms just enumerated have also been dealt with in another connexion, but it seemed advisable to collect them together here.

Thirty-two patients showed these symptoms. The symptoms shown in individual cases were varied. R. S. developed splitting headaches and odd pains as soon as she was told to get up or go home; her descriptions were exaggerated, her mood varied somewhat and she responded to her environment. M. H. had much vomiting at the onset of her illness; she felt weight upon her head; her head felt numb; at times she felt she wanted to dance; she worried about her eyes, felt irritable and dissatisfied; she varied with her surroundings, and from day to day. E. J. had vomiting after every meal at the beginning of her illness. A. H. stammered a good deal, and was anxious to impress one with his knowledge of medical terms. E. J. F. stuttered after having a vaginal douche; her manner at one time was histrionic and artificial; she complained of a lump in her throat. F. N. wandered away from home for two days; he got into strong effective relationship with those around him. E. W. D. also wandered away, in order to avoid going into hospital for an operation. F. H. was exaggerated and histrionic; she felt she could not stand. E. P. had 'deliberately tried to fall' whenever she was got on to her feet in the earlier stage of her illness.

D. C. likewise tottered and stumbled; she was very irritable and histrionic, and she desired sympathy; she complained of pains in her back, face, etc. L. L. C. fainted in shops, had 'hysterical outbursts'; she wrote in exaggerated high-flown style with endearments and cajolery; she threatened to 'hunger-strike', having heard another patient do so; she clutched one's arm and was appealing in her manner; she said the other patients depressed her. E. W. sought for sympathy; seemed at times to take pleasure in relating her great wickedness; she responded to changes in her surroundings. G. S. was histrionic and stilted, both in speech and manner; she talked with pedantic formality, like a bad caricature of Dr Johnson, e.g., she said, 'Sir, a catastrophe has occurred.' D. N. was melodramatic in the expression of her sufferings and intimate and appealing in her manner; her letters read like novelettes. M. L. got into strong affective relations with those around her, at one time professing a strong attachment, which later became active dislike; she was dependent on the physician; she was irresolute, and constantly deterred from action by scruples. A. F. was always seeking for attention, asking for interviews. M. F. was self-pitying; she gave highly-coloured descriptions of her agonies and suffering, and would show the same symptoms as her neighbours; she would occasionally laugh and cry alternately, both without giving an impression of much 'depth'. J. C. was very self-pitying, calling out for attention, and even appropriating another patient's pillow. E. R. had vague pains in her head, and in various joints and muscles; she was dissatisfied. E. N. said she had a pain in her heart and a pricking in her left breast and pains in her legs, indigestion, a feeling of weight on her head and headache. A. E. N. had headaches, abdominal discomfort and pains. I. M. said she got pains in her head whenever she tried to do anything; she called attention to herself a lot, asked for interviews, and was appealing and confiding, and complained of abdominal and other pains which cleared up quickly. G. M.'s illness had set in with sudden tiredness and pains in her left side, where her ribs had been fractured; she felt breathless during the night (her sister had had consumption); she worried about her eyes, and later about her ears, and said she felt pain on taking a deep breath though the injury to her chest had occurred 16 months before, and there was no evidence of any local cause for her pain. H. O. H. had a feeling of tightness in her throat. R. D. felt a sudden blank feeling in his head; he was dependent and sought reassurance. M. C. complained of pain over the top of her head and of peculiar feelings in her head. H. C. complained of pains in her head and back when she was agitated. L. C. likewise, and M. T.; the latter also felt that her eyes 'were fixed'. D. P. felt pressure in her head and her eyes felt fixed in her head. E. B. said her eyes kept revolving in her head, at other times that they felt staring. This is a neurotic symptom to which Abraham has called particular attention. M. S. was stated by her uncle, a doctor, to have shown some symptoms of conversion hysteria.

If it be objected that these symptoms can be accounted for otherwise than as part of the psychoneurotic reaction, there is no reply. Many of them have been, in other parts of this study. These heterogeneous symptoms have been collected together here because many British and German psychiatrists insist on a differentiation to which they are indispensable (unless clinical groupings and reaction types are to be classified and determined solely on criteria of pre-psychotic personality and inferences as to 'mechanism' of development). Reference need only be made to the two English discussions already alluded to, one in February, 1930, at which only one speaker refused to distinguish sharply between psycho-neuroses and psychoses, and the earlier one in 1926, at which sharp and unanimous exception was taken to Mapother's view that there was no essential difference between the 'manic-depressive' and the 'psycho-neurotic' syndromes (such as 'anxiety-neurosis'). Buzzard, for example, said that 'the distinction between these two conditions, although sometimes difficult, was of fundamental importance in regard to prognosis and treatment, as well as in the interests of academic accuracy'. Since these views have their origin in the teaching of Kraepelin and his followers (adapting the *dégénération* and *folie circulaire* groupings of the French), and have obtained their most effective expression at the hands of German writers, it will be as well to see what has been the development of these conceptions in Germany. Kraepelin began by differentiating 'konstitutionelle Erregung' and 'konstitutionelle Verstimmung' from manic-depressive insanity; later he included these groupings, as fundamental states (*Grundzustände*) in the new disease. These *Grundzustände* were really types of personality which showed the pre-disposition to the particular disorder. Then Bumke suggested on various grounds that manic-depressive insanity and the 'degenerative' conditions should be included under one grouping. Reiss wrote a famous paper in 1910 in which he described the depressive personality ('die konstitutionelle Verstimmung') with considerable skill, and incidentally pointed out that reactive depression could occur in persons of such a make-up, and that there was no satisfactory clinical means of distinguishing such reactive depression from 'endogenous' depression; further, that in these people the resulting illness might have either 'sensitive', 'psychasthenic', 'obessional' features or 'hysterical' ones. Thus, amid a welter of controversy about cyclothymia, depressive disposition and reactive depression, the view emerged that the manic-depressive psychosis occurred in people of a certain make-up in whom the illness might be a response to situations without or an apparently endogenous one, and that 'neurotic' or 'degenerative' features might occur. The view was not accepted. Alzheimer rejected it vigorously. The concept of cyclothymia received further attention. Lange and K. Schneider entered the field, the one with a clinical, genetic and constitutional study of thirty-one depressive cases, divided into endogenous, physically provoked, reactive and psychogenic depressions, the other with a formulation based on Scheler's philosophy, and with insistence on the 'vital' character of endogenous depression, as contrasted with the reactive psychopathic variety. Lange's views were largely in accordance with Kretschmer's; Schneider's found an enthusiastic advocate in Otto Kant. Meanwhile Bonhoeffer, Dattner, Stocker, Kleist and others attacked the problem from different points of view. Now one finds Lange in his recent monograph taking up a less emphatic standpoint, certainly not claiming that there is any fundamental distinction. Bumke, Kraepelin's successor in Munich, writes in the 1929 edition of his textbook: 'But there is such a mixing-up of the endogenous forms that it is often quite arbitrary whether one speaks of mere nervousness or of manic-depressive psychosis or hysteria. . . . To this extent the not infrequent question as to whether there is a fundamental distinction between mild melancholia and neurotic depression seems to me a false one (or wrongly posited).' These, then, are the changes which German psychiatry has gone through in regard to this matter; in this country a lingering formalism has persisted, with its roots in the outworn notion of endogenous-physical constitutional factors in psychosis as against environmental-psychic and constitutional factors in neurosis; Gillespie's study of depressive reactions, for example, follows close in the footsteps of Lange and Cimbal; while contesting Lange's view that endogenous depressions run a course independent of environmental factors, he yet calls one of his own groups autonomous, and describes it as 'showing no reactivity beyond at most an initial precipitation'. The discussions referred to above indicate that the distinction is regarded by many British psychiatrists as fundamental, with a decisive bearing on treatment.

There can be little doubt that this view is false. Every illness is the product of two factors—of environment working on the organism; whether the constitutional factor is the predominant and determining influence, or the environmental one, is never a question of kind, never a question to be dealt with as an 'either-or' problem; there will be a great number of possible combinations according to the individual inherited endowment and training, and the particular constellation of environmental forces. To set up a sharp distinction 'in the interests of academic accuracy' when the distinction is not found in nature and is no help to thought or action, when it is accurate only so long as it remains rigidly academic, but elsewhere inaccurate and misleading—this is not the current conception of the purpose of psychiatric classification, which essays to delimit only types of reaction, with every possibility of intermingling, and no certain independence. Biological and genetic studies have not confirmed the existence of separate and independent types of reaction or even diseases, but have indicated the great complexity of the constitutional factors and predispositions. 'Pure' syndromes and reaction-types are less and less often found as more careful examination of the patient and his illness is made. No one has declared this more emphatically than Adolf Meyer. In his paper on the interrelations of the domain of neuro-psychiatry he made it clear that no sharp line could be drawn between the psychoses and the neuroses; many neuroses represented a more far-reaching disturbance in the general adjustive equilibrium of the individual than some psychoses. If the occurrence of compulsive, anxiety, and other 'psycho-neurotic' symptoms be considered, as enumerated in the preceding sections of this study, the inapplicability of any other view, except on pragmatic grounds of didactic value, etc., is clear.

COMPULSIVE SYMPTOMS

Whether one uses the term 'obsession' or 'compulsion' is immaterial if to both the same meaning be given. The difficulties in the way of adequate definition of these terms are notoriously great. The most satisfactory appears to be: 'Contents of consciousness, which occur accompanied by an experience of subjective compulsion and which cannot be got rid of, although at quiet times they are recognized as senseless or as dominating without cause.' This is a rather clumsy translation of Schneider's definition; he gives a careful survey of the whole position with regard to compulsive symptoms, and with his conclusions one is in agreement. The relation of compulsive symptoms to anxiety needs no stressing.

Thirteen patients showed compulsive features during their illness. E. B. was obliged to make clicking movements with her tongue and to utter obscene words; obscene thoughts came into her mind against her will and distressed her. L. C. scratched her gum until it bled, and when remonstrated with, replied: 'I feel I must do that; I know it's wrong: I try not to.' E. J. said: 'Thoughts keep coming up and worrying me. I have tried to put it right, but I don't feel satisfied.' E. H. said: 'I try as hard as I can to put these thoughts out of mind, but I can't. I can't keep my thoughts off my private parts, and it's dreadful; it's abnormal. I try to fight it down.' A. M. P. had numerous repetitive compulsions with doubt, scruples and much anxiety; the latter were prominent symptoms also in M. L. H. C. would suddenly utter a rude remark, e.g., 'Get about your business,' or would clutch a door handle tightly, so that one could not open the door; she said, 'I don't know why I do it; I can't help it . . . these silly things I do.' She also washed with excessive frequency. This continual washing was also observed in 6 other cases. E. J. F. felt obliged to make a sucking noise with her tongue continually though she tried not to. M. H., in addition to washing herself, took to washing her house with superfluous assiduity; 'she had a mania for cleaning—washed the floors twice over'. M. S., in addition to washing, also kept picking her lower lip until it was excoriated; she said she didn't want to do it, but couldn't help it.

The dividing line between stereotyped actions, the picking and rubbing movements of the agitated, on the one hand, and compulsive phenomena on the other, is difficult to mark; the subjective experience of compulsion is the chief criterion, and by this the above would be regarded as compulsive. Many cases in which the compulsions were franker and more prominent, associated with a depressive type of reaction, were excluded from this study on diagnostic grounds; Bonhoeffer, however, in his well-known paper on the relation of compulsive ideas to manic-depressive disorders, goes so far as to say that the periodicity and other features of many obsessional illnesses make it probable that the occurrence of compulsive ideas has extraordinarily intimate relations to the manic-depressive disposition, and that in many cases the compulsive symptoms are prominent because the depressive patient is troubled most by them and therefore puts them in the foreground; the depressive symptom-complex that so commonly accompanies obsessions is not secondary, a consequence of them, but rather the essential illness; the patients view it, of course, otherwise, and many doctors, even psychiatrists, are misled by the patient's insistence of the primary nature of the obsessions: 'Where there is a depressive syndrome with obsessional ideas it is not a matter of a psychological consequence or secondary phenomenon, but of an intrinsic clinical relation.' Bonhoeffer also points out the obsessional features in the ideas of poverty and self-reproach which melancholics express though aware of their falsity, and he adduces the close relations between manic-depressive features in one generation and compulsive in another, just as Abraham has done. The views of this distinguished psychiatrist on the question coincided with those of Heilbronner, and have been confirmed or arrived at independently by Dattner, Strauss, Stöcker and Mapother (the last of whom considers that 'like the allusions (the obsessions) are as a rule of the readily intelligible type'. The point deserves a little labouring, because it is not mentioned in British works on psychiatry (though the psycho-analysts, following Abraham, give it prominence), and has actually been regarded by one psychiatrist (Gillespie) as a recent and novel observation ('that "obsessions were common in melancholics" was an original observation which he would have liked to see expanded'). There can be no doubt that compulsive phenomena occur in 'true' melancholia; how far this is to be regarded as indicative of a close relation in manner of development is a more difficult question. Bumke (who makes a clear, rather too formal distinction between 'dominant ideas', 'compulsive ideas', 'over-valued ideas' and 'delusions') points out that the periodic occurrence of obsessional states, often commented on, is not in itself a reason for including them among the manic-depressive disorders, since periodicity is a normal property of the human psyche, but he adds that melancholia can certainly be accompanied or ushered in by compulsive phenomena: 'There is, besides a relationship to the circular depressions—in my opinion not an essential one—in so far as in many obsessional patients a depressive state could be demonstrated as having preceded the obsessions.' There is another point which must be mentioned in this connexion. Gillespie insisted on the therapeutic criterion: 'The distinction between neuroses and psychoses rested not upon the problem of certification so much as upon the problem of treatment. The treatment that was suitable for a manic-depressive was fatal to a psychoneurotic'; similarly Ross, on the same occasion, 'absolutely controverted the view that the two states showed no difference in reaction to treatment'. But there is not merely the evidence of many cases in this series who got rid of 'psychoneurotic' symptoms (manifest not only during the illness, but also in the pre-psychotic personality) after a period of treatment in which no 'active' psychotherapy was employed (see discussion below); there is also the opinion of a psychiatrist of the eminence of Bonhoeffer, who writes: 'A confirmation of the view here presented as to the nosological position of obsessions is perhaps also to be seen in the similarity between genuine depressions and obsessional states in the matter of therapeutic successes. In both the credit goes to the therapist who has the luck to get the patient at the time when the disorder, according to the unknown laws of endogenous illness, is spontaneously tending to end. In this phase everything appears useful that in another phase was futile.'

One would expect that compulsive features would be more common in those who had had similar tendencies or symptoms before they felt ill. This was found to be the case. Nineteen patients showed obsessive character-traits or frank obsessive symptoms, and of these 5 had had many doubts and scruples: they often went back to make sure of having turned off the gas or locked the door; they repeated actions which seemed trivial or purposeless and did not know why. R. R. S. had a horror of trains and closed spaces. E. B. was often worried by questioning thoughts about the origin and nature of things—thoughts which never came to an end and were not to be escaped from. A strong desire to keep everything excessively clean and orderly, to have things always in the same place, to wash frequently, were reported in 15 cases. Extreme conscientiousness had been a characteristic in ten cases. These are features of the 'obsessive character' described, with different-preconceptions, by Schneider as 'anankasten' (or 'selbstunsichere'), by Kretschmer as 'sensitive', by Abraham as anal-erotic (or, in part, oral-erotic). It will be seen that the relation between the pre-psychotic and the psychotic features is striking. In all but one of the patients who had compulsive symptoms during their illness, the tendency was recognizable in their ordinary conduct before they had fallen ill. (The solitary exception, M. S., was a girl, about whom it was difficult to obtain any adequate and reliable description of the pre-psychotic personality, so that it might well be only a matter of an inadequate record.) There are the patients who, with obsessive characteristics, showed no compulsive features during their illness. It has been suggested by Lange that it is only in atypical mixed states that the requirements for the occurrence of compulsive symptoms obtain; this is speculative, however, as he admits. Investigations on a larger, specially selected case-material are being conducted, but as the number of these cases that have been included in the 61 is small, one cannot say more here than that it appears that it is almost always possible, by careful inquiry, to discover compulsive features during the psychosis in patients who previously had shown such tendencies.

It is worth recording that W. J. Pinard, working at the Maudsley Hospital, on the lines of Spearman's psychological researches, has found that depressive states, paranoid states and obsessional states all have a high correlation with strong 'perseveration' ('perseveration' in Wiersma's sense).

PERSONALITY

No thorough examination of personality is contemplated in this paper, for reasons given elsewhere. It seems necessary to give a brief reference to some features of character, not already enumerated in connexion with the clinical features, which need brief mention. Hoch and others have emphasized the frequency with which a gloomy, pessimistic, worrying disposition is found in those patients; in the present series it was reported in 30 cases. Variability of mood was found in 19 cases; sensitiveness, 'touchiness', in 32; 9 patients had always been rather suspicious; while 12 were seclusive, shy, unsociable.

The inadequacy of this affixing of epithets is so great that it was proposed to abstain from it in favour of the more plastic delineation of the reactions of the personality, but as it has some bearing on the paranoid features of the illness alluded to above, it has been included.

ASPECTS OMITTED

An intentional omission of much that is of the first importance in psychiatry calls for some explanation. Neither therapeutics, nor prognosis nor personality have received any but casual mention; the occurrence of previous illnesses, especially similar ones, the childhood, the sexual life, the physical and metabolic changes, the outcome, the duration and the family history have been left untouched. This is not because they are considered unimportant. On the contrary, they are more important than the comparatively static and descriptive investigation of clinical features. But the last is not a useless exercise, but rather an essential part of the whole. On large sections of the omitted material conclusions have been reached in the course of the present and other investigations, but it seemed best to limit this paper definitely. The general attitude of the writer towards the dynamic aspects of the disorder, which may seem to have received scanty consideration, may be gathered from the following section.

REACTION, PSYCHOGENESIS

As the result of the investigations of Bonhoeffer, the teachings of Adolf Meyer, and the growing influence of constitutional and genetic conceptions, it is now customary to speak of depressive as well as other psycho-pathological states as types of reaction. It is assumed that people of a certain make-up will react to certain situations, both external and internal, in this typical way But this is a biological conception; and wherever else in medicine such biological views of reaction to a situation are considered, they have a strong teleological bias. Inflammation, fever and other morbid processes are regarded as beneficial reactions tending to preserve the organism from harm: 'Where damage has been done or the conditions are abnormal, a series of reactive processes come into play. They have for their object the getting rid of the irritant or abnormal state, and the repair of the damage. The reactions are thus defensive and reparative in nature.' They may prove inadequate, but that is nothing against their purpose.

Psychiatry as a branch of medicine uses the medical conceptions of symptoms as evidence of disordered function, reaction as an attempt to deal with noxae, usually to the benefit of the organism. The end of mental, as of physical disorder, if the painful dichotomy may be permitted for a moment, is harmonious adaptation to the conditions of the environment. Mental disorder therefore tends to result in a change of the individual or a change in the environment which may make each tolerable to the other. Nowhere is such a relation more clearly seen than in depressive states. Schizophrenia, one might say, offers as many difficulties to this point of view in psychopathology as does tumour-formations in general pathology. But depressive states might almost be a paradigm. Many result in a complete recovery, in which the patient seems better than he has been for years; it is exemplified in many patients of this series. Others, removed from their noxious environment, speedily repair the damage, and the organism can again cope for a time with a renewal of those irritant situations, for example, on discharge from hospital, by a number of minor symptoms, or, less effectively, by a renewal of the whole process, only effective in so far as it brings the organism again into an easier environment. Still others are comparable to such damaging extreme processes as keloid formation or pyaemia. There is, however, no need of comparisons. Unless didactic ends intervene or a fatalistic conception of genetics, there is general agreement as to the adaptive nature of the reactions; the form of the adaptation may be determined by a system of values different from that of the physician or of society generally, but it is difficult to hold the dynamic view without seeing an end to the 'dynamism', a purpose to which, however obscurely, it works. Into the problems of entelechy, libido, *élan vital*, and other more or less metaphysical explanations, this is not the place to enter. It is assumed here that the patterns of reaction are inherent in the organism, but are susceptible of infinite variety through combination of elements—what the elements are is a problem to be solved by researches in heredity, what the determinants of their form by studies in constitution and the influence of environment.

Many writers who hold the dynamic views describe varieties of depression, which they designate 'autonomous' and 'reactive' (Gillespie), 'constitutional' and 'reactive' (Dawson), 'vital' and 'psychoneurotic' or 'psychogenic' (Schneider, Kant). But this appears to be unjustified. Its justification would lie in the possibility of separating most cases of depression into one or other group. Though there were a continuous graded series between them, there would be good pragmatic grounds for the distinction if one could usually say of any case that it was one or the other; the exceptions would be material for a special study, much like mixed manic-depressive schizophrenic states, which do not prevent us from grouping cases in these two categories. The writers are aware of this. Thus Dawson writes: 'Although in a sense most depressions are reactive, in so far as the individual is depressed as a result of difficulties within himself or in his environment, a special group may be distinguished in which the precipitating factors are adequate and outstanding, and in which the depression appears clearly to follow upon a certain situation.' If these be the criteria of a reactive depression, they are surely most difficult of application. What is an 'adequate' situation to precipitate mental disorder? Inasmuch as many others have passed through similar situations without showing mental disorder, the situation for those who did must appear adequate only if one takes into consideration their tendencies, their previous personality, their inherited endowment and their disposition to certain forms of reaction. The attempt was made in the course of the present investigation to decide with regard to each case whether there was a definite situational factor responsible for the precipitating or the maintenance of the symptoms. The criteria were the previous good health of the patient before this situation arose, the temporal relationship between the situation and the beginning of the illness, and the apparent adequacy of the situation from a 'common-sense' point of view. As Wertham has pointed out in connexion with 'reactive mania', the adequacy of environmental factors must be assessed by ordinary experience—so-called 'common sense'—since the attribution of great significance to trivial happenings because of their emotional value for the patient, though perfectly correct psychopathologically, is foreign to the implications of the term 'reactive' in this connexion. Dawson remarks that precipitating situations should always be considered in the light of their meaning to the patient; 'in this way apparently trivial incidents may lead to widespread emotional changes', but this is very different from 'adequate and outstanding precipitating factors'.

The criteria just mentioned were applied to the 61 cases. But the more one knew about the patient, the harder this became. A very small group of nine cases emerged about whom one was almost satisfied. Although one had to invoke much more than the situation to account for the psychosis, it could be said that the situation in these cases had been an indispensable efficient cause for this attack—perhaps the main precipitating cause. There was a small group of 10 in whom one could not in the least discover anything in their environment which could have been held responsible for the outbreak of the attacks. But all the others were understandable examples of the interaction of organism and environment, i.e., personality and situation; it was impossible to say which of the factors was decidedly preponderant. It is to be emphasized that considerable pains were taken to elucidate the development of the illness in all these cases; the available data as collected by lengthy and detailed questioning of the patient and of the relatives, inquiries from employers, secretaries of clubs, etc., were in most cases copious, and short of an analytical technique, employing free association, it is doubtful whether in any large series of cases it would be possible to collect more relevant material; in spite of this there were ten patients in whom one had not the slightest inkling of why the illness had broken out; this may reasonably be attributed to the reticence of the patient and the relatives, or to the importance for the patient of events, not striking to the observer, but 'conditioned' for the patients by previous experience. Apart from these one could always recognize some of the factors operative. But to resolve the whole problem of causation is not possible; comprehensible relations, which were recognized with relative ease, are by no means the same as causal relations.

There are, to be sure, other criteria of a 'reactive' disorder besides those mentioned. Jaspers gives as his criteria: (1) The illness must be determined by a psychogenic factor; (2) there must be corresponding uniformity of the content of the psychoses with the causal factor; (3) the course of the psychoses must be dependent on changes in the situation; (4) the morbid phenomena must disappear, with unconditional return to the normal state, when the traumatic factor is got rid of. It may as well be said at once that not a single patient was found in whose illness these requirements were satisfied. The second requirement was met in three cases; the third requirement was satisfied in four, the fourth in two, but in no patient were they all satisfied.

It would appear that the effort at subdivision is, on the one hand, a setting up of types or ideal forms (*Hilfskonstruktionen*), a concession to the requirements of convenient thinking in categories, and, on the other hand, a relic of

Kraepelinian nosology, mediated largely through his pupils and successors, like Lange. The straits to which writers are put who wish to do justice to the great variety of clinical appearances can be well seen in Lange's generally admired paper of 1926, where he divides depressive states into endogenous melancholia, psychically provoked melancholia, reactive melancholia and psychogenic depression. Gillespie, though professedly a follower of Adolf Meyer, has manifestly been greatly influenced by the nosological views of Kraepelinians like Lange and Cimbal, and he divides reactive depressions into psychoneurotic depression and depressions in constitutional psychopaths; the difficulties involved in his differentiation have already been considered in connexion with 'reactivity', and are manifest in the conclusions at the end of his original paper; he remarks, moreover, that 'precipitating causes were rather frequently traceable in both groups (autonomous and reactive) and were of a similar kind'.

Dawson remarks of constitutional depressions that the depression here 'results from a lack of inner harmony, from conflicting impulses, from a failure to achieve certain ideals, to a large extent apparently independently of adverse environmental conditions. Since these individuals have been grappling with personality problems for many years, they come to the clinic for the most part with an exacerbation of a long-continued state rather than with a more or less clear-cut attack. There are rarely any prominent precipitating factors.' (He includes among them the paranoid cases.) Here an important aspect of the problem is touched on. In attempting to discover the psychogenic and the constitutional cases among these 61, a note was made in each case as to whether there had been any symptoms of mental disorder prior to the occurrence of what might reasonably have been regarded as a psychogenic happening. The more intimate the knowledge of the patient's previous behaviour, the more definitely did such prodromal features become evident. Of the large number of patients in whom a disturbing experience (being jilted, the death of a near relative, a painful overt sexual experience, abortion, loss of wealth or occupation, etc.) appeared at first sight to have precipitated the illness and to have influenced its content, there was a considerable proportion in whom antecedent disorder was found to have been evident; the patient had been tired, irritable, quarrelsome, quieter, rather worried, a little preoccupied, 'not quite herself', 'nothing much, but just a bit off colour', 'worried about things rather', 'didn't seem to be his usual self', 'a bit nervous'. Statements such as these were obtained in about 19 cases. If one examined these one found that in some there was a cumulative situation, as it were; each difficulty had reduced the patient's good spirits and capacity, and over a period of weeks, months or even years there had been a gradually increasing worry, irritability, depression, inadequacy; finally the burden became so heavy that the patient was referred to a hospital. In others the personality had always been a mild, persistent picture of depression—pessimistic, hesitating, gloomy, anxious, unreliant; where the personality stopped and the illness began was a point calling for skilful casuistry, if thought worth deciding at all.

One was impressed with the purely temporal relation of the apparent psychogenic factor with the onset of the illness in some cases, with its purely pathoplastic or rationalizing use in others, where it formed the manifest content of the psychosis. If the patient reports a recent sexual trauma which colours all her psychotic life, and which was promptly followed by the outbreak of the psychosis, one calls it a psychogenic factor; if the patient reports a remote sexual trauma which now colours all her psychotic life, but was followed only after an interval of years by the outbreak of the psychosis, one scarcely calls it psychogenic; but surely the only difference is a temporal one. This is well exemplified in such cases as that of D. N., where the physician who saw the girl first in the out-patient department was misled by the patient's and her mother's insistence on the importance of a false accusation of fornication that had been made, so that he put this down as the psychogenic factor in a reactive depression; later, when it was discovered that between the accusation referred to and the onset of the psychosis there was an interval of a year or more, it was regarded as an example of the familiar phenomenon of the patient bringing up remote happenings, peccadilloes and slights, and interpreting them in the light of present mood. In many the earlier episode will fit well into a less rigid conception of the development of the disorder, figuring as a contributory cause, one of a chain of events, leading to the illness as one sees it on admission. Similarly if the illness occurs during the puerperium, this is regarded as establishing a probable aetiological relationship, as well as a temporal one, even though the patient had passed through previous confinements without any illness; and if one takes into account the many additional factors, both environmental and 'psychic', that have been operative during the interval between the two confinements, one is recognizing the pluridimensional nature of the 'illness' and the multiplicity of its 'causes'. One does not call the last straw the cause of the camel's broken back, at any rate if one is talking scientific language. The 'influenzal' cases and the 'post-operative' cases are in large measure illustrations of this.

Since, therefore, the delimitation of 'reactive' depression is justifiable only so far as it is serviceable and approximates to the facts (the pragmatic requirements), the discovery that it clouds the issue, makes difficulties that are not intrinsic in the data, and is unequivocally applicable only to a small percentage of the cases (Bonhoeffer found among 117 mild depressive states only 8 or 10 that were reactive, i.e., psychogenic, according to Reiss's definition), all this suggests that the term and the grouping it denotes would be better done away with. Gillespie thinks the delimitation of it is of value in determining therapy; his views are not confirmed by the cases here under consideration. Since Reiss first set up this group of reactive depressions, it has been subject to criticisms, especially from Bonhoeffer, Birnbaum and Stransky.

Another aspect of the problem that is often sacrificed to apparent lucidity is the fluidity of personality, modifying and being modified by environment. It is the great merit of William Stern in recent years to have emphasized that human personality is neither static nor secluded; it exists only in virtue of its environment, and in order to react on that environment, adapting it and being itself adapted. When, therefore, one says environmental factors did this and personality factors did that, one is again using an artificial construction, useful no doubt, but full of pitfalls. The personality often makes the situation, as it were, and then is appalled by it—a reciprocal action, not easily reducible to descriptive terms, but comprehensible as a sequence in which neither is independent or itself responsible for the product.

It may appear that too much attention has been paid to the reactive types and too little to the constitutional or autonomous. But what are the criteria of the latter? Periodicity?—it is a function of all the activities of the organism. Recurrence?—it occurs in the most clearly psychogenic. So do 'autonomous' course and apparent freedom from modifiability by extraneous factors. What remains is negative; there is no evident psychogenesis, and the illness does not respond to any treatment but that of care and abstention from all interference (except that needed to preserve life). Such cases unquestionably occur. The absence of psychogenesis or environmental influence, largely apparent, is due to our distinction between somatic and psychic, and our inability or disinclination to probe deeply into the total previous experience and reactions of the sick man; the autonomous course is a particular aspect of the general problem of illness. How far one does good, otherwise than by removing painful stimuli, whether outside or in the organism, is always dubious, and the tendency of the process, as suggested above, is towards recovery, i.e., harmonious adaptation. Von Monakow has insisted on the chronogenic as well as the spatial determinism of the organism; this applies not only to growth, one would say, but also to variation of function in unfavourable circumstances; the time factor is as important as the form factor in determining the course of an illness. On this point, as on many others in connexion with the problem of 'psychogenic' and 'autonomous' mental illnesses, I am in agreement with Erwin Straus's subtle and profound analysis of the problem. No doubt there are changes in the internal structure of the body, its chemical and vegetative regulation which play a great part in determining its course. But these are only part of the total reaction of the organism, and it is by no means in denial of their fundamental importance in the illness that one refuses them independent and preponderant significance, either aetiologically or as part of the process of the illness. With justice does Rosenfeld in his *Referat* on the vegetative and endocrine changes say 'Since physical and psychic functions are fused into an indissoluble unity—and not only in respect of sex—there will also be possible in endogenous psychoses an active interplay between the psychic processes, the cerebral processes and the endocrines. It will often be difficult, perhaps impossible, to decide which processes are to be regarded as primary.'

Finally, Lange and others, including Gillespie, have laid down clinical criteria by which one may distinguish endogenous and reactive depressions, e.g., loss of weight, attitude towards illness and towards environment, nature of retardation, etc.; Gillespie even gives a table showing the differences, so that the general practitioner and the student can carry out the diagnostic exercise readily. But it has been made sufficiently apparent in the various sections of this study that these criteria fail; they may be combined in the most varied ways, and the factors which determine them are by no means the factors concerned in the antithesis environment—person. It may be said that sixty-one cases are not many; but they are varied, and they are more than either Lange or Gillespie included in their studies. The conclusion would seem to be that reached by J. H. Schultz, who can scarcely be accused of bias against the differentiation of psychoneurotic or reactive conditions: 'The question whether an illness is reactive or endogenous is often put too schematically; it might more sensibly be formulated as: How far are reactive processes, in the widest sense, concerned in this case, and how far obscure hereditary or somatic determinants of a fateful sort?'

CONCLUSION

It has been the object of this study to determine the clinical features of 'depressive states'. From a series of personally observed cases, in which the diagnosis might fairly be regarded as unexceptionable, a fuller description of the range and form of the clinical features has been obtained than has been available in English. The consideration of relevant writings in English, German and French has been full because of the great diversity of statement about matters of observation, as well as of theory. The findings have compelled divergence in many points from the accepted views, as presented in textbooks and monographs, or amplification of them; these are discussed at length in the body of the paper, and do not permit of brief recapitulation. Particular reference, however, may be made to the discussion of several matters in which the divergence was great or the necessity for more adequate differentiation striking; such may be found in the sections dealing with paranoid features and the patient's attitude to his environment; the phenomena generally grouped under the heading 'retardation'; feelings of unreality; anxiety and compulsive symptoms; and the validity of current grouping of the types of depression.

It has to be pointed out that this paper was originally written in 1931. Its publication has been deferred until 1934, when a prognostic study of the patients in question can with propriety also be put forward.

REFERENCES

AVELING. 'The psychology of conation and volition', *Brit. J. of Psychol.*, 1926, **16** (also in Wittenberg Symposium, Worcester, 1928).

ABRAHAM. *Selected Papers*, London, 1927.

BALLET. 'Sur le caractère de certaines idées de persécution, etc.' (Congrès de Blois), *Le Mercredi Méd.*, 1892, no. 33.

BENON, P. 'Les Alternatives d'excitation et de dépression', *Rev. Neurol.*, 1920, no. 1.

BENON, P. *La Mélancolie, Clin. et Ther.*, Paris, 1925.
BERINGER. 'Denkstörungen und Sprache bei Schizophrenen', *Zeitschr. f. d. ges. Neur. u. Psych.*, 1926, Bd. ciii.
BIRNBAUM. 'Die Psychoreaktiven (Psychogenen) Symptombildungen', in Bumke, *Handbuch der Psychiatrie*, Bd. ii, Allg. Teil, Berlin, 1928.
BLACKER. 'Life and death instincts', *Brit. Journ. Med. Psych.*, 1929.
BLEULER. *Textbook of Psychiatry*, 4th ed., London, 1924.
Idem. Affektivität, Suggestibilität, Paranoia, Halle, 1906.
Idem. 'Zur Unterscheidung des Physiogenen und des Psychogenen,' *Allg. Zeitschr. f. Psych.*, 1926, Bd. lxxxiv.
BONHOEFFER. 'Über die Beziehung der Zwangsvorstellungen zum Manisch-depressiven', *Monats. f. Psych. u. Neur.*, 1913, Bd. xxxiii.
Idem. 'Wie weit kommen psychogene Krankheitszustände vor', *Allg. Zeitschr. f. Psych.*, 1911, Bd. lxviii.
BOSTROEM. 'Störungen des Wollens', in Bumke, *Handbuch der Psychiatrie*, Bd. ii, Allg. Teil, Berlin, 1928.
BUMKE. *Lehrbuch der Geisteskrankheiten*, München, 1929.
BUZZARD, YELLOWLEES, RIDDOCH *et al.* 'Discussion on diagnosis and treatment of the milder forms of the manic-depressive psychosis', *Proc. Roy. Soc. Med.*, 1930, **23**.
CARP. 'Zur psychoanalytischen Auffassung der Hypochondrie', *Zeitschr. f. d. ges. Neur. u. Psych.*, 1928, Bd. cxv.
CAMPBELL, MACFIE. 'Schizophrenia', *Association for Research in Nervous and Mental Diseases*, vol. v, article 2, New York, 1928.
COTARD. 'Du délire des négations', *Gaz. des Hôp.*, no. 32, 66e Année, 1893.
CRAIG AND BEATON. *Psychological Medicine*, London, 1926.
CRAMER. 'Über eine bestimmte Gruppe von Sinnestäuschungen bei primären Stimmungsanomalien', *Allg. Zeitschr. f. Psych.*, 1890, Bd. xlvii.
DAWSON. 'A study of the depressive reaction', *Mott. Memorial*, London, 1929.
DERON. *Le Syndrome Maniaque*, Paris, 1928.
DOERING. 'Über Herabsetzung der Thränensekretion bei Melancholie', *Inaug. Dissert.*, Freiberg, 1898.
DOMARUS. 'Über das Denken der Manischen und Depressiven', *Zeitschr. f. d. ges. Neur. u. Psych.*, 1928, Bd. cxii.
DREYFUS. *Die Melancholie*, Jena, 1907.
DUNLAP. 'Response Psychology', *Psychologies of* 1930 (Internat. Univ. Series), Worcester, 1930.
EWALD. 'Die biologischen Grundlagen von Temperament und Charakter, und ihre Bedeutung für die Abgrenzung des Manisch-depressiven Irreseins', *Zeitschr. f. d. ges. Neur. u. Psych.*, 1923, Bd. lxxxiv.
FREUD. *The Ego and the Id.*, London, 1926.
GILLESPIE. *Hypochondria*, London, 1929.
Idem. 'The clinical differentiation of types of depression', *Guy's Hosp. Reports*, 1929, **79**.
Idem. 'Some common functional nervous and mental conditions, etc.', *Med. World*, 1930, **32**.
GREENACRE. 'The content of the schizophrenic characteristics occurring in affective disorders', *Amer. J. of Insanity*, 1918, **75**.
GRUHLE. *Psychologie der Schizophrenie*, Berlin, 1929.
HEILBRONNER. 'Über Krankheitseinsicht', *Allg. Zeitschr. f. Psych.*, 1900–1901, Bd. lviii.
HENDERSON AND GILLESPIE. *Textbook of Psychiatry*, London, 1926.
HOCH. *Benign Stupors*, New York, 1921.
Idem. 'A study of the mental make-up in the functional psychoses', *J. Nerv. and Ment. Dis.*, 1909, **36**.

HOCH AND AMSDEN. 'A guide to the descriptive study of the personality', *Rev. Neur. and Psych.*, 1913.

JAHREISS. 'Störungen des Denkens', in Bumke, *Handbuch der Psychiatrie*, Bd. i, Allg. Teil, Berlin, 1928.

JANET. *Fear of Action as an Essential Element in the Sentiment of Melancholia* (Feelings and Emotions: The Wittenberg Symposium), Worcester, 1928.

Idem. 'Les Sentiments du vide', *J. de Psychol.*, 24me Année, no. 10, 1927.

JASPERS. *Allgemeine Psychopathologie*, Berlin, 1920.

KAHN. 'Über Wahnbildung', *Arch. f. Psychiat.*, 1929, Bd. lxxxviii.

KANT. 'Depression und Psychopathische Verstimmung', *Klin. Wochenschr.*, Jg. vi no. 34, 1927.

KEHRER. 'Paranoische Zustände', in Bumke, *Handbuch der Psychiatrie*, Bd. vi, Spez. Teil 2, Berlin, 1928.

KIRCHHOFF. 'Der melancholische Gesichtsausdruck und seine Bahn', *Allg. Zeitschr. f. Psych.*, 1900, Bd. lvii.

KRAEPELIN. *Psychiatrie*, Bd. iii, 8te Auflage, Leipzig, 1913.

Idem. 'Die klinische Stellung der Melancholie', *Monats. f. Psych. u. Neurol.*, 1899, Bd. vi.

KRETSCHMER. 'Störungen des Gefühlslebens', in Bumke, *Handbuch der Psychiatrie*, Bd. i, Allg. Teil, Berlin, 1928.

Idem. Der Sensitive Beziehungswahn, Berlin, 1926.

LAIGNEL-LAVASTINE, BARBÉ ET DELMAS. *La Pratique Psychiatrique*, Paris, 1929.

LANGE. 'Die endogenen und reaktiven Gemütserkrankungen und die manisch-depressive Konstitution', in Bumke, *Handbuch der Geisteskrankheiten*, Bd. vi, Spez. Teil 2, Berlin, 1928.

Idem. 'Über Melancholie', *Zeitschr. f. d. ges. Neur. u. Psych.*, 1926, Bd. ci.

LUGARO. *Modern Problems in Psychiatry*, Manchester, 1909.

MACCURDY. *The Psychology of Emotion*, London, 1925.

MALAMUD. 'The sense of reality in mental disease', *Arch. of Neur. and Psychiat.*, 1930, **23.**

MAPOTHER. 'The schizophrenic-paranoid series (early mental disease)', *Lancet*, London, 1926.

MAPOTHER *et al.* 'Manic-depressive-psychosis' (Discussion), *Brit. Med. J.*, November, 1926.

MARCUSE. *Die Psychischen Reaktionsformen*, Berlin, 1929.

MAYER-GROSS. 'Pathologie der Wahrnehmung', in Bumke, *Handbuch der Psychiatrie*, Bd. i, Allg. Teil, Berlin, 1928.

Idem. Selbstschilderungen der Verwirrtheit. Die oneiroide Erlebnisform, Berlin, 1924.

MEYER, ADOLF. 'Interrelations of the domain of neuro-psychiatry', *Arch. Neur. and Psych.*, 1922, **15.**

V. MONAKOW ET MOURGUE. *Introduction Biologique à l'étude de la Neurologie et de la Psychopathologie*, Paris, 1928.

MORSELLI. *Suicide* (Internat. Scientific Series), London, 1881.

NATHAN. *Manuel de Psychiatrie*, Paris, 1930.

PASKIND. 'Brief attacks of manic-depressive depression', *Arch. of Neur. and Psychiat.*, 1929, **22.**

PFERRSDORF. 'Rededrang mit Denkhemmung', *ibid.*, 1906, Bd. lxiii.

PICK. 'Zur Lehre von der Hypochondrie', *Allg. Zeitschr. f. Psych.*, 1903, Bd. lx.

RAECKE. 'Über Hypochondrie', *ibid.*, 1902, Bd. lix.

RICKMAN. *The Development of the Psycho-analytical Theory of the Psychoses*, London, 1928.

ROSENFELD. 'Die Beziehungen Innersekretorischer Vorgänge zu Psychopathologischen Phänomenen', *Zentralbl. f. d. ges. Neur. u. Psych.*, 1930, Bd. lvii.

Idem. Die Störungen des Bewusstseins, Leipzig, 1929.

SCHILDER. *Selbstbewusstsein und Persönlichkeitsbewusstsein*, Berlin, 1914.
Idem. 'Zur Lehre von der Hypochondrie', *Monats. f. Psych. u. Neur.*, 1924, Bd. lvi.
SCHNEIDER, CARL. *Die Psychologie der Schizophrenen*, Leipzig, 1930.
SCHNEIDER, KURT. 'Pathopsychologische Beiträge aur Phänomenologie von Liebe und Mitfühlen', *Zeitschr. f. d. ges. Neur. u. Psych.*, 1921, Bd. lxv.
Idem. 'Die Schichtung des emotionalen Lebens und der Aufbau der Depressionszustände', *Zeitschr. f. d. ges. Neur. u. Psych.*, 1920, Bd. lix.
Idem. Die psychopathischen Persönlichkeiten, Leipzig, 1928.
SCHROEDER, J. 'Über gedankenflüchtige Denkhemmung', *Zeitschr. f. d. ges. Neur. u. Psych.*, 1910, Bd. ii.
Idem. 'Das Halluzinieren', *Zeitschr. f. d. ges. Neur. u. Psych.*, 1926, Bd. ci.
SCHULTZ, J. H. 'Das Endgültigkeitsproblem', *ibid.*, Weygandt-Festschrift, 1930.
Idem. 'Der Angstsymptom in seiner klinischen Stellung und allgemein-biologischen Bedeutung', *Monats. f. Psych. u. Neur.*, 1929, Bd. lxxiii.
SÉGLAS. 'Idées de Persécution' (Congrès de Blois), *Le Mercredi Méd.*, no. 33, 1892.
SPECHT. 'Struktur und klinische Stellung der Melancholie', *Zentralbl. f. Nervenheilk.*, 1908, Bd. xxxi, no. 449.
STODDART. *Mind and its Disorders*, London, 1919.
STRAUS. *Geschehnis und Erlebnis*, Berlin, 1930.
Idem. 'Das Zeiterlebnis in der endogenen Depression und in der psychopathischen Verstimmung', *Monats. f. Psych. u. Neur.*, 1928, Bd. lxviii.
STRECKER AND EBAUGH. *Practical Clinical Psychiatry*, London, 1928.
THALBITZER. 'Melancholie und Depression', *Allg. Zeitschr. f. Psych.*, 1905, Bd. lxii.
TOULOUSE. 'Le Délire des Négations', *Gaz. des. Hôp.*, 1893, no. 32, 66e Année.
WERNICKE. *Grundriss der Psychiatrie*, Leipzig, 1906.
WILMANNS. 'Die Differentialdiagnostik der funktionellen Psychosen', *Zentralbl. f. Nervenheilk.*, 1907.
WILSON AND DEMING. 'Statistical comparison of psychiatric diagnosis', *Quart. Bull. Mass. Dept. Ment. Dis.*, 1930, **11**.
WITMAACK. *Die Hypochondrie*, Leipzig, 1857.
ZIEHEN. *Die Erkennung und Behandlung der Melancholie*, Halle, 1896.

4

MELANCHOLIA: A PROGNOSTIC STUDY

I HOPE it will not be a waste of time to begin by seeing what can be meant by prognosis in this difficult kind of illness. Prognosis is often conceived as the natural history of disease—or the course it will follow if it is not interfered with. Treatment is valued for the good modification it produces in this 'natural' course of events; it may hurry up the processes of recovery or it may bring about recovery that would not otherwise occur, or it may lessen the harm the disease does; in other words, the efficacy of treatment is assessed by the changes produced in the time the illness takes and the shape it takes. In the case of such a disease as malaria, this conception of prognosis, and this use of it for assessing treatment, can be demonstrated. In psychiatry, however, one is not as a rule dealing with parasites, bacteria, or other exogenous agents which live and exert their influence in a definite order of time and place. Causes of mental illness have no set sequence or constancy. Those external to the patient are as variable and manifold as the pattern of daily life around us and those intrinsic in him are seldom capable of forcing their way and becoming manifest as illness, no matter what befalls the patient. They are for the most part dependent on circumstance, and of their particular transmission and manifestation we know little; we infer hereditary and constitutional causes with good grounds, but of the details of heredity in any of the individual forms of mental illness we cannot be sure. Consequently we cannot find now any accuracy of prognosis, in the sense of predictable sequence in an individual, based on comparable experience of many others; the variations will be too many; we may expect such accuracy when we know more of the nature and mode of transmission, and of the influence of external circumstances upon time and form and degree of manifestation of each kind of mental illness. Without accurate knowledge of how the causal and modifying factors act, prognosis must be uncertain to a greater extent than in many other illnesses. In medicine, it is true, prognosis can hardly ever be exact, but here it is more inexact than usual.

It will be seen that I make a distinction between prognosis pure and simple and the prognosis which takes account of treatment. In clinical practice this

This paper is reprinted from the *Journal of Mental Science* (September 1936), **82**, 488–558.

is customary; 'follow this treatment', one says to the patient, 'and such and such will happen; if you do not, then I am afraid . . .'. Now, in psychiatry the number of possibilities is wide, for the reasons I have just spoken of—the variety of external circumstances that may act on the patient, and the variety of ways in which he may be constitutionally prone to respond to them. There is, in short, no such thing as an abstract pure prognosis of manic-depressive insanity as it occurs in any single patient; there are a number of chances or prognoses which we may foresee, sometimes clearly, sometimes darkly, and with wide conjecture. This I hope to illustrate presently. Such simple statements as that the prognosis for recovery from the attack is good in correctly-diagnosed cases have to be qualified. We have changed the Kraepelinian view as to the prognosis in dementia praecox without revising it in manic-depressive psychosis.

When I speak of prognosis in manic-depressive psychosis, it is necessary that I should state whether I have in mind a type, an ideal form, 'the manic-depressive psychosis', or whether I mean the illness of a particular patient which approximates to this diagnostic grouping. In the one instance I am dealing with an abstraction, or at best with a statistical estimate of the chances in a somewhat heterogeneous group, and in the other with an attempt to evaluate individual causal and clinical facts which bear on individual prognosis. In fact I have both in mind, in that in discussing the literature of the subject I shall be dealing mainly with the former, i.e., with a more or less fictitious Kraepelinian entity, whereas in discussing a small group of patients whom I have followed for some years I shall raise the latter issue, though without any pretence at disposing of it.

Before considering these two matters, viz., the general course and the individual prognosis, it is also proper, I think, to recall that the word 'prognosis' sums up a number of questions which should be dealt with separately. There is first the genetic prognosis—the chances of a child later showing manic-depressive illness because of his inherited predisposition. The probability is an actuarial matter, which belongs to another discussion in this symposium. Then there is the time of occurrence of the illness; will it coincide with adolescence, marriage, pregnancy, menstruation, menopause, season, bereavement, infection, promotion, etc.? What will be the duration of the attack? And what the probable sequence of events in it? Will the patient get worse before he gets better? Will his symptoms become more florid? Will his judgment be impaired? Will he need hospital treatment or certification? Will he recover suddenly or gradually? Will he pass into a manic or depressive phase? Will he remain capable of attending to his business? Will he attempt suicide, and, if so, how and when? There are any number of important practical issues which one would like to be able to forecast from one's knowledge of the past clinical form, the causes and psychopathology of the condition. There is the question whether the man with cyclothymia must fear a severe attack of depression or elation. Also, after recovery from an attack, will the patient have another, how long will he remain well before the sword falls, what will be its form and duration, how bad will it be, what might occasion it? And, a more important question than is commonly thought, how will he be after this attack, how complete will be his recovery or how satisfactory his improvement? Will his attacks gradually get more severe or different? Will he eventually die of this illness? What physical changes may occur in him as he grows older which will be related to his mental disorder? And finally, this all-important question of treatment—what effect will it have in ending the attack happily and in staving off further attacks? I should say, here, that as I am not considering the relative value of methods of treatment, I shall assume that in other people's reports, as in my own group of cases, the treatment used was that considered orthodox and best in psychiatric clinics at the time of the respective inquiries. No doubt different kinds of treatment influence the course of the illness differently. I do not think that anyone can reasonably sustain the view sometimes hinted at, that people get better of manic-depressive illness equally well whatever you do. But as I cannot judge the relative value and effects of different methods of treatment, I shall, by a convention which I hope may be excused, neglect this factor of different treatment. Unfortunately—or fortunately—one cannot get hold of any adequate psychiatric reports of manic-depressive cases left entirely to their own and their neighbours' devices; some sort of treatment there always is, even if it be bad treatment. A pure prognosis, independent of circumstances, is, as I said earlier, a figment, a thing of naught. The most important circumstances will, of course, be those specially designed to meet the needs of the patient's situation—in other words, therapeutic circumstances.

In reading through the literature of this subject one is struck by a discrepancy between the findings of investigators with a Kraepelinian notion of the disease and those of the latitudinarian party; by which I mean those psychiatrists who deal with reactions rather than diseases, and to whom the term 'manic-depressive insanity' implies an arbitrary frontier rather than a true division. Thus French psychiatry is less rigid in this respect than the Kraepelinian; Rouart, for example, in the most recent monograph on the subject says:

'Manic-depressive psychosis corresponds to a mild paroxysmal causal disturbance. Indeed, pure manic and melancholic states imply a fundamental mental integrity, no intellectual defect, and a return to normality during the intervals between attacks. These characteristics necessarily put a limit to what may be included in this disorder; but it seems that one can extend it beyond Falret's periodic intensity to cover intermittent forms, forms with less regular and simply intermittent manifestations, and forms in which the attacks include morbid states of a more understandable kind (paranoiac delusional states) or with rather more dissociation (more schizoid types of attack). These latter variations would depend on the patient's previous personality. And, finally, confusional states can be observed at the beginning or the end of the attack or during it.' He recognizes a different evolution for these types from that of the Kraepelinian manic-depressive psychosis. Benon, giving the prognosis of pure melancholia—pure in Tastevin's sense—says that before the age of 30, 25% recover, 40% develop into a chronic hypothymia (dementia praecox), 20% have a periodic dysthenia, 5% chronic asthenia, 5% chronic persecutory delusions; while of patients over 30, 60% recover, 5% pass into chronic asthenia, 5% into hypochondria, 5% periodic dysthenia, 5% chronic persecutory delusions, 10% are incurable, 10% die. This is very different indeed from, say, Gruhle's categorical statement, 'Immer geht der einzelne Fall in Heilung aus, die Persönlichkeit wird vollkommen wiederhergestellt.' [The single case always ends in recovery, the personality is completely restored.]

Such conflicts of statement are due in part, it is true, to different circumstances of observation—private practice as against psychiatric clinic—but much more, I think, to different conceptions of the illness. Statistics of outcome which are based on certified cases in mental hospitals will differ from those obtained, like Paskind's, in private practice or in the psychiatric clinic with a big out-patient department; those based on a distinction between 'true manic-depressive psychoses' and 'reactive depression' or 'constitutional or neurotic dysthymia' will not be comparable with those which include all predominantly affective disturbances, whatever their severity or periodicity; involutional melancholia is included by some, and not by others in their material of investigation, and there is to be reckoned with the variation in opinion between different observers as to whether a case is to be diagnosed as mainly schizophrenic or mainly affective; finally the possibility that cases of an organic or symptomatic psychosis are included, some of which will be incurable and progressive, others deceptively speedy in recovery. It would be going too far to show how all these factors have actually entered into the data on prognosis published by different workers. Perhaps the most striking example is to be seen in the interesting paper of Strecker of Philadelphia and his co-workers; they picked 50 recovered and 50 unrecovered cases of manic-depressive psychosis from the patients admitted to a mental hospital during a four-year period; they deliberately excluded all uncertain psychotic reactions and the various acute affective reactions accompanying toxic-infective-exhaustion processes, as well as mixed schizophrenic affective ones, also borderline neuroses and the purely situation psychoses; they then compared the two groups for significant differences. One of the most striking points was that in the unrecovered group there was very much more cardio-vascular and renal disease, so that they concluded that the presence of this disease-complex rendered the outlook for recovery less favourable. Examination of their material shows, however, that of their 50 unrecovered patients only 13 were under the age of 40, as against 25 in the 50 recovered cases; of the 50 unrecovered, 23 were over the age of 50 as against 11 of the other group. It will thus be seen that the apparently unfavourable prognostic significance of vascular disease may be, in part, an expression of the greater age of this unrecovered group, and in part an expression of the liability of all manic-depressive patients to show vascular disease in later life; vascular disease may, on the face of this evidence, be insignificant prognostically except as to mortality risk; to test its psychiatric significance comparable age-groups should be taken and the presence of dementia due to it reckoned separately, since the arterio-sclerotic cerebral conditions will notoriously confuse the issue in middle and later life.

In this single instance one can see how important it is to consider the method of collection in any prognostic study. Broadly, the choice lies between applying an arbitrary, hard and fast criterion of some diagnostic group, collecting a large number of such cases and seeing what becomes of them; and, on the other hand, using a flexible diagnosis, taking a small number of such cases fully studied, and seeking to relate what one knows of their development prior to the illness and the phenomena of the illness itself to the later course of their lives. By the former method one obtains what Bleuler calls the 'Richtungsprognose' or general drift of the illness; and by the latter one aims at discovering what details of form and development throw light on the individual prognosis. The former method has great advantages; it can be employed and controlled systematically, it *must* yield *some* results, and it permits of a statement of probabilities, at least for the group so defined. It is the method employed by Kraepelin, and by most of the writers on prognosis in manic-depressive insanity. The other method is more in keeping with recent tendencies in psychiatry; it is concerned with the individual patient rather than with the fictitious disease or type, and anything established by it could immediately be used in practice. But as a method it is open to great objections; it is less controllable, its necessarily small material may be exceptional and, therefore, unsuited for clinical application; statistical treatment of it is difficult because of the smallness of the sample; it may be misused to confirm false impressions and prejudices, it requires much more time and its results may, after all, be nugatory. If, for example, physiological or psychological phenomena as yet undiscovered are the most significant prognostically in this illness our elaborate study may be fruitless. As my own investigation was of the sort whose defects I have just been cataloguing, perhaps it will be best if I rapidly review the findings arrived at by the other, or Kraepelinian method as one might call it for short, and then pass on to the more detailed, if more dubious, investigations.

The general findings of the German investigators have been these. In diagnostically 'pure' cases the attack always clears up, leaving not a wrack behind. If mild dementia seems to follow such an attack the diagnosis was wrong, or the effects are those of arterio-sclerosis or of mental hospital life—certainly not of the illness itself. The duration of single phases of illness is on the average 6–8 months; gain in weight is a reliable prognostic sign. There is no rule as to when another attack will occur, or whether it will occur at all. Bumke and Gruhle, to take two outstanding authorities, deny flatly that one can venture on any prediction as to this. Gruhle adds, 'The duration of any single attack entirely defies prediction.' If it is a first attack of mania, it will almost certainly not be the only attack; if of melancholia it may be. In nearly half the cases of manic-depressive illness the first attack is the last. Melancholias are not repeated if they appear for the first time in men about the age of 45. Puberty melancholias are sometimes the only attack during a lifetime, or are followed only by an involutional melancholia. Melancholia ushers in 70–80% of all truly circular cases of manic-depressive psychosis. It is rare for an attack of mania to pass into a chronic state with occasional flare-ups; this occurs more commonly with depression. Severe mania or depression is seldom superimposed on a cyclothymia. The more chronic the illness the less severe the manifestations. A transition from mania to melancholia, or the reverse, is commonly gradual, by way of a mixed picture. Recovery from an attack is likewise gradual as a rule. Complete insight is by no means universal after recovery from manic upsets. In patients who have had several attacks one can say that the attacks will get longer and the intervals shorter. Kraepelin, however, says that after rather long intervals an attack can be very brief. Lange, arriving at higher figures than his master, gives 10 years as the average length of the interval after the first attack, 6 after the second, 4 years after the third and so on; apparently, however, he had little more than a hundred cases, and, as I shall presently mention, my own observations do not accord with his. The question of ultimate cessation of attacks or passage into chronicity is answered to the effect that if truly circular, i.e., mania alternating with depression, or if 'mixed', then the chances are definitely poor; with periodic manias, especially those beginning in the twenties, however, an end to the attacks may come in the fifth decade of life; it is less often so with periodic depressions. Later attacks will probably be of the same kind as earlier ones; if the mania is severe a later depression will be severe, if there have been delusions and hallucinations in the one, there will probably be in the other. Melancholia in the so-called involutional period tends to a much longer duration. The prognosis is much better in the following conditions of 'purity', viz., the 'purer' the clinical picture, i.e., the fewer the heterogeneous pathoplastic elements; the 'purer' the manic-depressive heredity; the 'purer' the pykinic habitus and the 'purer' the syntonic pre-morbid personality; the last kind of 'purity' is particularly favourable if the subjects have had mentally robust, well-developed, healthy personalities. In attacks of depression somatic factors have an unfavourable influence; infections and vascular diseases in particular prolong the illness. Death is a rare outcome, apart from suicide and arterio-sclerotic accidents, like apoplexy. Defective nutrition is the common cause where death occurs; inexplicable deaths are unknown, unlike those in schizophrenia.

In the foregoing statement of the findings, which may be found recapitulated in Lange's authoritative monograph or in the most recent work on the subject, that of Müller, the facts are derived mainly from the publications of Kraepelin, Rehm, von Hoesslin, Reiss and Lange himself. I shall not weary you with the figures and material in the original papers (Rehm is not available at first hand). I would only point out that these findings are contested in some particulars by other German writers. Thus, Bumke considers that psychic invalidism can follow cases of quickly alternating mania and melancholia, or of mania with brief intervals between attacks; he describes the anomalous clinical picture that develops—of apathy or irritable silly unrest, with fantasies and hallucinations, though even from this the patient may recover. Jaspers again lays it down as a general rule that if the weight begins to increase regularly, and if in a woman the menstruation starts again without there being a pronounced improvement in the mental state, then it means that the condition is becoming chronic or hopeless.

There is one other German writer whose views on prognosis deserve attention—Mauz. In his monograph he gives evidence for the view that pyknic habitus, with syntonic temperament, is indicative of recovery from the *attack*, at all events he expresses himself with a cloudiness that defies translation: 'Wir finden dort die diäthetische Proportion in einer tief vitalen Schicht auf der sich das Leben in den Dingen, das Aufgehen in den Dingen, das Mitleben, Mitfühlen und Mitleiden zu einem festen Ringwall der Lebenskraft und des Lebensgefühls fügt. Dies scheint uns für die Prognosestellung wesentlich; die Geschlossenheit und Tiefe der diäthetischen Proportion, der elastische Tonus und Turgor der Schwingungsfähigkeit, der jede Bresche und Lücke, jeden Riss im Ringwall des Lebensgefühls wieder sich schliessen lässt, das Getragensein von einer elementaren Frische, die sichere und selbstverständliche Einheit (von Ich. u. Aussenwelt).' Other prognostic points he mentions bear rather on reactivity and on a distinction between 'true' manic-depressive psychosis and the reactive or psychogenic depressions. I must confess that his views about the prognostic influence of personality are not only hard to understand, but are unsupported by my own observations or by those of some other writers. His use of the pyknic habitus has diagnostic and perhaps prognostic value, but I have not investigated it because the bulk of my cases were women.

I must refer also to some American studies. In 1918 MacDonald published a retrospective study of 451 cases. There are objections to his method, which led him to the conclusion that a favourable outcome is more likely in depression than in elation, intervals being in general longer and the possibilities of non-recurrence greater. A series of careful studies has recently been published by Fuller, using the material of the New York State Hospitals; the cases were followed up for 10 years after discharge; half of the manic-depressive cases (excluding involutional melancholia) were living ordinary lives in the community at the end of this time, though only a third of them had done so without interruption by another attack of psychosis; over a fifth had died. Malzberg, on the same material, found that manic cases had the best outlook for recovery when the attack came on between the ages of 20 and 24, and Pollock, again on the New York cases, that manic-depressive patients between 20 and 40 years of age at the time of first admission had fewer recurrences than those younger or older. Steen published a brief inquiry with essentially negative results; the comparison of unrecovered with recovered cases did not bear out the customary views as to the importance of body-build, previous personality, or heredity, or as to the prognostic harmlessness of hallucinations and delusions. Paskind likewise could not confirm the assertion that a 'tainted' heredity was an unfavourable factor as to course or severity. Another American worker, Nolan D. C. Lewis, examined cases diagnosed as manic-depressive and later regarded as malignantly schizophrenic, and concluded that 'what seem to be malignantly destructive features in some patients are eventually dealt with in a benign and effective manner by others, but, speaking generally, persistent localized feelings of depersonalization, dominating hypochondriacal ideas with bizarre delusional elaborations, outspoken hallucinations with delusions, fortifications, and odd, disjointed paranoid mechanisms make for a comparatively early serious outcome. When the affect (elation or depression) is notably in excess of the schizophrenic components, one is inclined to give a favourable prognosis for the present attack, but definite schizophrenic elaborations appearing during the course of an affect disorder are unfavourable signs'. It would be going too far afield to enter into the discussions about Claude's 'schizomania' or the 'schizo-affective psychoses'. Nolan Lewis's paper is noteworthy because it belongs, not to the more or less Kraepelinian studies mentioned earlier, but to the more detailed inquiries into a group just large enough to be treated statistically, but small enough to be studied fully on the clinical side. Strecker's is another such study: he and his associates found, surprisingly, that the outlook in the mixed forms was somewhat better than in the other forms—I cannot confirm this with my material—and that a cycloid personality did not necessarily indicate a favourable prognosis; dependent and suspicious people had a poorer outlook; and paranoid or suicidal trends, stupor and somatic delusions and hallucinations were unfavourable, while frank erotic or psychoneurotic reactions had no significance.

That there are gaps and contradictions in the literature thus briefly surveyed is clear enough. Many of these gaps are not likely to be filled or the doubts settled until better ways of limiting and describing the phenomena are available; physiological, genetic and psychological advances will first be necessary. Perhaps I am the more ready to believe this because of the meagre fruits of my own inquiry.

The investigation of the after-history of 61 cases of depression, of which the immediate clinical features have already been published, has been carried out at regular intervals since 1928 and 1929, when the cases first came under my care at the Maudsley Hospital. The patients and their relatives have been visited at home by social workers, many of the patients have come to see me or have been treated at the hospital as out-patients or in-patients, and the records of mental hospitals have been seen in the appropriate instances. Of the 61 cases, one was lost sight of after a year and a half, and three others after three years; 10 have died since leaving hospital; the rest have been followed up satisfactorily. I need not now discuss the grounds of diagnosis or selection in these cases, but would only recall that the majority were women, a number of them were not certifiable as insane, and that their ages ranged from 15 to 63, the majority being between 20 and 40; 'involutional' and 'reactive' cases were included; early arterio-sclerotic dementias or definite schizophrenias with depression were excluded.

The cases were arranged in order of excellence of outcome, i.e., passing from those who had remained perfectly well since discharge to those who had never recovered from the attack and were now apparently hopeless cases of chronic insanity. This arrangement proved a very difficult business, because of the unexpected variety of results,—results of every shape and size, as it were; it was not a simple matter of 'recovered' or not, any subsequent attacks or not. The order finally was: Completely recovered and continuously well since attack (14); completely recovered, but subsequent attack from which completely recovered (4); fairly well since attack, i.e., those who have lived ordinary lives working and getting on in the community, but have been of a depressive or neurotic temperament since (as many of them were before) the attack (19); those who were fairly well until they had another attack from which they have emerged (7), or, next in order, in which they still are (4); then those who have been in a mental hospital ever since discharge from the Maudsley (7, counting 3 who have lately died), and, finally, those who have died. The many clinical features recorded in an earlier paper were then charted against this order of results, as were also data of heredity, previous attacks, personality, physical disease and a number of similar particulars, comprising almost all the facts that are commonly collected and used by psychiatrists in day-to-day work, though I think I may say that they were fuller and had been collected with more care than usual, because I was fortunate in being able almost always to fill up any gaps in my original records during the course of subsequent inquiries.

Clearly, in these charts, any data that were heaped up at either end of the scale were of prognostic value. I carried out a similar procedure with the patients arranged, not in order of result, but in order of duration of attack; the purpose of this is obvious.

After doing this I was chagrined to find that there were no unequivocal prognostic signs, either as to duration of the current attack or as to the subsequent history. There was no feature of the case, and indeed no combination of features, which was found emphatically clustered at one or other end of this scale in either of the two arrangements of cases. Certain features there were, it is true, which seemed somewhat favourable or unfavourable; thus, in respect of subsequent history it emerged that the retardation-disproportion,* the doing of tests well, general retardation and stupor were favourable, also that puerperal cases did well; while agitation, incessant talk, self-reproach, ideas of influencing others, voracious eating, inexplicable loss of weight, vascular and endocrine disease, and, to a slight extent, greater age, were unfavourable symptoms. Somewhat similar findings were obtained in respect of duration of current attack, viz., retardation—disproportion, response to stimulation, adaptation and affectively labile personality were of good omen,

* See Chapter 3 p. 44.

and agitation, ideas of influencing others, disorder of perception and denial of mental nature of illness, voracity, compulsive symptoms and personality, and physical, especially vascular, disease were bad. But all these allegedly prognostic signs might be found, though less frequently, in patients who did the opposite. The patients who died illustrate this point strikingly; almost without exception they were hopeless, self-reproachful and unresponsive to any reassurance; vascular disease, a history of affective psychosis in a parent or sibling, suicidal inclinations and a history of only one previous attack also characterized them; but this combination of features could be found in other patients who did quite well. The explanation I would offer for the rather barren outcome of a fairly painstaking inquiry, such as this, is that the single data we usually contemplate cannot give us a good answer to our question. There is reason for supposing that by looking at the case as a whole and studying the patient's development we arrive at a better prognosis than by considering any single details or combination of details. But even if this be true—and there is no satisfactory evidence for it beyond personal impression—we probably take into account a number of supposedly valuable data which may, in fact, be prognostically worthless. Only by testing them as well as testing our general estimate can we get the ground clear for better methods.

I should like to say a few words about the deaths; 3 of these were suicides. The prognosis of suicide alone is a thorny problem, into which I shall not enter. These 3 cases went out of hospital before they were well and are of the same kind as those investigated by Minski. Of course the number of suicidal attempts in this series was high, but not significant prognostically; under other social and medical conditions the number of fatal attempts might have been higher. The rather high death-rate in the whole series seems surprising in view of Essen Möller's investigation; he found the mortality of discharged manic-depressives to be only one and a half times higher than in the general population; if, however, one excludes from my series those who committed suicide or had valvular disease of the heart, the remainder were all but one middle-aged patients; the exception was a young woman who persistently refused or vomited her food while in hospital and who was taken home by her family, against all common sense; her death was, I think, a true death from melancholia. Obviously larger statistics are necessary if one is concerned with time and cause of death in manic-depressives; previous studies have been chiefly on those who died in mental hospitals—obviously not a true sample.

There are a number of special points on which my findings do not tally with those of some other investigators, mentioned earlier. Thus my material included 34 who had had one or more previous attacks; the greatest number of attacks was 10, another had had 9, another 5; 5 of the patients had had 3 attacks, and so on. I did not find, however, that the intervals had grown shorter, but found such sequences as 2, 5, 7, 3, 3, years; 3, 8, 3; 2, 2, 8; 6, 10, 4, 10, 11; 4, 6, 2; 3, 6, 4; 17, 4, 12. Moreover, the duration of the intervals could often on inspection of the whole case be accounted for by the incidence of such environmental factors as pregnancy and puerperium, removal of a thyroid adenoma (resulting in 4 years' freedom from attack in a woman who had had 10 attacks in the previous 11 years); in other words, external as well as intrinsic constitutional factors were playing a considerable part in determining the length of intervals. It is such considerations as these that prompted my earlier statement that there was reason to believe a study of the case as a whole might give better prognostic indications than attention to the details often stressed in prognosis. As regards duration of previous successive attacks, they did tend, on the whole, to grow longer, but sometimes showed irregular relations, e.g., 5, 24, 18, 12, 12 months; but what was striking was the much greater duration of the attack for which they were in the hospital than of previous attacks; such figures as 7, 16 months; 3, 11; 6, 10; 6, 38; 13, 96; 1, 56; 9, 1, 56; 1, 8; 1, 84; $1\frac{1}{2}$, 3, 4, 14; 3, 12; 2, 5, 8; 4, 20; 1, 1, 1, 10; 1, 2, 3; 2, 4, 8, 17, $\frac{1}{2}$, 6, 48; and so on. This is partly due to the actual tendency of later attacks to last a long while, partly to errors of recollection and report as to attacks long past, but much more, I think, to the care that is taken, once a patient has come into a hospital, to ensure that he does not go out until he is quite well, and to the strict criteria used in this investigation for determining when the patient had recovered. There are, in short, grounds for concluding, on the one hand, that the previous attacks, measured by the same standards as this one, were longer than reported, and also for suspecting that we keep patients sometimes longer in hospital than is necessary for their safety or their recovery. On this point I have looked into the cases that got better after having left the Maudsley while still definitely ill; there are 14 such cases, of whom only 6 effected their further improvement in a mental hospital. The rest, i.e., non-mental-hospital cases, showed a recovery which was in some cases amazingly rapid. The reactivity of such patients was high, and one concluded that the hospital situation had an adverse influence on their recovery after a certain point; some of them were pronouncedly 'endogenous' cases who had got into the doldrums in hospital. In other instances surgery had been beneficial. A hypochondriac melancholic woman near the menopause who believed she had caused a uterine tumour to grow by attempts to induce an abortion, recovered promptly after the operation which she had long clamoured for vainly; after she left the Maudsley a gynaecologist removed her appendix and a small cyst of her ovary. Another, who had her teeth removed some months after leaving immediately lost the troublesome vestiges of her depression, which had earlier been accompanied by the idea that her breath was foul from venereal disease because of an illegitimate pregnancy, etc. It is easily seen that such individual matters do not lend themselves to systematic treatment in a prognostic inquiry. The patients who are taken home against advice while still apparently very ill mentally and who then make rapid recovery call for special study; the number in the series was not large enough, however, to attempt any generalization.

Among other special points may be mentioned the influence of the puerperium; 9 such cases were included and all but 2 did surprisingly well, in view of the poor outlook in puerperal cases of schizophrenia.

Heredity, moreover, had no special significance, so far as my data went. I divided the cases into those who had a parent or sibling with affective disorder and those whose relatives had been otherwise ill mentally.

I have spoken of the disappointing aspects of this investigation. It has, however, had for me at any rate some positive value, some gain as well. For one thing it has shown, if any demonstration was needed, that short cuts and clear sign-posts do not exist in this disorder, and that one's impressions about prognostic signs may be deceptive. I had, for example, a strong impression that previous pelvic operations, especially hysterectomy, were an unfavourable indication; it turned out that this was based on four cases only, which all did badly, it is true, but such a number is statistically unreliable, to say the least; the same proved to be true regarding thyroid disease.

The other thing that emerged from the inquiry was the wide range of results in the disorder. Psychiatrists have tended to continue the error with manic-depressive psychosis, which, in its converse, we have given up in schizophrenia. It proved extraordinarily difficult to classify the patients in order of favourable result, or of duration of attack. Some were perfectly well for a while and then passed into a severe psychosis, which has in some cases not cleared up; or mania supervened upon the depression and has been followed by years of normal life, though the patient has persistent auditory hallucinations all along; or the illness has died down into a chronic depressive outlook upon life, compatible with daily work and varied by brief periods of cheerfulness or of increased depression; two- or three-day depressions, either at the menstrual periods or occurring at regular intervals, are found in many patients otherwise well; neurotic symptoms—anxiety, obsessions, irritability, self-consciousness—may make the recovery a dubious matter, especially if these psychopathic features were present before the attack occurred; sometimes the patients are worse after the attack; or again there may be a slight deterioration of personality after the manic phase, a very definite deterioration according to relatives, although the patient can still earn her living and is regarded as normal; in others who are still in mental hospitals a settled apathy seems to be as much a reaction to their environment as a residue of their illness; or they are kept in hospital because they still express vague ideas of self-reproach and gloom which seem to have lost their affective basis; or after a year or more of apparent deterioration in the mental hospital they rapidly recover either there or at home. Others—actually only two of this series—are diagnosed now, after a considerable stay in a mental hospital, as 'dementia praecox', though in one case one could question the diagnosis—a case of recurrent stupor with bizarre somatic delusions—and in the other a whining contentless apathy is her present condition; she had not been regarded as showing any schizophrenic symptoms during her illness at the Maudsley Hospital; she had a reactive psychosis, which came on during her honeymoon. A review of the cases which had exhibited schizophrenic symptoms did not reveal that these had any prognostic value. I question whether a good deal of the literature on the subject is not vitiated by an unintentional bias, through knowledge of the final issue. Some of the patients are better than they were before the illness, not, I think, because of any virtue in the illness as such, but because their experiences during treatment in hospital have taught them to order their lives better. Whether they are sheltered or not also affects the outcome; some live quiet but useful lives who, in more exacting or different social circumstances, would inevitably have to go into a mental hospital. A patient with mild hypomania is often not regarded as ill or 'nervous' by his associates, so that in some instances a misleading after-history is obtained. Whether mental hospital treatment is deemed necessary will reasonably turn on whether the attack is manic or depressive in form. Thus, a patient who had for years had attacks of gastric neurosis, associated with depression, has lately been readmitted to a mental hospital in a state of acute mania; one sees how empty would be a dispute as to whether hers is a neurosis or a psychosis. In several cases where the blood-pressure had been high, with some anxiety and irritability, there has been a persistence of the character anomalies, without any dementia.

There are finally some comments to be made on the collection of the facts for such an inquiry. One reads prognostic studies which use after-histories based on letters, and on opinions formed by the doctor who is treating the patient. My collection of data in this inquiry contains some striking instances of the untrustworthiness of such information. Letters from psychotherapists, for example, reporting that the patient is well or otherwise must be checked by additional information from near relatives and the patient herself, for such statements may sometimes be misleading, because of the therapist's limited means of ascertaining the true state of affairs. Similarly the patient himself may give a partial and even false account of his adjustment to daily life, or a relative may be unaware of various subjective discomforts the patient suffers; in the accounts of personality which I have, these discrepancies become exceptionally prominent.

There are also practical difficulties of ascertainment. A few patients have an abiding dislike of the place and the people associated in their memories with a horrible illness; they do not welcome inquiries. If I had not been exceptionally fortunate in social work helpers, especially Mrs Werth and Miss Galloway, I should have been at a loss for adequate information and contacts in some of the cases. In others, of course, the attachment to the hospital or the doctor who looked after them is considerable, and there is no such difficulty. On the whole, however, it is striking how few avail themselves of the opportunity of further treatment offered them after they have got over the acute attack; where there were persistent neurotic or mild depressive symptoms the patients preferred to put up with them, and a willingness to have treatment as a prophylactic against further illness or for residual symptoms was rare. When another attack threatens they are usually prompt in coming again for help. I have, however, as I said at the beginning, deliberately assumed treatment to be a constant factor. Of course it was not, but one cannot deal with such an abstraction as 'prognosis in manic-depressive psychosis' without begging a lot of questions or assuming some constants. Prognosis is the most severe test of our clinical judgment, no matter in what branch of medicine it be asked for. Manic-depressive psychosis is a provisional group of heterogeneous disorders. It is not surprising or disconcerting if we have to confess that we cannot find a clear and easy answer to our questions about the future in such an illness.

REFERENCES

BENON, R. *La Mélancolie*, Paris, Doin, 1925.

BLEULER, E. *Lehrbuch der Psychiatrie*, Berlin, Springer, 1930.

BUMKE, O. *Lehrbuch der Psychiatrie*, München, Bergmann, 1929.

Commonwealth of Massachusetts: Annual Report of Commissioner of Mental Diseases, Public Document No. 117, Boston, 1935.

DERBY, I. 'Manic-depressive "exhaustion" deaths', *Psychiat. Quarterly*, 1933, **7**, p. 419.

DERON, R. *Le Syndrome Maniaque*, Paris, Doin, 1928.

ESSEN-MOLLER, E. *Untersuchungen über die Fruchtbarkeit gewisser Gruppen von Geisteskranken*, Copenhagen, Levin & Munksgaard, 1935.

FULLER, R. G. 'What happens to mental patients after discharge from hospital?' *Psychiat. Quarterly*, 1935, **9**, p. 95.

GRIESINGER, W. 'Prognosis in mental disease', *J. Ment. Sci.*, 1865, **11**, p. 317.

GRUHLE, H. *Psychiatrie für Aerzte*, Berlin, Springer, 1918.

HINSIE, L. 'Successful socialization and compensation in manic-depressive psychosis', *Psychiat. Quarterly*, 1931, **5**, p. 312.

JASPERS, K. *Allgemeine Psychopathologie*, Berlin, Springer, 1923.

KASANIN, J. 'The acute schizo-affective psychoses', *Amer. J. Psychiat.*, 1933, **13**, p. 97.

KRAEPELIN, E. *Psychiatrie*, 8th edn., Leipzig, Barth, 1915.

LANGE, J. 'Die Endogenen und Reaktiven Gemütserkrankungen', in Bumke, *Handbuch der Geisteskrankheiten*, Berlin, Springer, 1928.

LEWIS, A. J. 'Melancholia: A clinical survey of depressive states', *J. Ment. Sci.*, 1934, **80**, p. 277. (See also this volume, pp. 30–117.)

LEWIS, N. D. C., and HUBBARD, L. 'Prognostic aspects of manic-depressive schizophrenic combinations', *Proc. Assoc. Research Nerv. and Ment. Dis.*, 1931, **11**, Baltimore, Williams & Wilkins.

MACDONALD, J. B. 'Prognosis in manic-depressive insanity', *J. Nerve and Ment. Dis.*, 1918, **47**, p. 20.

MAUZ, F. *Die Prognostik der Endogenen Psychosen*, Leipzig, Thieme, 1930.

MINSKI, L. 'Investigation into the after-history of 90 patients discharged against advice', *J. Ment. Sci.*, 1935, **81**, p. 509.

MULLER, M. *Prognose und Therapie der Geisteskrankheiten*, Leipzig, Thieme, 1936.

PANSE, F. 'Untersuchung über Verlauf und Prognose beim Manisch-depressiven Irresein', *Monats. f. Psychiat. u. Neurol.*, 1924, **56**, p. 15.

PASKIND, H. A. 'Relation of hereditary factors to clinical course in the manic-depressive psychosis', *Arch. Neur. and Psychiat.*, 1931, **25**, p. 145.

POLLOCK, H. M. 'Recurrence of attacks in manic-depressive psychoses', *Amer. J. Psychiat.*, 1931, **11**, p. 567.

REISS, E. 'Konstitutionelle Verstimmung und Manisch-Depressives Irresein', *Zeitschr. f. d. ges. Neur. u. Psych.*, 1910, **22**, p. 347.

ROBERTSON, C. L. 'Prognosis in mental disorder', *J. Ment. Sci.*, 1859, **5**, p. 257.

ROUART, J. *Psychose maniaque-dépressive et folies discordantes*, Paris, Doin, 1936.

SLATER, E. 'Incidence of mental disorder', *Ann. Eugen.*, 1935, **6**, p. 173.

STEEN, R. 'Prognosis in manic-depressive psychoses', *Psychiat. Quarterly*, 1933, **7**, p. 419.

STRECKER, E. A., APPEL, K., EYMAN, FARR, LAMAR, PALMER and SMITH. 'Prognosis in manic-depressive psychosis', *Proc. Assoc. Research Nerv. and Ment. Dis.*, 1931, **11**, Baltimore, Williams & Wilkins.

URQUHART, A. R. Morison lectures, *J. Ment. Sc.*., 1907, **53**, p. 233.

WILSON, E. B., and DEMING, J. 'Statistical comparison of psychiatric diagnoses in some Massachusetts state hospitals during 1925 and 1926', *Quart. Bull. Massachusetts Department of Mental Disease*, Boston, 1927, **11**.

5

STATES OF DEPRESSION: THEIR CLINICAL AND AETIOLOGICAL DIFFERENTIATION

CLASSIFICATION AND diagnosis have been so derided in psychiatry that the subject of our discussion today is almost a shady one. No doubt the shadow under which it lies comes also from the solid difficulties, which are plain when any of the current ways of differentiating between depressions are applied to a series of cases. It is, I think, at all events correct to say that (although a fair amount has been written) no fresh light has been cast on the subject for several years, since it is much easier to show the inadequacy of proposed methods than to substitute for them a useful and valid one. Useful and valid are the two epithets which any classification should deserve. In considering them the opportunities and difficulties can be brought into clearer view.

VALID CLASSIFICATION

The usefulness of a classification will vary according to who uses it. One that serves the clinician well may be of little value to the research worker: it may even make his task harder. The clinician wants classes into which he can put his patient's illness after a reasonably brief period of investigation, and which will assist him to make a prognosis and decide on treatment. So long as the classes do this, it does not matter how illogical, psychologically or pathologically unsound, and expressive of his own idiosyncrasies they may be: they provide him with extra knowledge of the sort he wants, and he does not care whether they represent his own, more or less incommunicable, experience or the fruits of others' study. The man who treats patients only in private practice may find a classification useful which the physician in the

---

This paper was read in opening a discussion in the Section of Neurology and Psychological Medicine at the Annual Meeting of the British Medical Association, Plymouth, 1938. It is reprinted from the *British Medical Journal* (29 October 1938), 2, 875–78.

mental hospital regards as illusory, and the latter may use one which the consulting-room psychotherapist detests or cannot understand: both these classifications may be useless to the general practitioner. If all three physicians had the same clinical material and problems they would no doubt come to use the same classification; but at present they do not, although they may use the same words for their classes: to realize this one has only to compare the letters sent by each of them when referring depressed patients to an out-patient clinic. Because of the peculiar phenomena of mental disorder, so much harder to describe in agreed conventional terms than those of other illnesses, it is customary for clinicians to use their words, and their classes, with an individual twist. This is what distinguishes them from those of the research worker. He wants his classes, and his words, to have some fixity, so that he can generalize and summarize and communicate his observations: he cannot work in circumstances where the illness that he calls endogenous melancholia another man may call a reactive depression, and a third man call a paranoid schizophrenic. He may be satisfied if he can delimit a class of depressions in which the only distinguishing feature common to all members of the class is some chemical anomaly, even though for the clinician this turns out to be a woefully heterogeneous group. Many quarrels about the justness of classifications in psychiatry are usually due to these differing needs of the clinician and the research worker. In an ideal state of knowledge the schism would end, but that is still a distant time.

It might seem that validity is here merely a synonym for usefulness. But classifications may be useful for the wrong ends: they may be used to separate off cases which are regarded—wrongly—as hopeless, or as needing a particular type of treatment; the clinician may never come to see how vicious are the uses to which he has been, contentedly, putting his classification. The research worker, on his side, may have delimited classes of which the characteristic is irrelevant to his problem, much as though he were to divide depressives into those with and those without naevi, or those whose parents had hernia and those who had not. A valid classification is one which is not only useful, but useful for sound medical or scientific ends. It is necessary to see how far the available classifications are valid in this sense.

The first task of classification is obviously to recognize the depression itself. This is too often taken to be a diagnostic act. It should be concerned with nothing further than description of the emotional state. Any person who is unhappy, and ill with his unhappiness, may properly be said to be in a state of depression. To lay down other criteria for a depression is to raise fundamental problems. For convenience we may restrict the term to those states of depression in which we cannot discover any other significant illness—for example, schizophrenia, cerebral tumour, arteriosclerosis. But the elimination of these is the second task. It is common ground that depression may be the conspicuous or the only clinical evidence of almost any mental illness at some stage: everyone will aim at spotting the G.P.I., say, or cerebral tumour, or schizophrenia which hides behind a depressive front. What is more, the psychiatrist cannot dismiss this depressive front as a false one, a screen, but has to consider how far it stands for an independent contribution to the total illness. It is at this point that the clinician's private notion of depression creeps in, bringing confusion. If he regards 'true' depression as an endogenous illness, of good prognosis, and itself recognizable, he will be interested to see whether this patient's depression conforms to his notion of 'true' depression, in which case, if there is also another disorder present, such as a schizophrenic or an obsessional one, he says, 'We have here a mixed picture': or he may regard this depression as the normal response to the abnormal situation created by the concomitant, or screened, illness, and may dismiss it as secondary and rather irrelevant. In short, the moment description is deserted, at the second stage of the classifying process, influences get to work which are often only in part consciously recognized as such by the clinician, though they may greatly modify his decisions.

HEREDITARY AND ENVIRONMENTAL FACTORS

The most popular classification is, on the surface, an aetiological one. It says that there are depressions due to heredity (autonomous, autogenous, endogenous, manic-depressive, cyclothymic, vital, constitutional, are among the words employed) and others due to the environment (psychogenic, exogenous, extraneous, reactive, psychoneurotic). But this is purely theoretical. We have no means of detecting such causes satisfactorily, except in a minority of cases. Moreover, as theory it is bad. It derives from the days when Nature and nurture could be contrasted in an epigram. It assumes that heredity commonly operates with that high probability of manifestation which we see in Huntington's chorea or the height of sweet peas: and that environment can work on an almost illimitably plastic and responsive human organism. As biology has moved beyond these excessively simple views, and recognizes that hereditary and environmental factor commonly interact, it is reactionary to uphold them in the case of a depressive illness, especially when it is so extremely difficult to determine the relative importance of hereditary and environmental factors in any such case. It is probably true that in some depressions the hereditary factor vastly outweighs the environmental, and that in others the reverse is the case, but to detect such cases we have only dubious means—study of the parentage and sibship, observation of the bodily habit, assessment of the relation between the outbreak of the illness and the external factors which might have conduced to it. In the present state of knowledge these are dubious means when applied to the individual case, though they serve well enough for the analysis of a collection of cases, statistically. The number of cases in which critical and experienced psychiatrists with different theoretical standpoints would be found to agree that the hereditary factors were almost certainly responsible for the attack (or, in the alternative instance, that environmental ones were) is, I believe, so small that the subjectiveness of many of our judgments on this matter can scarcely be gainsaid. There are some cases in which a recent distress seems to account for the depression, which is then properly called a reactive one, but since profound melancholia or mania may likewise ensue upon a sorrow, reactivity does not mean only psychogenesis. The more thorough the analysis that can be made of the life of the patient, and of his responses to circumstances, the stronger is one's inclination to attribute his morbid behaviour mostly to post-natal influences; genetic studies have the opposite effect. There is no reliable evidence as to the heredity of so-called psychogenic depression; and as for the other varieties, what has been reported does not justify distinctions upon a hereditary basis.

DIFFERENTIATION BY STUDY OF SYMPTOMS

A differentiation that can be made by study of the symptoms is of value to the practising physician. When he sees a patient who has fits it is more convenient for him to run over in his mind the differential points given in the textbook tables than to inquire at length into the previous personality, make an encephalogram, etc. At any rate he tries the short method first, preparatory to further search. If he could similarly separate forms of depression he would not be put off by any uncertainty about causes. I have taken a very recent table of the sort: the author says that the differences between neurotic and manic-depressive depression are usually clearly marked: they lie in the constancy of the depression during the attack; the patient's ability to be amused by a joke, to weep, or to appreciate beauty; his interest in himself and his surroundings, his self-reproach, his good health in the period before or between attacks, and his admission that he is ill. Also it is said that in manic-depressive depression 'the patient gets well obviously spontaneously. He has been unresponsive to all therapeutic efforts, and the doctor is never given the impression that he has done anything.' Nothing could better illustrate what I said earlier about the personal and partly incommunicable value of the classification which a particular clinician may find useful. The psychiatrist quoted works very satisfactorily with a scheme which to me is useless: when I try to apply it it fails, because the same cases will fall on one count into the left-hand side of the table and on another count into the right-hand side. It is true that when first seen in the out-patient department cases often seem to me to fall readily into one or the other category, but when they are gone into more fully in the course of treatment this facility of classification turns out to have been spurious. And I take it that this is partly because my notions of spontaneous or aided recovery, of variability and responsiveness in the depression, and so forth, are not those of the author of the table. Also it is because of a disagreement about facts: patients with severe self-reproachful depression sometimes weep, sometimes even laugh, sometimes worry about their relatives, are mildly depressed and anxious between attacks, or admit that they are ill; patients with chronic reactive depression may be self-reproachful, incapable of appreciating beauty and never weep. Moreover, in a series of cases I have lately looked through for the purpose, illnesses that fulfil all these clinical requirements of a reactive depression have occurred preceding an acute mania and a severe involutional melancholia, either as an initial stage or as a previous attack (in my earlier published series the same sequence can be found): some of them have been treated as such psychotherapeutically, and with benefit, in previous attacks. Even this shows only how useless the scheme is to me: not that it is generally useless. Actually it is a question of how many patients fit comfortably into either group, so characterized. As is fairly plain in the series I reported, I find that few do; Curran reaches the same conclusion. I think these groups are extreme types rather than clinical realities: a few others, however, find good reason to hold the contrary view. Clouston, who believed in the importance of a distinction (between 'melancholy' and 'melancholia'), put the matter quite simply in 1904: 'Typical cases exhibiting these two conditions are totally different and distinguishable, and the only excuses for confounding them are that they shade off into each other, that we have no absolutely definite scientific test to distinguish them, that they are both in many cases the outcome of the same temperament and diathesis, and that they both have something of the same nature, both psychologically and physiologically.' These are good excuses. Probably there are genuine differences between cases of mainly hereditary causation and those in which environmental causes predominate, possibly also between cases with different kinds of hereditary causation, but the clinical differences given in such tables as I have mentioned do not at present serve to distinguish them. And it is well to remember, as Newman has recently concluded from his studies, that in many ways what heredity can do environment can also do.

There is another such table which includes bodily features—anorexia, constipation, loss of weight. Muncie has stressed the sleep disturbance. Various writers have thought that metabolic variations, especially in respect of nitrogen and carbohydrate metabolism, occur in manic-depressive depression and not in reactive depression. Such claims have not been substantiated as yet. When classes can be separated which are marked by significant somatic differences, it will have the advantage that trained observers will presumably be able to agree as to the presence or absence of these somatic characteristics in any patient.

In recent contributions to the subject emphasis is variously laid upon periodicity, concomitant depersonalization or anxiety and tension, sleep, personality, heredity, psychopathology, and somatic pathology (Rouart, Muncie, Titley, Schnitzenberger, Brockhausen, Montassut, Anthonisen, Schilder, Armenise, Lorand, Baruk and Gevaudan, Georgi, etc.). But periodicity would be more valuable if it could be demonstrated to be a frequent characteristic, whereas actually it is rare; recurrence is of course a different thing, and may be no more indicative of an intrinsic rhythm, a biological periodicity, than is a series of colds in the head; it may indicate recoverability only. As for the anxiety or tension depressions, they cannot be made to form a homogeneous group, for they have only the phenomena of the anxiety attack in common, all the rest being expressible in terms of mild and severe, or proportions of fear and misery. Personality and heredity have not so much cast light on involutional melancholia as left it in a penumbra. Twin studies should, of course, elucidate the whole problem, but until Dr Slater's material is published nothing is available on this aspect of the classification of depressive states. Psychopathology is as variable as ever in its voices, and no somatic changes are of sufficient definiteness and constancy to be the basis or the buttress of a differentiation.

DISTINCTION BETWEEN REACTIVE AND MANIC-DEPRESSIVE VARIETIES

Apart from some English writers, it is difficult in the literature of the last five or even ten years to find support for any sharp distinction between reactive and manic-depressive varieties of depression. But a distinction of this sort is often implied in what is written, especially (if it may be said without offence) in the more elementary presentations, in which an almost entirely hereditary psychosis is kept remote from the 'neurasthenia' of year-long neurotics and the mourning and unhappiness of those who have lost something of immense emotional value to them. Moreover, in many writings the intelligibility of the occurrence is taken as a criterion: if the physician can enter into the patient's feelings and understand the illness as the natural outcome of situations in which the patient has been, then he calls it psychogenic or reactive; if he cannot, then he calls it autonomous (thus Adolf Meyer talks of a 'true simple melancholia, or "unjustified depression" '). No doubt this too is a personally valuable way of reviewing the illness, but it has the disadvantages already mentioned as attaching to such subjective judgments. For psycho-analysts it is out of the question, because of the universally explanatory value of their views and method.

There could be no more convincing evidence of the way classifications epitomize theory, and can be serviceable for very limited groups while worthless to others, than the psycho-analytical classification put forward by Glover. Psycho-analytical work in the field of depression during the last few years (for example, Schilder, Klein) has shed as little light on the topic of this discussion as have published studies in heredity, psychology, or somatic pathology.

It is very probable that all the tables and classifications in terms of symptoms are nothing more than attempts to distinguish between acute and chronic, mild and severe: and where two categories only are presented, the one—manic depressive—gives the characteristics of acute severe depression, the other of chronic mild depression. I am using acute and chronic as temporal words, and mild and severe as indicating the degree of the overt mental disturbance. This, if recognized for what it is, is a useful division, provided the vulgar error is avoided of thinking that every manic-depressive should get well inevitably and spontaneously, and that every case of reactive depression calls for intensive psychotherapy which, if well given, should bring recovery. It also rather fails to provide for the acute mild and the severe chronic cases, which are numerous.

The danger of these classifications, for the clinician, lies in two directions. First there is the assumption, just alluded to, that when a patient's illness seems to fit into the manic-depressive category there is nothing to be done but to fold one's arms in resignation, or, at most, to employ 'reassurance and safeguarding' until he gets better of his own accord; and, alternatively, that if it falls into the other group, psychotherapy, and nothing but psychotherapy, will restore him to active life. Treatment should be based on a knowledge of the patient's constitutional qualities and the stresses he has met, not on a schematic and rigid plan, a short cut to the wrong shop. Secondly, it is dangerous because it says, as one of these tables does, that in reactive depression suicide is 'sometimes talked but not attempted'. Now and again there appears in the account of some inquest the evidence of the doctor who had concluded that it was 'only a neurotic depression', and had his views confirmed by a psychiatrist, who found no sign of a 'genuine psychosis'. Of course, everyone makes mistakes in assessing the likelihood of suicide, and it is quite possible that in these cases the suicide would have occurred anyhow, since one cannot send into a mental hospital every doubtful case of suicidal risk. And, again, it may be conceded that in the hands of some clinicians this method of assessing the risk of suicide works very well. But it is surely bad when that immensely important question of suicide can be disposed of in the practitioner's mind by reference to a classification that creaks at the joints, and is applied differently by different people. Classifications cannot take the place of experience, or of knowledge of one's patient, of the depth of his despair, and the strength of his impulses.

INVOLUTIONAL DEPRESSION

These are the two varieties of depression chiefly dwelt upon in textbooks and articles. Attention is also paid to involutional depression. Thus, one authority speaks of five varieties: constitutional depression, prolonged neurasthenic malaise, true simple melancholia, depressive delusion with intense fear, and catatonic melancholia (but the last two are, of course, usually involutional, and the first covers Reiss's group of 1910, now swallowed up in the reactive group). It is true that some features common in involutional melancholia are rare in other forms of depression, but since these probably depend on the patient's age and on degenerative cerebral disease (often of the vessels), or on schizophrenic admixture, it does not seem necessary for classification to stress them as such, but rather to use the patient's age as the sole reason for calling the depression 'involutional', and to seek for further data which will illuminate the prognosis and treatment.

The necessity for making sure that a depression is not due to G.P.I., pernicious anaemia, or other organic disease is present to everyone's mind. But it is less often remembered that the discovery of hysterical, obsessional, or other psychopathic trends in the patient may be important too. A very depressed young woman may be troubled by the thought that she has injured her child through leaving pins about which he could swallow; the obsessional component in this needs examination. A depression in a patient aged 50 may be accompanied by many hysterical symptoms; if the patient has most of his life shown nothing hysterical in his behaviour the possibility of a cerebral arteriosclerosis must then be reckoned with. Or a depression may be found to have developed in a person of schizoid personality, and to be ushering in a schizophrenia. Depression is a very ready psychic response; hence it cannot be evaluated and pigeon-holed without a survey of the patient's life. It was not for lack of instances to support their view that the psychiatrists of the last century believed that most mental diseases began with a stage of depression.

CONCLUSION

The classification, or avoidance of classification, which I would propose is: first, to determine whether the depression is severe or mild—melancholia or neurasthenia, descriptively speaking; and, of course, there are many grades. Next, does it depend on physical disease, and, if so, how completely? What happened in any previous attacks? On what discoverable influences does it depend: age; constitutional morbid trends; lifelong environmental factors, recent more acutely disturbing ones? What, in sum, is the presumptive balance of environmental forces responsible for the illness as against inherited ones; and what is the balance between environmental influences that may be modified for the better and those that are irremediable? Has the morbid condition been going on long enough to have, so to speak, established an autonomy, set up bodily and mental habits that are inveterate? Have the patient's character and surroundings worked to his advantage or disadvantage during the illness? These are points to weigh rather than points on which to classify; matters of clinical judgment, not solely of observation. A classification can, however, be built upon them. It is because we have no sure means of distinguishing exactly the numerous causes in each case, and their effects, that we must deny ourselves the ease of a simple classification: I think it is a deceptive ease and a deceptive simplicity. No doubt increasing knowledge will bring an improved, eventually even a stable, classification based on aetiology, and pointing, it may be hoped, to treatment: whether it comes by way of genetics, psychology, or somatic pathology, it will be welcome so long as it is useful and valid.

6

PROBLEMS OF OBSESSIONAL ILLNESS

IN A would-be definite inquiry that I have been making into obsessional illness, I have been struck by the variety of problems and the difficulty of stating them. This would no doubt be true of any psychiatric topic as wide as obsessional illness, but here I found to my surprise that it would be harder to state the problems clearly than to present the alleged solutions offered in the literature. Some of these solutions deal with problems that are indefinite and indeed unsubstantial; others are global; they cover so wide a field that it is difficult to examine them without examining also the nature of man. It may well be that obsessional illness cannot be understood altogether without understanding the nature of man, or perhaps inquired into profitably without much bold speculation and the use of methods as yet unthought of or suspect; but one is reminded of Descartes' rules—to doubt everything that is not clear, to avoid precipitancy, and to divide up every difficulty into as many parts as are possible and necessary for its better solution: also to proceed from the simplest and plainest facts. Obsessional illness has not usually been treated on such lines. I have tried in this paper to raise the difficult issues that seem to need clarification before an answer can well be sought, much less accepted.

The first of them is definition or, if one likes to call it so, diagnosis. Whether one is seeing a patient oneself or reading the literature of the subject, doubt as to diagnosis often turns out to rest upon vagueness as to what are the essential features of an obsessional symptom. This is of some consequence; a great deal of psychopathological literature about obsessions is made dubious for the reader by carelessness on this point. Dynamisms and relationships are discovered which depend upon hardly tenable notions of what is obsessional. Those who have occupied themselves with this question, from St Ignatius Loyola onward, are divided by their emphasis on the formal disorder of thought on the one hand, and on the disorder of affect on the other. The definition that I have found at once precise and practicable is Schneider's, which defines obsessions as 'contents of consciousness which, when they

This paper was first delivered to the Psychiatric Section of the Royal Society of Medicine in December 1935, and is reprinted from the *Proceedings of the Royal Society of Medicine* (1936), **29**, 325–36.

occur, are accompanied by the experience of subjective compulsion, and which cannot be got rid of, though on quiet reflection they are recognized as senseless'. This is a practicable definition though not the ideal one. It can be applied readily to the recorded cases of other psychiatrists—a merit which I have appreciated in working through more than a hundred old cases for an investigation of which I shall speak presently. But it contains more than it need, and omits an important point. The recognition that the obsession is senseless is not an essential characteristic; there should, instead, be mention of the feeling that one must resist the obsession. This resistance is experienced as that of one's free will. The innumerable devices, rituals and repetitions of the obsessional are secondary expressions of this immediate experience; they carry into effect the urge to ward off the painful and overwhelming obsession. The more overwhelming and painful the obsession, the more urgent and unsuccessful the devices to ward it off. It is misleading to consider such devices as essential. They certainly cannot be judged on behaviouristic grounds. Constantly in the writings of some psychopathologists it is assumed that a ritual or ceremonial is, *ipso facto*, obsessional—ignoring the absence of the essential subjective features of compulsion. Repetitive mental happenings and more or less stereotyped motor activities occur in a wide range of illnesses—schizophrenia, idiocy, diseases of the basal ganglia, frontal lobe lesions and others; interference with their performance, in all of these, may cause the patient distress, as it also does in the obsessional rituals or repetitions. But clearly, by observing that a ritual or repetitive motor activity is pursued, whether it be with or without anxiety, with or without evident purpose, one cannot tell that it is an obsessional activity. Many reports on obsessional behaviour in children fall into this error. The more the doing of the repetitive act is enjoyed, the less is it like an obsessional act.

The experience of subjective compulsion is the essential feature of obsessions; others follow from it. Critical appraisal of the obsession, and recognition that it is absurd represents a defensive, intellectual effort, intended to destroy it: it is not always present, nor is the obsessional idea always absurd. Perhaps it is emphasis on this criterion that has in part led to the belief that intelligent people are more prone than stupid ones to obsessional neurosis. It need hardly be pointed out that an obsession cannot be experienced except in relation to a freely conducted psychic life; that although psychic activity be fully determined, the quality in conscious experience which is commonly attributed to free will must be present before an obsession can occur. This active experience of willing is, so far as obsessions are concerned, characterized by its feeling of integration with the whole stream of psychic life, indeed with one's self.

The ignoring of this aspect of experience by dynamic psychology has tended to a blurring of the issue here between obsessions, and other compelled mental happenings, especially those of schizophrenia. It has repeatedly been pointed out by Jaspers and others, that an 'obsessive' hallucination or an interpolated, passively experienced autochthonous idea, cannot be obsessional.

In thus considering the problem of definition a number of fresh problems have been opened up—problems of dynamic causation, of constitution and of the relationship to other morbid activities of the mind. Definition itself can only be concerned with abstracting from the complex phenomena certain features which are so constant as to be final criteria. But without such final criteria all other problems of obsessional disorder lose their sharpness and even their reality; the very term or conception 'obsessional' becomes worthless, because it can then be extended to cover everything, as 'neurasthenia' was yesterday, or 'anxiety neurosis' is today.

There are some other features of obsessional illness which are conspicuous. Everyone has been impressed by the frequency with which filth, harm, sex, or religion give the content to the obsessional idea. There are other recurring features: the seemingly 'trivial' content of many obsessions; the 'au delà', literally interminable nature of much obsessional thinking; the hindrance there is to decisive action; the self-tormenting aspect; the apparent contrasts between kindness and cruelty, logicality and unreason, fear and desire, and so on. It is impossible sometimes to escape from the impressions that many of the writers have founded their interpretation of the genesis of obsessions on a few cases that had come their way and in which one or more of these aspects were very conspicuous; some writers seem to publish revised versions of their theory with every two or three new patients they see.

In considering the psychopathology of the obsessional symptom—I shall speak of the obsessional neurosis in a moment—the first and easiest point must be to discover what has determined the content of the obsession. Individual experience is here clearly responsible, and the familiar psychological mechanisms of repression, displacement and substitution are at work, resulting in symbolic representation of harmful or significant earlier happenings. These mechanisms do not differ from those found in other types of mental disorder. Consequently they tell us nothing of the specific obsessional quality and its modes of development. The theories concerning this are, with one exception, concerned with the battle of instinctual drives: the exception is the view that the specifically obsessional characteristic is a repetitive, perseverating quality which cannot be further analysed. All the theories work back to a constitutional, i.e., hereditary basis for the disorder. The most developed and dialectically impregnable of these, the psycho-analytic, rests on a mythology, which is the Freudian theory of instincts; the others are equally unsure of their foundations.

But, as usually conceived and with no more than our present knowledge, the psychopathological problem, genetically speaking, seems to me so difficult to state and so far from being answered, that I should prefer to leave it alone, in its general form. It is well, I think, to remember that psychopathology is properly only an answer to the question 'How?' To answer this does not perhaps call for much of the speculation and metaphor that make psychopathology sometimes sound like metaphysical allegory. I hope I may be forgiven for saying that more than one of the sometimes conflicting theories seem to account plausibly for the facts, but can neither be proved nor disproved because of the nature of its assumptions: Dr Glover has his theory, and Dr Mayer-Gross has his, and Dr Kronfeld and Dr Schilder have theirs, and even I—*sed longo intervallo*—have mine; all of them, I suppose, based on fairly good opportunities of seeing some of the facts.

The more limited question 'How does the quality which appears as obsessional disturbance of function show itself during development?' can, however, in some measure be studied and tested. Most of the work that has been done, has been based on recollection by the patient under special conditions, and on observation of children, again under very special conditions. It would be more convincing if there were less tendency to infer that behaviour is obsessional because it is repetitive and anxious, and if the behaviour and observations had not been influenced by the interposition of verbal suggestions to test theory. It is necessary that we should know more of the development of the average child and the appearance in him of the supposed manifestations of obsessional tendencies. Gesell, for example, finds that little children show a tendency to ritualization; spontaneously they pour pellets out of the bottle in one of his tests and reinsert them without suggestion or command. 'Ritualization is a reinstatement of the situation, a method of defining, and perhaps improving, new abilities; but it is itself a general ability, an intrinsic product of growth.' A few others have examined magical thinking and ordered ways of behaviour in normal children, but the material is meagre. We do not even know whether well-marked obsessional features in early childhood are more often the precursors of obsessional illness in later years than of other morbid states; the children that Ziehen reported, for example, have not, as far as I know, been followed up. The occurrence of slight obsessional symptoms in everyone's psychic life is a reminder that the problem is better posed if one asks what have been the previous manifestations of obsessional tendency in persons who now show obsessional neurosis. There is, moreover, little but psycho-analytic evidence for assigning to the first three or four years of life so prepotent a rôle or supposing that they are the microcosm of which all mental disorder is the larger repetition.

The question worth considering at this point is whether it is sound to regard obsessional neurosis—or Janet's 'psychasthenia'—as a special type of morbid reaction, or as merely a manifestation of universal psychic attributes, aggravated and furthered by the occurrence of some morbid state such as severe anxiety or depression. Thus Bleuler considers obsessional neurosis to be latent schizophrenia. Stöcker and Henry Maudsley aligned it with affective psychosis. The syndromes of psychiatry, however, have at present only a provisional heuristic value: they have not yet the firm biological foundation which one anticipates and strives after. It is therefore still convenient to speak of obsessional neurosis, though it seems to me that the obsessional experience is so widespread over psychic activity and so commonly found with other abnormal psychic states that this neurosis is almost as insecure a category as anxiety neurosis, however hard one may try to delimit both and prop them up. The obsessional neurosis, qua neurosis, rests more on its occasional tendency to become stabilized and systematic than on its exhibiting a constant grouping of symptoms. It is tempting here to stop to classify the manifold phenomena of the obsessional neurosis, but it has been done so successfully by Kronfeld and Janet and Friedman that one may take for granted the general subdivisions into obsessional ideas or images, impulses, phobias, and thinking or rumination.

It is, however, in relation to personality that one sees another aspect of the problem of psychopathology. In the personality of a patient who has pronounced obsessional neurosis, have there been features which betokened this predisposition? This is to ask for late childhood and postpubertal life the question above raised with regard to young children. The question has of course often been answered: and every book on psychopathic personality now describes the anankastic character, just as Freudian manuals take the anal-erotic character for granted. But if we are concerned only with the demonstration of a sequence of related phenomena, with answering the question 'How?', in short, then much that is summed up in the concept of an anal-erotic character will remain unproven. Of course many obsessionals have shown excessive cleanliness, orderliness, pedantry, conscientiousness, uncertainty, inconclusive ways of thinking and acting. These are sometimes obsessional symptoms themselves, sometimes character traits devoid of any immediate experience of subjective compulsion. They are, however, especially in the latter case, just as commonly found among patients who never have an obsessional neurosis, but who get an agitated melancholia during the involutional period; I have verified this on a large number of patients at the Maudsley Hospital. The traits are also, of course, common among healthy people. They are, conversely, sometimes undiscoverable in the previous personality of patients who now have a severe obsessional neurosis. I have collected a number of such instances. For example, a woman aged 23, who had shown none of the accepted obsessional traits either in childhood or since, became depressed during her pregnancy and afterwards worried that her child was swallowing pins and nails; this spread, other compulsive thoughts and fears troubled her. With treatment lasting nearly a year she improved.

Sometimes these supposedly obsessional character-traits have been restricted to one field, e.g. repetition of acts to make sure things are right; in others there has been no such special attitude towards money and possessions, cleanliness and defaecation, or other matters as the name 'anal-erotic' implies. It is perhaps true that the rigid view of regression and fixation at a particular stage of instinctual development, whether it be called anal- or oral-aggressive, has been by some modified into a conception of the primacy of developmental phases and mechanisms. But in any case it is not sufficient for the character-trait, in so far as it is not itself an obsessional symptom, to show a connexion with the neurosis that is essential and understandable in the light of a special theory; it is necessary that it shall be at least significantly more frequent in those who show obsessional neurosis than in others. At present one can say only that to the 'nuclear' group of chronic severe obsessionals who have shown symptoms since childhood, there correspond two types of personality—the one obstinate, morose, irritable, the other vacillating, uncertain of himself, submissive. There are more detailed descriptions of these matters in Kahn's monograph and other well-known works. The evidence is incomplete for the common assumptions underlying the phrase 'an obsessional personality', just as one has to beware of the careless use of 'schizoid' and 'paranoid' when applied to personality.

Before going on to consider the vexed problem of the relation of obsessional neurosis to schizophrenia and other mental illness, it is appropriate to consider where else in psychic happenings do we find the obsessional characteristic, viz.: the experience that some part of one's self or one's mind is working independently, that it is not an integrated part of oneself. There is first the experience of internal speech, as it is known to some people with strong auditory imagery: what is said to them is repeated in their minds, they formulate verbally their own utterances before speaking, and they cannot escape this necessity. M. Henry Ey has recently discussed fully the bearing of this on auditory hallucinations, and the value in regard to it of the conception of mental automatism, so widely used in France. He remarks, concerning this internal speech:

'Où cette conduite interne manque de vigneur, òu l'esprit vagabonde, òu la forme, l'aspect, l'image des mots et des choses l'emportent sur leur signification, il a l'impression de ne plus être maître de sa pensée, d'être parasité par ses propres idées, par la masse de tous ses automatismes toujours en éveil.'

It is, I think, more common in patients who have tinnitus with loss of bone-conduction but no local lesion. Thus a woman of 36 who had all her life been a worrier and a great hand-washer came to hospital complaining of having been bothered for several years by a hissing noise in her ears and by having to repeat in her head all that people said to her: she had also to speak her own thoughts over and over internally: 'As I talked my own words used to come back into my head.' She had to fight against it, and against the thoughts of injuring herself or her child which beset her. The compulsive inner speech and repetition are still, seven years later, very distressing; the tinnitus also persists.

The transition from this to the experience of hearing one's thoughts spoken aloud outside one's head is an understandable one, though fortunately rare (Gedankenlautwerden) and, in both, motor accompaniments of inner speech are conspicuous. I have found it sometimes difficult to distinguish between 'Gedankenlautwerden' and obsessions, as in a young man I lately saw who had also visual hallucinations and forced movements of one leg. I have been impressed also by the frequency with which obsessional patients who are depersonalized complain of this necessity for inner verbal repetition of all they hear and precise verbal formulation of their own thoughts. Of course in depersonalization the patient is commonly so far from feeling the master of his own thoughts that he has almost no personal or free share in them at all, but this is true of all his thinking, not of small parts of it, as is the case in obsessions.

There are, then, these allied experiences in which subjective compulsion and an incomplete integration are noticeable. But it is in relation to more pronounced disorders that obsessions have been actively discussed. On the one hand are Bonhoeffer, Stöcker, Reiss, and others, who insist on the close connexion between the manic-depressive psychosis and obsessions; on the other hand, Bleuler, Schneider and Jahrreiss who point out transitions to schizophrenia. At the Maudsley Hospital it has been taught and often demonstrated that obsessional symptoms are not uncommon in depressive illnesses, and that obsessions may develop into definitely schizophrenic symptoms such as hallucinations and ideas of reference.

Taking the depressive illnesses first, I found in an earlier investigation that there were indubitable obsessional symptoms in at least a fifth of a series of casually selected depressive patients; a third of the patients had shown the so-called obsessional character-traits. If one takes only the patients with agitated depression the proportion is much higher. As I discussed the matter rather fully on that occasion, I shall pass to the more difficult question of schizophrenia.

The surprising thing here is not that some obsessionals become obviously schizophrenic, but that only a few do so. It must be a very short step, one might suppose, from feeling that one must struggle against thoughts that are not one's own, to believing that these thoughts are forced upon one by an external agency; and indeed a religious patient who has never been anything but obsessional will sometimes go so far as to impute his obsession to the devil. The actual projection, however, is rarely made; the patient does not, any more than in depersonalization, make the causal interpretation which would be understandable. It is a useful warning against the more facile explanations of what happens in the genesis of schizophrenia. It is also surprising that the projection should not occur, seeing how close are the links between compulsions and ideas of reference; Ewald and Kehrer and one or two of the Freudians have even thought that there were affinities between obsessions and paranoia. One can easily, of course, be led astray into supposing that a stereotyped, outwardly affectless, compulsive action is in fact a catatonic manifestation, or that the more bizarre rituals or compulsive movements are schizophrenic symptoms. Jahrreiss puts some weight on the normal tendency towards persistence or perseveration as explaining the common features in stereotypies and long-standing compulsions, but prefers to insist on the differences rather than on the points in common. I have been collecting relevant cases, but they are not easy to unearth from the mass of records; from such material as I have I should say that as a rule it is only under the influence of drugs (such as bromide) or organic cerebral changes that a long-standing obsessional can come to show schizophrenic features or a hallucinosis that looks schizophrenic; but that florid schizophrenia may be preceded by, or may set in with obsessions often of a stormy and imperative kind, and that this is especially true of adolescents. Schizophrenics may however have shown numerous obsessional features together with the more usual schizophrenic ones all along. The following cases illustrate some of these points:

A woman of 38 had since childhood been abnormally clean and afraid of contamination. At the age of 32 she had a mild attack of depression, with some fears (walls falling). At 34 she became afraid she would get vermin on her from contact with menstruating women. She became irritable and had outbursts of screaming, especially at her periods. She described her fear of contamination as 'this mania of mine'. 'It's as if there's some unseen power; the Devil's been persecuting me ever since I married—a figure of speech really.' She also said, a month after she had begun to attend hospital, 'I get a lot of hallucinations. All Derby week I could see a white fish in green water. Silly imaginings, I know. I think my father has bits on him that smell. I tell my mother not to touch him.' (The visual phenomena were mostly, as is usual in these cases, hypnagogic.) During the two years she attended the outpatient department these symptoms became rather worse; she believed that the physician was hypnotizing her, she had ideas of reference, was uncertain as to the reality of the visual images, and included more and more contaminating objects. She has twice been a voluntary patient in a mental hospital during the last six months. There were grounds for regarding many of the apparently schizophrenic features as hysterical.

A younger case:

A boy of 18 had been irritable, sensitive, timid, and excessively clean from the age of 6. At 16, a month after a blow on the head, he suffered much from fears of death, such as he had had mildly for years. He had to touch things. He had been having intensive psychotherapy for several months before he came to the Maudsley Hospital. He described his fears: 'Wherever my eyes direct me I see these thoughts. I've got to gesture and take them up and throw them out of the window. I'm afraid of putting them on anybody.' In fact he did make throwing-away gestures. He also had ideas of reference and believed his body was changing its shape and appearance. He felt that his own thoughts were trying to harm him. His condition fluctuated, depending on external circumstances.

Another adolescent, a girl of 17, had been obstinate, jolly, sociable, free from any obsessional traits, until an illness at 16, characterized by depression and inclinations to suicide. She was treated at a Child Guidance Clinic, but made an attempt to gas herself. In a mental hospital to which she was sent she expressed hypochondriacal fears. She was referred to the Maudsley Hospital after she had left the mental hospital: When I saw her she said: 'Always there seems to be someone speaking to me. If a bus goes along it says "Why don't you jump under it?" I can't tell what kind of voice; it's just a voice, inside my head. Well, I don't know really, it seems inside. It makes me walk over to the gas-stove at home and tells me to do things. I think it always comes from my own mind.' She felt she must obey the voice. She also said: 'Sometimes I hear a voice, a deep commanding voice over my shoulder behind me; sometimes it's in my head; it must be, because other people don't hear it.'

And one more example, this time of obsessions passing over into hallucinations as dementia progressed.

The patient was a woman, aged 56 when first seen, who had developed obsessional thoughts, chiefly blasphemous and obscene, after the suicide of her husband two years before. She also had impulses to injure herself and others, and to take sexual liberties with women. She was depressed. The physician who treated her at Maudsley Hospital recorded 'the thoughts and impulses are so alien to her that she thinks she must be mad, and though she does not actually hear them as voices or think they are put into her mind by some external agency, yet her attitude towards them suggests that further projection is likely to occur.' In the eleven years since then she has been in a mental hospital. She has gradually lost the acute depression and anxiety she had, but has complained more of the weariness and loss of feeling—'no life in me'—akin to depersonalization, and often found in one group of chronic obsessionals. As her arteriosclerotic dementia advanced she became so certain that the abusive and obscene voices were external to her that she now stuffs her ears to keep them out.

Even more important in its bearing on the aetiological problem is the occurrence of obsessions in persons who have had encephalitis lethargica.

Thus a woman of 28, a severe encephalitic of ten years' standing, with oculogyric crises, is obsessed by the ruminative thoughts 'what is what' and 'did you say did I say'. These she has to revolve and rearrange endlessly in her mind, e.g. 'What is what, did you say did I say, what word is that word what, what do the words the word what mean.' Besides this thought, so reminiscent of the literary output of Gertrude Stein, she sometimes sees her obsessing sentences as though spelt, and spelt wrongly, e.g. 'what is thē or thĕ', the first 'the' being spelt 'thee', and the second 'ong'. She also has premonitions of evil and anxiety attacks. The obsessional thoughts occur independently of her oculogyric crises.

Another, a man of 25, whose encephalitic attack occurred when he was 11, had had to clap his hands and perform other habitual movements which made him a butt at school. At 16 he was in court for stealing; at 18 he began to fear that buildings would collapse on him; a year later oculogyric crises began. Now, besides depressive inclinations to kill himself, he has obsessional symptoms. 'I have to fight against thinking. I keep on continually thinking: "What's going to become of the country? Where do clothes come from, and electricity and wireless?" I can't stop myself. I feel frightened—I feel something terrible is going to happen—buildings will fall; and then I think where cement comes from, where wood comes from, how trees grow? And I think I'm a murderer—I'm a spy. I know they're silly ideas, but I can't help thinking them. I try to put it out of my mind, but it seems impossible.' Here, too, the ideas did not occur during an oculogyric crisis, but might occur just before or just after it.

In many of these cases there have been no indications, before the febrile illness, of any obsessional predisposition—nothing more than we all have. But either with the oculogyric crises or independently these typical obsessional features appear. It has been questioned whether they are in fact typical: some writers have emphasized that they are often formal and do not tend to become systematized. But systematization, which I should have liked to discuss more fully, is not a necessary characteristic of obsessional neurosis, and, where it occurs, suggests connexions with schizophrenic and paranoiac development. A more important point is the readiness with which they are translated into or associated with motor iterations. This is not always so, but it is significant that in this disorder subjective compulsion in the sense referred to in the outset of this paper should so often go hand in hand with objective compulsions in the field of motor behaviour. Compulsive laughing and crying, bellowing, turning of the eyes, chewing, and other actions are common enough in encephalitis lethargica: is one to call them obsessional because the patient is aware of them, and dislikes them, and fights unavailingly to suppress them? I should say not, because they are either accompanied by the appropriate effect (in which case the same objections apply as to preoccupations and delusions, and Jaspers' requirement as to freely conducted activity is not fully met); or, on the other hand, the appropriate effect is lacking and the movement is a forced one, viewed with as much detachment as any other unwilled movement. And, still more important, these movements are the primary happening, which the patient perhaps resists, they are not the secondary happening, expressions of a resistance, which we have seen to be the case with almost all obsessional actions. Only the very rare impulsive obsession that is carried into action, e.g. jumping out of a window, corresponds to these, and even then the action is preceded by a conscious image or idea of it to which there is nothing intrinsically corresponding in the forced movement. If one is to regard forced movements, however purposive or however emotionally expressive, as obsessional, one must say the same of a great variety of motor phenomena determined by structural changes in the central nervous system but also open to psychic influences—certain tics, coprolalia, automatoses, torticollis and more. This is to extend the conception of obsession as unwarrantably and loosely on the one side as it has been stretched on the other side to include dominant preoccupations, delusions, autochthonous ideas, impulses and disagreeable effects. It may be objected that although for the sake of precision these motor phenomena can justly be denied the epithet 'obsessional', they are dynamically and functionally akin to obsession. Some such view is held, though in very different ways, by Goldstein, Stern, Jelliffe, and Schilder. That the iterative and forced quality of these motor phenomena enters into and is indeed a part of the structure of the personality of these patients is certain, but whether it modifies it in the direction of obsessional modes of mental behaviour is undecided. I should think it is so; and Dr Mayer-Gross has based his psychopathology of obsessions on some implications of this view. But as both Dr Guttmann and Gabriel Steiner have pointed out, we know very little indeed about the incorporation of motor expressions and attitudes in the personality or of the relations between them that are favourable to the peculiar obsessional experience. Explanations have been, of course, offered, and with varying confidence; it would be very tempting to enter more fully now into this fascinating and controversial field. The significance here of motor expression of instinct especially in early life may be mentioned, and I might quote the case of a man of 46, always very cleanly, conscientious, and tidy, who had an attack of encephalitis lethargica seventeen years ago. He is now troubled by obsessional palilalia. 'I can't help repeating things, I try not to. Singing a song, for example, I keep on repeating over and over again "Is it in the trees, is it in the trees, is it in the trees?" It's when I'm agitated, too, I'll keep on saying things "I'm going to hang that cup up, I'm going to hang that cup up, I'm going to hang that cup up," I can't stop myself and when I go to wash my face, I keep splashing the water, I can't get my hand to my face. Everything I do seems to be wrong. I used to say "Damn" all the time, I couldn't help it.'

It is perhaps sufficient, in leaving this topic, to emphasize the problem that is offered by obsessions occurring otherwise than on a demonstrable constitutional basis. Before I pass on to consider constitution in its hereditary aspects, I should perhaps mention that I have observed over a long period a woman in whom obsessional features appeared only during the years she had an untreated myxoedema and disappeared completely after adequate treatment had been instituted; and that in the early stages of an arteriosclerotic dementia I have seen obsessional symptoms make their appearance for the first time in the patient's life.

Constitution is universally recognized as the essential determinant of obsessional illness; all else is only the manner of its working out. Constitution, however, is the loose term we use for the more or less stable product of the interaction of heredity and environment while the organism is developing. It would be more precise to speak of the hereditary determinant of obsessions than of the constitutional factors.

The literature on the heredity of obsessional neurosis is meagre. Apart from a few individual pedigrees and some unsystematic collections I know only of Jahrreiss's report on the families of his sixteen schizophrenic obsessionals, and Luxenburger's brief presentation of his findings on 71 families. In order to make use for this purpose of the very large material which the Maudsley Hospital affords I took fifty obsessional cases. I was fortunate in having the collaboration of Miss Ashdown, to whom is due whatever credit may attach to such an investigation. We were able to get detailed information not only about the mental illnesses of all the patient's immediate relatives but also of their personalities, a valuable but hitherto neglected aspect of such inquiries. As this is being published in full elsewhere, I shall only say here that of the 100 parents of the patients four were psychotic, 22 had been treated for neurotic illnesses, 30 had been regarded by their families as eccentric, unusual or different (these were classed as 'psychopathic personality') and 18, though normal, showed either the accepted obsessional traits, e.g. being very methodical, or else a kind of personality which was surprisingly frequent—a mixture of strong religious feelings, irritability and strictness. The number of parents who showed pronounced obsessional traits in one form or another was 37: in a number of instances both parents had been obsessional, and in several cases grandparents were likewise: I shall not now, however, speak of the findings in any but parents and siblings. Of 206 siblings who had survived beyond childhood, twelve had been in mental hospitals, 55 had been treated for neurosis, 27 had some kind of psychopathic personality and 20 showed such obsessional traits as may occur in healthy normal people: 43 of these 206 siblings showed mild or severe obsessional traits. My findings differ from those of Luxenburger in that he found a much higher proportion of schizoid persons, but I think he reckoned those stern, harsh domineering people as schizoid. There are many other aspects of the inquiry which I must now omit.

It is agreed that one cannot distinguish satisfactorily by this method between hereditary influences and the environment that is constituted by the parents. Moreover, to find the meaning of such statistics, one must have comparable data about the incidence of psychopathy and varieties of personality in normal or average families, and in those of propositi with other than obsessional illness: these data are as yet only available for definite pyschoses among the relatives.

For the determination of the relative importance of hereditary and environmental factors twin studies are an obvious mode of research. I need not detail the reasons why this method is invaluable but only remind you that a striking concordance in one or two pairs of monozygotic twins proves nothing: one needs a series and a control group of fraternal twins. Specially valuable also is the monozygotic pair in whom the conditions of the environment have been very different. I have one such pair: healthy girls of 17 who have lived apart from the age of 3 months. They are both very particular about their clothes and other details and fussy about tidiness, but the one who was brought up by her mother at home shows these tendencies more, and was a sleepwalker till puberty; she had clung to a dummy till she went to school. I have also been fortunate enough to find a pair of male monozygotic twins, one of whom is a severe and typical obsessional, with complicated rituals, and chronic course: many of his obsessions were concerned with bodily functions, e.g. he blew his nose thirty times, always having to stand in a particular place to do it; his bowels and cleanliness were other topics. His twin had a brief spell of hypochondriac pre-occupation two years ago, being convinced his eyesight was bad; the symptoms cleared up without medical aid. Dr F. E. Pilkington has kindly let me see the record of another pair of probably identical twins who show striking similarity in their respective obsessional illnesses. But two or three pairs tell very little; it is a pity that twins are so rare.

The value of treatment and the choice of procedure are the most urgent questions for the practising psychiatrist. All of us who have treated obsessionals know how exacting it can be. Most writers are gloomy as to the prospect of recovery and the duration of treatment. Fenichel, a psychoanalyst, says:

> 'Every analysis of a compulsion neurosis is a difficult and time-consuming undertaking. . . . Cases of short standing are the most amenable to analysis; those called "terminal states" and those forms which present transitions to schizophrenia are the least amenable. However, since other types of therapy are so fruitless in such cases, it is pertinent to advise that any compulsion-neurosis, generally speaking, should at least try psychoanalysis, providing the external circumstances permit it.'

This is now echoed by many writers who are not adherents to the analytic theory. It is difficult to understand why this sad belief should prevail. I suspect it has little to do with observed results of treatment, and a great deal to do with less rational considerations, such as the irksomeness of having to deal with some of these patients, and their attitude towards treatment.

In order to find out what happened to obsessional patients, I collected from the Maudsley records 50 patients in whom the diagnosis was certain, and in whom there had been an interval of at least five years, often much more, since they were under treatment there. The inquiry into their present state, and the interval history was as complete as one could hope to make it. In most instances the patient and one or more relatives were seen and any hospital records were obtained; in no case was the conclusion as to the patient's present state based only on letters from himself or his relatives, which are, as I have often found in investigations of this sort, fallacious. Now taking the outcome, irrespective of what treatment had been given, 16 of the patients are quite well and have been so for years; seven are much improved; five quite well for years but have had a recurrence from which they recovered or they are now in it; five patients are a little improved; 17 are no better or are worse. It must be remembered that this group has not been selected because of supposedly good or bad prognosis; it is a sample of the obsessional patients who are referred to the Maudsley Hospital either as in-patients or out-patients, and there is reason to suppose that it is a good sample of the obsessionals of London. Certainly it contains examples of every variety of obsessional state. There are of course many provisos and explanations necessary before one makes use of these figures: I quote them cursorily now only to indicate that in an unselected sample of obsessional patients, roughly one-half may be expected to do well. I do not consider that one is justified, from such a series as this, in deciding on the value of one or other form of treatment. Two of the patients have had no continued medical treatment; one is very much worse—she spends her day sitting naked behind a screen to avoid any contamination—and the other has been quite well for eleven years. By 'quite well' I mean what everybody means, i.e. freedom from symptoms. An attempt to distinguish between the value of one form of treatment and another proved futile because there had been no rigidity of method, and sometimes the change in the patient had less apparent connexion with the medical treatment than with external happenings, such as obtaining employment, getting married and so forth. Actually in this series 31 had psychotherapy conjoined with medicinal treatment and hospital régime: 17 had more intensive psychotherapy of an analytic kind, though not strictly Freudian. Of the former group a considerable majority had done very well; of the latter group a majority had done badly, not because of any insufficiency in the method or its application, one may suppose, but because the most difficult and demanding cases were referred for this treatment.

One has so many things to correlate—the patient's attributes (heredity, personality, form and duration of illness), the doctor's treatment, the other external happenings in the patient's life, and the course of his illness and health since the treatment. For these reasons assertions about the superior merits of any one form of treatment seem premature.

There are many other points in this inquiry which I can only touch on here. Some of them are: The capacity of all but the most severe obsessionals to continue to work; the very gradual return to health in many, sometimes beginning years after treatment has stopped; the influence of intercurrent happening on the course of the illness, e.g. a very severe case in which all the obsessional symptoms disappeared completely during the patient's period of war service —with its routine and lack of responsibility or need for decisions—to return and persist afterwards; the inherently cyclical nature of one large group, quite apart from any accompanying depressive or other affective features; the persistence in some cases of the obsessional idea after it had lost its obsessional quality, viz.: the obsessional experience, so that there was no complaint about it any more than about any other integrated habit. The following case-history emphasizes that it is not always safe to assume a bad prognosis or a need for long analytical treatment because the symptoms have been present for many years or since childhood.

A chorus girl of 22 had had obsessional symptoms since the age of 15, and obsessional traits for years before that. At 15 she had washing mania and feared she had picked up some germ. She thought she might somehow have dirtied her tongue by licking the pavement. She was afraid she had harmed a baby by looking at it and touching it. At 16, when her periods started, these symptoms were a little relieved, though she has never been rid of them, e.g. at 17 she thought she might have been implicated in a murder that she had read of on the page which had a favourable press notice of her dancing. Following the suicide of a friend the symptoms became more severe. Her last obsession before being referred to hospital had been the fear that she might have written notes to people encouraging them to hurt her friends. She was an in-patient for six months at the end of 1930. A week after admission she was referred to a colleague who had been through the Freudian discipline. After a month during which he saw her twice a week, he stopped it, as he considered her unsuitable for the modified analytical method he had been using. She became clinically worse during that month. From then on she had no other psychotherapy than brief occasional reassuring conversations on topics which she herself raised. Later she began to improve. She has been seen since, and both she and her mother are quite certain that she is cured; she has been happy and free from obsessional symptoms now for five years.

These cases do not confirm the belief that schizophrenic features are necessarily ominous, even in young persons. I could quote several instances to the contrary.

I should say, if I may sum up my own impressions, that the choice of treatment in obsessional disorders is to be decided on the same general grounds as in depressive disorders, and that the prognostic considerations are much the same. In both the constitutional basis is conspicuous and may show itself either by outbursts of acute illness, or by a long-continued psychopathic personality with neurotic symptoms; gradations of every sort occur between these two forms. The important matter in settling on treatment is to discover how far the patient is responsive to external happenings, especially as regards her obsessions; how his character will enter into his attitude towards treatment and symptoms; and how far the lasting obsessions have become formalized, systematic, progressive. I doubt whether the content of the obsessions is of much consequence as a prognostic or therapeutic signal. I do not think age is, either—I have known a patient aged 88 with pronounced obsessions who has been well since, he is now 93; and several people over 50 who recovered. Perhaps it is worth saying that so many of these obsessional patients have been happy and well on their own telling and that of their families for six to ten years since they were treated by non-Freudian methods, that one may think it would have been superfluous, if not unkind, to have taken them through the storms and sacrifices of a Freudian analysis: in some cases one would say, of any analysis at all. What psychoanalysis can do for some of the intractable, progressive forms is a matter not for assertion but for demonstration; the same is true of its efficacy or inefficacy in improving obsessional character and in warding off later obsessional illness by treatment of children or adults. The published records of the London psycho-analysts are informative but clinically unconvincing.

There is one other aspect of the illness to be alluded to before I end. It has a forensic bearing. How far do obsessionals give way to their impulses; are their fears of wrongdoing realized? When 'kleptomania' or 'irresistible impulse' are mentioned in a court it is often put forward that these are of the nature of obsessional acts. But the obsessional does not in fact commit criminal acts, nor does he, except in rare instances, yield to his sudden obsessional impulses. Suicide may occur, but even then it is when the patient is also depressed. None of the patients in this series have committed suicide, though two, while depressed, made abortive attempts: none of the patients committed any legal offence, though several were dogged by the fear of it. Those who have much to do with criminals arrive at the same conclusion as this. Sexual offences or perversions are sometimes referred to as though they were obsessional: they are really no more so than gluttony. The patient enters into the act and willingly entertains the anticipations of it; he has none of the true obsessional experience, even though afterwards he recognizes the unwisdom of his act and may say that he had a preliminary repugnance which had been more of the intellect than of the will, if one may so express it. There are, of course, rare instances, in which sexual offences have been of an obsessional nature (Mercklin's case). When an impulsive act has occurred in a person with obsessional traits, other morbid qualities will generally be found to have been responsible. Encephalitics are a very special case.

In this paper I have been concerned with the difficulties that present themselves in a typical neurotic disturbance. They are clearly manifold, and have been tackled by clinical psychiatrists and psychologists, neurologists and psycho-analysts. Anthropologists with their observations on magical thinking and primitive rituals, and geneticists with their special methods have indicated further approaches to the phenomena. But about these phenomena, seen with the least distortion and the most detail, we still know too little. Heredity and psychopathology may be feeling their way to a grounded doctrine of transmission and development and function; no doubt it is fascinating to guess and grope with them in their search. But the problem is primarily a clinical one; it turns about this end-product, the obsessional symptom, which has to be accounted for. It would be a pity if other quests kept us from making sure of all the plain clinical things that are yet to be seen and studied.

7

OBSESSIONAL ILLNESS

THIS MAY seem an unprofitable subject to review at the present time. There has been no marked increase in our knowledge of it in recent years, and indeed much of what can be found on the subject in current textbooks had already been fully stated and closely discussed in the first two decades of the century —a period during which Janet's monumental work on Obsessions and Psychasthenia appeared, as well as the detailed studies by Friedmann, Löwenfeld and Bumke: Freud, Abraham and Jones also put forward at that time their views of the varieties and mechanisms of obsessional neurosis. The clinical phenomena have been well recognized and described for over half a century, and little new information has accumulated in recent years regarding the treatment and course of the illness.

Some aspects of the problem are, however, worth looking at again, in the light of recent evidence, and I propose in this paper to examine the relationship of obsessional illness to other forms of mental illness, its forensic implications, its relation to personality, and some biographical instances. Before tackling these themes I should like to state briefly and dogmatically, the distinctive characteristics of the illness, which I shall be taking for granted in what I subsequently say.

The essence of an obsession is the fruitless struggle against a disturbance that seems isolated from the rest of mental activity. It is not sufficient that the disturbance be recognized as senseless or obnoxious—that may be true of dominant ideas, sexual images, hallucinations, suicidal inclinations and other morbid experiences which the patient may accept or dally with, even though they strike him as senseless and absurd. But the subjective element of compulsion is lacking in them: therefore they cannot be obsessional. This is, if you like, a verbal point: but it is not for that reason less important to clarify it. Semantic carelessness over the meaning of terms in psychiatry leads easily, as we all know, to faulty diagnosis and sometimes in consequence to faulty treatment.

This article is based on a lecture delivered in the Royal Medico-Psychological Association Maudesley Bequest Refresher Course in November 1957. It is reprinted from *Acta Neuro-psiquiátrica Argentinia* (1957), **3**, 323–35.

The indispensable subjective component of an obsession lies in the *consciousness* of the patient: to him it is an act of *will*, which he cannot help making, to try and suppress or destroy the unwelcome intruder upon his mental integrity; but the effort is always in vain. It does not matter whether the intruder is a thought, an idea, or an image, or an impulse, accompanied by appropriate affect.

Along with this subjective feeling of compulsion goes an inability to accept the experience as part of one's proper and integrated mental activity: it is a foreign body, not implanted from without (as a disordered schizophrenic experience might be held to be by the patient) but arising from within, home-made but disowned, a sort of mental sequestrum, a calculus that keeps on causing trouble. Isolation as dynamic process in the genesis of the obsessional symptom has of course been stressed by Fenichel and Freud: they have extended it to the attempt obsessionals sometimes make to keep various spheres of their life strictly apart from each other. Erwin Straus, using the concept in yet another wide sense, applies it to the obsessional's drive to sever contacts with the outside world and become a solitary: obviously this is not true of all obsessional patients and I refer to it, not in order to discuss Erwin Straus's very thoughtful and independent analysis of the obsessional process, but as a reminder of the ambiguity and looseness with which technical and other terms are used in this connexion.

Obsession can conveniently be divided into primary and secondary. An example would be first the insistent feeling that one is dirty—that is the primary phenomenon: and then there is the impulse to wash—the secondary phenomenon, developed in order to obtain relief from the primary disturbance. The second phenomenon can be regarded as defensive and aimed at preventing or relieving tension. They can themselves be obsessional, that is, the patient has to struggle against them and may indeed develop defensive rituals or tricks against them in turn: or they may remain neutral and unresisted, they may indeed be prized for their protective efficacy. The distinction is of importance since it concerns, particularly, obsessional acts, and has forensic implications. The primary obsessional phenomenon is far more private than the secondary; its sources lie deep in the individual's constitution and past life: whereas the secondary phenomenon is, as a rule, resisted (or accepted) according to the extent to which it offends against familiar social, hygienic or moral canons of conduct. If an unobtrusive gesture or unspoken phrase can avert the impending obsessional thought with its attendant discomfort, this gesture or phrase will be indulged in without any reluctance: but if the secondary phenomenon is such as to arouse ridicule or censure, or to prejudice health, it may be ineffectually resisted, or half-heartedly yielded to, or wholly abstained from. There is, in short, a great difference between, say, the impulse to steal or strike, as a primary obsessional symptom, and the execution of some ceremonial or cleansing or propitiatory act, as a defensive secondary symptom. This is a matter we shall come back to when the connexion with criminal acts has to be considered.

Now let us look at the relation of obsessions to other psychiatric symptoms and diseases. Here a number of alluring antitheses lie in wait for us. Is obsessional disorder a hereditary or an acquired condition? Is it organic or psychogenic? Is it a psychosis or a neurosis? Is it linked with manic-depressive psychosis or with schizophrenia? There are some in psychiatry who like the definiteness of such sharp alternatives; but their preference is not in keeping with our knowledge on these matters, which repudiates the either-or, black-or-white approach.

Obsessions may occur as symptoms in any form of mental disorder. What then do we mean by the 'obsessional neurosis' or 'obsessive-ruminative tension state' or 'obsessive-compulsive reaction'? I think we mean no more than that obsessions can make up the whole of the clinical picture the patient presents—and be disturbing enough to him to warrant our regarding it as an illness. But that it exhibits a consistent pattern, as most of the major psychiatric syndromes do; or has a regular or predictable course, or a psychopathology going beyond the genesis of the obsessional symptom—none of these things can be said of it. As with other neurotic syndromes, its boundaries are indistinct, and its identity insecure. To dwell further on this would be to examine the basis of our current style of classification. It is a matter profitably discussed in Professor Bumke's recent essay on the 'Psychopathology of Compulsion Phenomena'.

The most authoritative attempt to make an honest syndrome of it was Janet's, when he invented 'psychasthenia'. The theoretical substructure need not detain us, since concepts of nervous exhaustion and psychological tension have gone out of currency; but the clinical picture he drew emphasized some features worth our attention. Besides weariness and lack of perseverance, Janet stressed the 'sentiment d'incomplétude', leading the patient to stop midway, to go back and verify, to be irresolute and hesitant; he stressed also the tendency to introspection and rumination, and to depersonalization—a condition described neatly in 1873 by Krishaber, and given its modern name in 1898 by Dugas, but not recognized as often associated with obsessions until Janet noted it. It would be necessary to cover a lot of ground if one wanted to review the reasons for Janet's proposal that we recognize a single neurosis, psychasthenia, instead of 'the innumerable obsessions, manias, tics, phobias, folies du doute ou du contact' and so on. But it is useful to recall that from the time of Esquirol, until the eighteen-seventies, obsessions were a monopoly of the French psychiatrists, and have always intrigued those subtle and logical analysts of mental disorder. For a recent conspectus of French views, Madame Favez-Boutonier's article in the new Encyclopedia is illuminating, and so is the appreciation by a veteran, Hesnard:

'. . . or c'est à P. Janet que devait revenir le mérite de montrer que tous ces syndromes divers—névrose d'angoisse avec ses épisodes variés, dont quelques-uns à prédominance somatique, phobies plus ou moins spécialisées, idées obsédantes avec les sentiments de doute, de scrupule qui les accompagnent, manies mentales, cérémoniaux, obsédants, certains traits de caractère, aussi, annonçant aux périodes climactiques de la vie des poussées anxieuses—n'étaient que les symptomes différents, de premier plan, d'un état morbide particulier de même nature foncière et qui pouvait s'étendre à tous les modes de penser et d'agir. Etat qu'il appela.... psychasthénie, en le différenciant catégoriquement des états dits hystériques. Nous verrons qu'une telle conception devenue classique, paraît encore satisfaisante aujourd'hui, si l'on n'abandonne pas le domaine de la clinique pour se cantonner dans la recherche exclusive du 'sens' des symptômes névrotiques.'

Hesnard rightly suggests that Janet's formulation was not in opposition to Freud's, but that these were at the time complementary and mutually corrective ways of studying the obsessional syndrome.

All writers about obsessional neurosis recognize points of similarity between it and other forms of mental disorder: sometimes the point of likeness is in the psychopathology, sometimes in the course, sometimes in the family history of the illness.

Let us take schizophrenia first. Views on its relationship to obsessional neurosis are sharply opposed. Some, including Kraepelin, Hoche, Kehrer and Carl Schneider, deny any intrinsic connexion: others, more numerous, see obsessional neurosis as a muted variant or prodrome of schizophrenia: Bleuler was the leader of this party. It would be wearisome to examine the conflicting evidence and arguments. No one could maintain, after reading what has been written about it, that people who were diagnosed as having an obsessional neurosis never developed unequivocal schizophrenia, or that obsessional symptoms have never been noted in the course of a schizophrenic illness, or that psychopathological similarity between some features of the obsessional and of the schizophrenic illness has not been noted. But, even putting aside any doubts about the precision of diagnosis, we remind ourselves that mixtures of syndromes are the rule rather than the exception in psychiatry, and that if we assume some intrinsic connexion whenever we find such mixtures, or whenever what appeared to be one illness apparently demands a change of diagnosis later on, then we should be forced to assume this kinship between all the syndromes—a sort of nosological incest or endogamous chaos. Rosen in his recent study of 30 schizophrenic patients who had had obsessional symptoms at some time in their lives, recognized that he could not, on clinical evidence, decide whether this showed the phases of a single developing illness, or the occurrence of two reaction-types in the same individual—on the whole his case material supported Professor Stengel's ingenious division into four groups, of which the last showed interplay whereby the persisting obsessional neurosis could be thought of as inhibiting the development of the schizophrenia. Ultimately the question is one regarding genetics.

The relationship to manic-depressive psychosis has preoccupied psychiatrists for nearly a hundred years: Griesinger raised it in 1867. Anxiety is so prominent in obsessional conditions that a link with the anxiety and depression of the affective psychoses seemed likely: later more subtle and stronger links were detected or alleged. Again there is a great array of famous psychiatrists who got excited because they found obsessional symptoms in melancholics; some have stressed in particular the obsessional personality that may precede the onset of involutional melancholia; others have inferred, because obsessional attacks occurred periodically without external occasion, that they were exhibiting the periodicity of the affective psychoses, behind a mask. One authority (Stöcker) attributed obsessional symptoms to the conflict of manic and depressive tendencies in mixed states, an extreme and unacceptable view. But no less a clinician than Bonhoeffer pointed to the periodic course, the concomitance of depressive syndromes with obsessional symptoms and the manic features which (in spite of occasional assertions to the contrary) can be seen in some obsessionals (garrulousness, excitability, flight of unspoken ideas, distractability). Indeed the sponsor of these lectures, Henry Maudsley, subscribed to the view that the obsessional disorder is a variety of affective illness. In *The Pathology of Mind* he described the condition in a chapter headed 'Insanity with Depression—Melancholia': after stating that in this melancholia without delusion 'there is no real derangement of mind: there is only a profound pain of mind . . . an essential psychalgia', he introduces a vivid description of obsessional urges, as follows:

'In another group of cases of simple melancholy the cause of affliction is a morbid impulse to utter a bad word or to do an ill deed. The impulse is bad enough, but the essence of the misery is not always so much the fear of actually yielding as the haunting fear of the fear. . . . It is not easy to persuade him who suffers in one or other of these ways that he is not doomed to madness.'

In the search for an essential identity underlying the difference between two psychiatric syndromes the safest indication is a greater frequency of one of the syndromes in the families of propositi exhibiting the other syndrome than would be the case in families drawn at random from the general population. Evidence as to whether this is so in regard to obsessional propositi has been rather conflicting. The latest and fullest data are those of Edith Rüdin. In her series of families of 130 obsessional propositi she found that in the sibs manic-depressive psychosis was no more frequent than in the average population, but it was higher than this in the uncles and aunts, grandparents and parents of the patients. The frequency of suicide was also somewhat greater in the relatives than in the population at large.

It would be possible to infer from these figures that there is some genetic factor common to both obsessional and manic-depressive disorder. But to this there are two main objections. First, schizophrenia is likewise more frequent in the relatives of the obsessional patients than it is in the general population: and secondly, the raised percentage of manic-depressive—and schizophrenic—relatives of obsessionals is still appreciably lower than the percentage of such affected relatives in the families of manic-depressive or schizophrenic propositi; there are evidently therefore essential differences genetically between the obsessional disorder and the two major psychoses. Dr Rüdin concludes—and I think she is right—that 'there is no close affinity between obsessional neurosis and schizophrenia or manic-depressive psychosis'. Her whole paper is an informative one, deserving of close attention.

The relation of obsessional symptoms to organic disease of the brain became a very lively topic, especially in the German literature, between 1921 and 1930. The post-encephalitic disturbances of behaviour and especially the obsessional troubles, the tics and the respiratory and oculogyric crises, revived a problem which had lain rather dormant since Meige and Feindel gave it prominence twenty years before. The localization and pathology of the lesion which could give rise to obsessions in a patient whose personality had before his encephalitis shown no such propensity; the psychopathology which could reconcile a somatic etiology with the presumed genesis of such symptoms in a patient with pronounced and lifelong 'anal-erotic character'; the significance of psychomotor behaviour as the link between somatic and psychological aspects of such illness—these issues were debated with much ingenuity and advantage. The argument extended more widely, to extra-pyramidal disorders, especially Parkinsonism and chorea, and eventually (in the way such things do) to all organic cerebral disease and to normal behaviour, in both of which obsessional traits are not uncommon. Dr Hoffer, in his recent Abraham Flexner Lectures, described an interesting psychoanalytic case-study bearing on this: Schilder, who was fascinated by the problem, believed that patients 'with a partially organic origin of the increase in aggressive impulses . . . react very well to psychoanalysis as well as to group psychotherapy.' I do not think this view would be so readily sustained now; it is, at any rate, as open to question as Schilder's opinion that 'about one-third of the obsessive and compulsive cases show organic signs pointing to pathology with the same localization as that found in encephalitis. These changes may be constitutional, or they may be due to lesions in foetal life, to birth traumas or to toxic and infectious processes of unknown origin'. Schilder's views on such a matter are entitled to much respect, but they depend on highly disputable evidence. The subject calls for more close study rather than assertions. In this it is very like the disputed value of various methods of treating obsessional illness.

I referred earlier to the forensic aspects of obsessional illness. They are illustrated in the following quotation from Maudsley's book on *Responsibility in Mental Disaese*:

'It may no doubt be fairly argued that a person is not to be counted insane simply because the idea of killing another person comes into his mind, more especially when he recognizes its atrocity and abhors it; but when he cannot dismiss it from his thoughts, although he feels keenly its enormity; when it is directed against someone against whom he has not the least animosity, perhaps against someone near and dear to him; when he is truly possessed by it, so that he is in an agony of fear lest he should yield to its influence, in spite of reason and against his will . . . then surely it must be acknowledged that his mental functions are not sound but diseased . . . the fact that he does successfully resist the insane impulse by calling up ideas to counteract it, or by getting out of the way of temptation is assuredly not, as many persons think and some argue, a proof that he might continue to do so on all occasions.'

This, however, is just what since then many people have maintained.

The generally accepted view today has been briefly stated by Norwood East:

'... obsessive-compulsive states are less frequently associated with criminal conduct than is often supposed. In a series of 406 offenders who were specially investigated because their mental condition appeared to be suitable for psychological treatment, only two showed an obsessional symptom which was undoubtedly connected with an offence. It is, however, common for an offender to allege that an obsession or compulsion so dominated him that he was obliged to commit theft, assault or other crime with which he is charged. His account is usually found to lack the essentials of a genuine obsessive or compulsive act.'

Let me now quote the other point of view, in its modern form—almost indistinguishable from what Maudsley wrote sixty years earlier. I am taking the quotation from Henri Ey's *Etudes Psychiatriques* (1950).

'Tantôt, en effet, c'est l'envie horrible de tuer un être cher, le besoin d'accomplir un acte terrifiant, sacrilège or criminel ... la lutte atteint un degré d'angoisse horrible, l'obsédé se trouvant attiré par le vertige de son effroyable impulsion. Tel est le drame de l'obsédé assiégé par lui-mêmc et contraint par lui-même à sortir de ses retranchements ... l'énergie du système pulsionnel se distribue en circuits labyrinthiques et sans cesse renouvelés. Parfois, cependant, après de grandes et douleureuses tentations, l'impulsion passe à l'acte. Cet homme dévoré par le désir, par le besoin, par l'envie de tuer quelqu'un, extenué d'angoisse et de lutte épuisante, va brusquement s'emparer d'une planche que porte un passant inconnu et l'assomme dans un crise de sauvagerie incroyable.'

It is common ground that criminal obsessional acts are rare: the real dispute centres not round their possible occurrence, but about the limits within which impulsive acts can still be correctly regarded as obsessional; and, of course, the bearing of this on 'responsibility'.

Violent impulsive acts, if correctly diagnosed as obsessional, will fall in the primary division of obsessions, which I spoke of at the beginning: secondary devices of defence against an obsession are hardly likely to take the form of a violent assault or similar outburst. It is, of course, true that minor primary obsessions are yielded to, e.g. the anankast avoids stepping on the alternate paving-stones or touches the lamp-posts as he goes along. But where vital interests (as Ziehen called them) are concerned in the primary obsessional urge, e.g. to throw oneself from a height, they are almost never yielded to. It is, however, generally conceded that in some few patients, on an exceptional occasion, the anxiety engendered with or by the obsessional urge reaches such an acme that judgment, restraint and self-control are overwhelmed. There is, inevitably, room for dispute about the correctness of the diagnosis in each case of this kind, but a few such patients have been so closely observed and reported by very competent psychiatrists that the extremely rare occurrence can hardly be denied.

Sexual acts of a perverse kind figure prominently in the literature on this matter, as do acts of arson. Arson is evidently a much commoner crime in Germany than it is with us, and it need not detain us today. Sexual offences, however, are a familiar problem, as in the case described by East and Hubert:

'A youth of twenty-three years periodically would put his hand up the skirts of girl children with whom he had entered into conversation. Interference never went further than touching the girl's thigh. He showed evidence of an obsessional personality by experiencing periodic exacerbations just before the offence occurred. For some weeks he would have to touch doorknobs, etc., a certain number of times, and carry out all sorts of complicated touching rituals. He showed some tendency also towards compulsions of the safeguarding kind—concerning knives, fires, lights, and so on, but to a much less extent. There was little evidence of abstract obsessional thinking and no hand-washing symptom. His symptoms, during an exacerbation, had been enough to prevent him carrying on with his work at school and later at his occupation for a week or two. He clearly remembered the first occasion when he had interfered with a girl between four and five years of age. His description of the offence showed none of the features of the ordinary sexual offender. He fought against it throughout, became exceedingly anxious beforehand and felt no pleasure save for a colourless feeling of relief afterwards. On one occasion he went to a local police station when he felt the temptation very strongly and asked for a police-sergeant's advice—behaviour hardly seen in the ordinary sexual offender. He served two sentences and received psychotherapeutic treatment during both. During this he showed a typical obsessional reaction.'

East and Hubert, in another section of their report, examine the activity of the exhibitionist, and, with a convincing array of arguments, demonstrate that his impulsive conduct is not obsessional. This is in sharp contrast to the most recent writer on the subject, Rickles, who tells us (1950) that among 48 exhibitionists whom he had examined, 17, i.e. a third, 'had a definite compulsive disorder': Rickles later asserts roundly 'the exhibitionist is a compulsive neurotic by all accepted definitions'. He buttresses this pronouncement with arguments drawn from dynamic psychopathology: they seem to me wholly misconceived. A far more penetrating and authoritative writer, Professor Binder of Rheinau, has analysed the matter, with a wealth of clinical illustrations: I will quote only his comment on a schizophrenic exhibitionist who had compulsions of this nature, and then his general conclusion. After describing the patient's outburst—in which he exposed himself naked to a party of young girls—Binder says:

'Man sieht wie hier der exhibitionistische Impuls urplötzlich alle zwanghaften Sicherungen durchbricht und sich schlagartig in Tat umsetzt. Bei nicht-psychotischen Fällen haben wir nie beobachtet dass ein Impuls solche Zwangsmechanismen, die ihm inhaltlich entgegengesetzt sind, mit dieser elementarer Direktheit einfach durchstossen könnte.'

Then, speaking of criminal acts in general, and particularly murder and other crimes of violence, many of which he has reported, he sums up:

'Die forensische Bedeutung der Zwangshandlungen (ist) ziemlich gering, da vorbedachte, compliziertere Willenshandlungen wie auch eruptive Affiekt-und Triebentladungen—darunter fallen aber fast alle grösseren Verbrechen—niemals zwangmässing geschehen können. Nur einfache, kurzdauernde, in ihrem Bewegungsentwurf einigermassen bereitliegende, triebhafte Handlungen können zwangmässig ablaufen, und auch bei diesen kommt es nicht selten vor dass die starke Bremswirkung . . . die Handlung zum Stillstand bringt, bevor sie zu ihrem natürlichen Ende gelangt ist. Somit fuhrt die echte Zwangshandlung, zum Unterschied von der Impulshandlung, nicht zum Ausleben der in ihr sich regenden Triebe und hinterlasst darum nicht Befreiung, sondern Unbefriedigung und ängstliche Ratlosigkeit. . . . Delikte die echte Zwangshandlungen darstellen, gibt es nur bei Zwangsneurosen ohne psychopathische Grundlage und bei solchen auf Grund einer anankastischen Psychopathie.'

Binder rightly stresses a distinction which is of wider application, I believe, than only to obsessionals who commit an offence. He insists that the delinquent act derives not from the neurosis but from the personality of the delinquent. Just as, in the war, the presence of neurotic symptoms was of far less relevance to the military fitness of an individual than his personality and attitude to his symptoms, so here it is not the obsessional's illness but his personality which decides whether he will commit an offence. Although as a rule the man of anankastic character has a rigid morality which can be expected to protect him from giving social offence, Binder rightly points out that there is a formal, lifeless, artificial flavour about the moral outlook and conduct of some such people: with their petty scruples and their harping on principles, some of them can nevertheless in actual dealings with other people resort to underhand methods. Several psycho-analysts, like Fenichel and Alexander, have remarked on the specious morality, the 'corruptibility of the super-ego', that may be met in obsessionals. Of course this aspect of character is not an essential or even regular feature of the obsessional: but when it is present it can favour the occurrence of that rare event—a minor offence by an obsessional (such as stealing) which is a genuine obsessional act.

This brings me to the most familiar question in obsessional illness—its relation to personality. In no psychiatric condition is there a more obvious and specific association between illness and preceding personality than here, yet we meet people with severe obsessional symptoms whose previous personality revealed no hint of predisposition; and we meet people with pronounced, unmistakable anankastic personality who never become mentally ill, in that way or any other.

What is more, there is not one typical obsessional personality. Dr Johnson was an obsessional, if ever there was one: so was Amiel. Yet what a world of difference between the two men. I do not say that there was not some fundamental identity in their personalities; we know a great deal about both of them but not enough to confirm or disprove that assumption. The differences, however, are gross, and they are differences which we daily detect between the personalities of our obsessional patients, some exhibiting the psychasthenic personality, so hesitant, so indirect, others the determined, driving ambition, the passion for detail, the robust assertiveness of the successful anankast. Take a characteristic passage from Amiel's *Journal*: 'Indecision being my principal defect I am fond of a plurality of phrases. . . . I see too many ways of saying things: a more decided mind hits on the right way at once . . . I wonder whether I should gain anything by the attempt to assume a character which is not mine. My wavering manner, born of doubt and scruple, has at least the advantage of rendering all the different shades of my thought, and of being sincere. If it were to become terse, affirmative, resolute, would it not be a mere imitation?' . . . 'Slumber of the will, lapses of the vital force, indolence of the whole being—how well I know you! To love, to dream, to feel, to learn, to understand—all these are possible if only I may be relieved from willing. It is my tendency, my instinct, my fault, my sin. I have a sort of primitive horror of ambition, of struggle, of hatred. . . . Intellectual Epicureanism is always threatening to overpower me.' At this point you may feel disposed to interject 'Pooh! These are the aboulic complaints of an introspective, schizoid hypochondriac; why call him an obsessional?' But remember all those patients of Janet's, so admirably delineated, who were like this. And hear other passages from that famous *Journal Intime*: 'If we are to give anything a form, we must, so to speak, be the tyrants of it, we must treat our subject brutally, and not be always trembling lest we are doing it a wrong. . . . This sort of confident effrontery is beyond me. . . . And then I am always retracing my steps: instead of going forward I work in a circle: I am afraid of having forgotten a point, of having exaggerated an expression, of having used a word out of place. . . . I do not know how to sacrifice anything, how to give up anything whatever. Hurtful timidity, unprofitable conscientiousness, fatal slavery to detail.'

And he apostrophizes himself 'What is your own particular absurdity? Why . . . that you are always making preparations for nothing, that you live without living. Contemplation which has not the courage to be purely contemplative, renunciation which does not renounce completely, chronic contradiction—there is your case! Inconsistent scepticism, irresolution, not convinced but incorrigible, weakness which will not accept itself and cannot transform itself into strength—there is your misery.' I need not quote more extracts from Amiel to confirm that he was at once an obsessional and a sensitive psychasthenic. Neither need I quote from Boswell and Mrs Thrale to remind you of the contrasted personality of Dr Johnson—so positive and definite, so determined on victory, so indolent and so productive. No one, contemplating these two men, Amiel and Johnson, could deny their obsessional traits, or deny their manifest unlikeness. Is it then permissible to take them, and scores of others like them, and to abstract from them one obsessional personality-type, or for that matter, two obsessional types—'the one obstinate, morose, irritable, the other vacillating, uncertain of himself, submissive'? Kretschmer has dealt with the problem by saying that they have a combination of schizothyme-hyperaesthetic and cyclothyme-melancholic disposition with a strain of altruism. Neither he nor any other observer but Kaila, however, has, as far as I know, made the systematic observations on physique and personality which would test this guess. Here we encounter one of the bugbears of psychiatry—the lack of an acceptable method of describing personality. We have, of course, many ways of doing so, and of delimiting types, but none has earned general acceptance. Swedish observers, to whom we owe the best investigations into the distribution of personality types and neuroses in the general population, use Sjöbring's classification, in which subvalidity corresponds closest to the psychasthenic obsessional pattern of personality: but the diagnostic procedure they adopt makes it difficult to relate personality variables satisfactorily to morbid patterns. The studies of Eysenck, Cattell and other psychologists who have occupied themselves with the description and typing of personality have suffered through paucity of obsessional subjects: at all events they throw no light as yet on the varieties of personality that may precede an overt obsessional illness.

A Finnish study, by Kauko Kaila (1949), has been devoted to this question. Dr Kaila examined 85 people with obsessional neurosis: he made exact somatometric observations à la Kretschmer and a neurological examination; the patient filled out a personality inventory; performed a test of ability for conceptual or abstract thinking and another test of the tendency to dissociate or 'split'; Jung's word-association test, two tests of psychomotor behaviour (tempo and handwriting), and the Rorschach. Before he carried out this study Kaila had satisfied himself from the literature that (1) there is a strong hereditary component in obsessional neurosis; (2) among the chief personality features are strong affective ambivalence, strong ambition, morbid introspection, pedantic fussiness, general social shyness, tendency to feelings of inferiority and sexual anomalies; (3) the disorder often begins about puberty, in which case it pursues a chronic course leading eventually to poverty of feeling and some autism with lessening prominence of the symptoms; (4) obsessional phenomena can appear in neuroses, in psychopathic personality (in the continental sense), in the early stage of schizophrenia, in depression, and after brain damage, especially encephalitis affecting the brain stem.

With these distillates of his reading before him, Kaila set about the examination of his own large series. His findings are illuminating. He saw good reason to deny that the differentiation between compulsion neurosis and the Freudian 'anxiety-hysteria' is valid: indeed he dismisses it as artificial. So far as this refers to the phobic class introduced into the international nomenclature, I believe he is justified in rejecting it as an independent or useful category. His subjects showed remarkable differences in personality—23 were straightforward schizothymes; 3 were cyclothymes in Kretschmer's terminology; and the remaining 59 were rather nondescript. The careful review of anthropometric indices did not point to any bodily habitus associated with this illness. Whereas bodily indices of habitus gave the proportions 42 leptosome to 27 pyknic, the corresponding temperament measures (schizoid and viscous to cyclothymic) gave 50 to 76. Without dwelling on the results in detail of the other tests, it was evident that no single personality type was to be detected in these people: so far as the Rorschach results went, they spoke in the same sense: Kaila inferred that Rorschach's equation of psychasthenia or obsessional phantasies with introversiveness, and of obsessional acts with the extratensive type, did not come out well in his material, but as the dichotomy introversive-extratensive has not commended itself to Rorschach workers latterly (Phillips and Smith 1953), Kaila's finding need not surprise us. In sum Kaila observed that 14 of his subjects had no definite predisposing features in their personality prior to the actual obsessional illness: 65 showed what Schneider stressed as self-insecurity, some showing it in the anankastic form, others as sensitiveness, in the form described by Kretschmer in his well-known monograph. Twenty-one of the insecure people showed schizoid features.

Some of you will think this sort of approach to the problem of personality *vis-à-vis* obsessional illness ill-advised and frustrating, when the all-embracing concepts of anal-erotic character are already available to clarify and explain the seeming confusion. 'In different types of obsessional neurosis', you will say, following Schilder, 'the proportion of homosexual, anal, aggressive and magic pattern may vary, hence the varied aspects that seem to have bothered Dr Kaila'. But the psycho-analytical explanations are not, of course, simple, nor of uniform application. To continue with Schilder, who took a keen interest in these phenomena, we have not only the anal drive to consider: 'Although in the majority of cases the anal drive is dominant, I do not doubt that there are cases in which the neurosis is chiefly based upon oral and genital drives and on their transformation. . . . Hitschmann has stressed the importance of urethral tendencies. The question remains why drives become the basis for an obsession.' 'The obsession-compulsion neurosis in which motor phenomena are of proven importance and the obsession-compulsion neurosis in which the internal drives are paramount lead to very similar pictures.' 'There is a decided difference between cases of this group (with strong motor drives) and the group of cases in which one gets the impression that attitudes of the parents and the formation of the Oedipus complex are the main factors in the genesis of the compulsion and obsession neurosis.' As I do not wish to rush to the destruction that awaits those who talk of matters they don't know about, I shall abstain from considering the present psycho-analytic standpoint on obsessional character, though from reading I take it to be complicated, more so than when Ernest Jones and Abraham wrote their essays on anal-erotic character traits (1918, 1921).

For rather similar reasons I shall not speak of von Gebsattel's existentialist analysis of the obsessional's world, in which the sufferer is forever in action against his tireless energy, a world in which pseudo-magical forces of unsubstantial ruin and decay seem to threaten him, with no prospect of truce or, for him, of victory. Von Gebsattel's thesis, which dwells on hostile forces of corruption and dissolution, putrefaction and death, has much in common with Erwin Straus's, and brings the obsessional half-way along the road which the paranoiac travels.

Having reached the point where personality impinges on philosophy, it is not inappropriate to turn very briefly to the realm in which one of the salient features of obsessional personality, the surrender to doubt figures as a great danger. In religion belief matters so much, doubt can be such an enemy to spiritual wellbeing, that it is no wonder that the obsessional, racked by his conscience, tormented by uncertainty, yet plainly ill and plainly an unwilling victim of disbelief, worries the theologians. Confessors know him as a man of scuples. A scruple, originally, was a rough pebble, an irritant to the tender conscience; as Jeremy Taylor put it, 'a scruple is a great trouble of mind proceeding from a little motive'. Henry VIII used the word to describe his struggles with himself. 'Whiche thing ingendered such a scrupulous doubt in me that my mind was incontinently accombred, vexed and disquyeted.' But the more technical meaning now commonly given equates scruples with obsessional doubts having a religious content (and to some extent, with depressive self-reproaches also).

It is sometimes forgotten that distempers of this nature, so severe as to cause profound psychological upheaval or to affect permanently the course of a man's life, can nevertheless consort with great practical abilities and a faith that moves mountains. The anankast who regards his neurosis as a sufficient reason, or it may be excuse, for leading an empty inept life, punctuated by visits to his psychotherapist, has as a social creature nothing in common with the scrupulous—I suppose we should now say over-scrupulous—man of affairs, or creative worker, who, as the cliché puts it, has learnt to live with his obsessional symptoms. We know little about those who struggle without our help and make much of their lives; there are some famous men, however, who point the moral in giant letters. I would mention two of these—both men of religion, unequal in their scope and influence, but notable examples of what the obsessional can do, though tormented with religious doubts and fears.

First John Bunyan. In *Grace Abounding* he tells us of his struggles. In his childhood—at 9 or 10 years old—he had nightmares of damnation and was greatly afflicted and troubled with the thoughts of the Day of Judgment, and that both night and day, and would tremble at the thought of the 'fearful torments of Hell-fire'. Then at about 19, he

'... would go to the steeple-house and look on, though I durst not ring.... But quickly after, I began to think: "How if one of the bells should fall?" Then I chose to stand under a main beam, that lay overthwart the steeple, from side to side, thinking here I might stand sure. But then I thought again, "Should the bell fall with a swing, it might first hit the wall and then rebounding on me might kill me, for all this beam." This made me stand in the steeple door.... But then it came into my head "How if the steeple itself should fall". And this thought ... did continually so shake my mind that I durst not stand at the steeple door any longer, but was forced to flee, for fear the steeple should fall on my head.'

A little later,

'I could not rest content until I did now come to some certain knowledge whether I had Faith or no, this always running in my mind "But how if you want Faith indeed? But how can you tell you have Faith?" ... While I was thus considering and being put to a plunge about it ... the Tempter came in with this Delusion "That there was no way for me to know I had Faith but by trying to work some miracles"... Nay, one day as I was between Elstow and Bedford the temptation was hot upon me, to try if I had Faith by doing some miracle ... I must say to the puddles that were in the horsepads, "Be dry" and to the dry places "Be you puddles" ... but just as I was about to speak, this thought came into my mind, "but go under yonder hedge and pray first"...'

and so on: the story he is telling us has a familiar ring. Another time:

'I durst not take a pin or stick, though not so big as a straw, for my conscience was sore and would smart at every touch. I could not now tell how to speak my words, for fear I should misplace them. Oh, how cautiously did I then go, in all I did or said: I found myself as in a miry bog, that shook if I did but stir...'

Presently he was assailed by blasphemous thoughts.

For, about the space of a month after, a very great storm came down upon me, which handled me twenty times worse than all I had met with before: it came stealing upon me, now by one piece, now by another. First all my comfort was taken from me; then darkness seized upon me; after which, whole floods of blasphemies... was poured upon my spirit, to my great Confusion and Astonishment.... Instead of lauding and magnifying God the Lord with others, if I had but hear him spoken of, presently some most horrible blasphemous thought or other would bolt out of my heart against Him.... I often, when these temptations had been with force upon me, did compare myself to the case of such a Child whom some gypsy hath by force took up in her arms, and is carrying from friend and country. Kick sometimes I did, and also shriek and cry; but yet I was bound in the wings of temptation, and the wind would carry me away.'

Very seldom has an obsessional been gifted with such powers of vivid statement as Bunyan had, to tell us of his trials.

'Sometimes it would run in my thoughts, not so little as a hundred times together "Sell Him, sell him, sell him."... This temptation did put me to such scares... that by the very force of my mind, in labouring to gainsay and resist this wickedness, my very body would be put into action or motion, by way of pushing or thrusting with my hands or elbow, still answering.... "I will not, I will not, I will not..." At these seasons he (the Devil) would not let me eat my food at quiet, but, forsooth when I was at the table at my meat, I must go hence to pray.'

On another occasion:

'Then would I be struck into a very great trembling... I felt also such a clogging and heat at my stomach by reason of this my terror that I was, especially at some times, as if my breastbone would split asunder.'

When Bunyan was persuaded to go about the country preaching, his obsessions troubled him there also. 'Sometimes again, when I have been preaching, I have been violently assaulted with thoughts of blasphemy and strongly tempted to speak the words with my mouth before the congregation.'

Doubts not dissimilar from those that beset Bunyan agitated Martin Luther. When at Erfurt in 1517 he was celebrating mass for the first time as priest, he was overwhelmed by an acute anxiety and violent scruples, and he would have fled from the altar if the Prior had not stopped him. 'Ita horrui ut fugissem de Altari nisi fuissem admonitus per Priorem.' 'Ego cum Erfurdiae meas celebrarem primitias, fere mortuus essem quia nulla aderat fides sed tantum respiciebam in dignitatem personae meae ne essem peccator, ne quid omitterem.' This was the prelude to a depressive period in which he worried greatly for fear he had carried out some trifling act of commission or omission which would be a sin: blasphemous thoughts pressed in on him, the master of novices did his best to comfort him, both in conversation and in the confessional: at this time Luther wanted to confess daily and sometimes several times on the same day. He would come back and say he had not confessed properly, he had forgotten something, he had not felt genuine repentance: eventually his preceptor in the monastery had to discipline him for this. Once, with metaphorical intention but not the less significantly, Luther said: 'Je länger wir uns waschen, desto ärger wird es mit uns.' Like Bunyan he was beset by blasphemous thoughts: 'Oblivio dei primum, deinde sempiterna blasphemia. Hic enim cura et amor sui ipsius regnat impetuosissima et confusissima sollicitudine, ideo misericordiam dei non potest ante oculos suos videre. Quaerit enim effugium et non invenit, tunc mox involvitur odium dei ardentissimum cupiens primo alium deum, deinde se non esse, ac sic blasphemat summam majestatem. . . .' Attacks of acute anxiety occurred, with palpitations and profuse sweating.

It is unnecessary to consider more fully the other affective disturbances which Luther had at different periods of his life: several psychiatrists (including Moebius) have occupied themselves with the problem, and I do not doubt that he was a man of cyclothymic temperament subject to severe attacks of depression. But I have not brought in Bunyan and Luther just to provide brief pathographies and still less do I wish to attempt to reformulate their profound and far-ranging religious experiences as symptoms of psychiatric illness—such a devaluing transformation serves no purpose. What I want to emphasize is that we have here, in two men of genius, a malady, well known to theologians and to psychiatrists alike, which is most painful, whether we view it from the religious or the medical standpoint, which goes with or precedes phases of utter depair, and is yet compatible with a life of the utmost mental vigour and practical activity. I would not dwell on this point, which can be illustrated from the history of lesser men also, if it were not so often implied, or stated, that the man who has obsessional character and obsessional illness is a social invalid, whose treatment can be regarded as fairly successful if it leaves him a contented weakling, withdrawn from every contest except perhaps that which goes on during the therapeutic hour.

The obsessional patient is often pitiably unhappy: he needs whatever help we can give him. But in seeking to give that help we have to recognize the uncertainties that attend our treatment of the condition, making all the stronger our obligation not to do harm in one great department of the patient's life while we are helping, or hoping to help, him in another. Whether treatment is psychological or surgical, by drugs or by regime, bold or prolonged, there are dangers, not always faced and avoided, which are as serious as those ensuing upon medical neglect and apathy towards the disorder. In no condition is it more essential than in this to study the patient closely, to diagnose his illness with caution, to understand his values and possibilities, and to define limited objectives before embarking upon treatment.

REFERENCES

AMIEL, H. F. *Journal Intime*, 1882–4 (English translation, Mrs H. Ward, 1909).
BINDER, H. *Schweiz. Arch. Neurol. Psychiat.*, 1945, **55,** 1.
BOSWELL, J. *Life of Samuel Johnson*, 1791.
BUNYAN, J. *Grace Abounding*, 1666.
CATTELL, R. B. *An Introduction to Personality Study*, London, Hutchinson, 1950.
EAST, W. N. and HUBERT, W. H. DE B. *Psychological Treatment of Crime*, London, H.M.S.O., 1939.
EY, H. *Etudes Psychiatriques*, Paris, 1950.
EYSENCK, H. J. *The Scientific Study of Personality*, London, Routledge, 1952.
FAVEZ-BOUTONIER, J. and LANTER, R. *La Psychonevrose Obsessionelle. Encyclop. Medico-Chirurgicale*, 1955, 37370, A–10.
FREUD, S. *Collected Papers*, Internat. Psychoanal. Press, 1926.
HESNARD, A. *Evol. Psychiat.*, 1950, 391.
HOFFER, W. *Psycho-Analysis. Practical and Research Aspects*. Baltimore, Williams & Wilkins, 1955.
JANET, P. *Les Obsessions et la Psychasthenie*, Paris, 1903.
KAILA, K. 'Uber den Zwangsneurotischen Symptomenkomplex', *Acta. Psychiat. Neurol. Scand.*, 1949, Suppl. 57.
KRETSCHMER, E. *Körperbau und Charakter*, Berlin, Springer, 1948.
LEWIS, A. *Proc. Roy. Soc. Med.*, 1936, **29,** 325. (See also this volume, pp. 141–56.)
LUTHER, M. *Sammtliche Werke*, Erlangen, 1830.
MAUDSLEY, H. *The Pathology of Mind*, London, 1895; *Responsibility in Mental Disease*, London, 1876.
PHILIPS, L. and SMITH, J. G. *Rorschach Interpretation: Advanced Technique*, New York, Grune & Stratton, 1953.
RICKLES, W. H. *Exhibitionism*, Philadelphia, Lippincott, 1950.
ROSEN, I. *The Clinical Significance of Obsessions in Schizophrenia*, M.D. thesis, University of Witwatersrand, 1954.
RÜDIN, E. *Arch. Psychiat, Nervenkr.*, 1953, **191,** 14.
RÜMKE, H. C. *Folia Psychiat. Neurol.*, 1952, **55,** 3.
SCHILDER, P. *Amer. J. Psychiat.*, 1938, **94,** 1397.
SJOBRING, H. In Wretmark, G., *Acta Psychiat. Neurol. Scand.*, 1953, Suppl. 84.
STENGEL, E. *J. ment. Sci.*, 1948, **94,** 650.
STRAUS, E. 'On obsessions: a clinical and methodological study', *Nerv. ment. Dis. Monogr.*, 1948, No. 73.

8

A STUDY OF CRETINISM IN LONDON

WITH ESPECIAL REFERENCE TO MENTAL DEVELOPMENT AND PROBLEMS OF GROWTH

THE FOLLOWING investigation was undertaken for the purpose of studying the psychological effects of thyroid deficiency in childhood, and what benefit substitution therapy provided for the mental retardation. As the material accumulated other questions presented themselves (chiefly concerned with growth), and led to some alteration in the intended method of presentation.

METHOD OF ASCERTAINMENT

For the first problem mentioned above, it was desirable to examine patients who had definite retardation: a search was therefore made in the institutions for mental deficiency. The permission of the medical superintendents of Leavesden, Darenth, The Manor, The Fountain, Caterham, and Tooting Bec Hospitals made it possible to examine all the patients diagnosed as 'cretins' in these institutions for defectives, conducted by the London County Council. As they represented a population selected for defect, it was impossible to use them for an assessment of the beneficial results of treatment. By the co-operation of a number of physicians, attached to voluntary hospitals, a collection of cases diagnosed as 'cretin' or 'juvenile myxoedema' was obtained, which was not open to this objection. The bulk of the cases from voluntary hospitals came from two sources—the London Hospital and St Thomas's Hospital. The latter were out-patients—23 of them—whom Dr H. Gardiner-Hill put at our disposal for this investigation. The records of the London Hospital, when searched through for the last thirty-five years, yielded the names of 40 in-patients in whom the diagnosis of juvenile myxoedema or cretinism had been made. Besides the patients from St Thomas's and the London, and those

This paper was written with the assistance of Nancy Samuel (late psychologist at the Maudsley Hospital) and Janet Galloway (late research psychiatric social worker at the Maudsley Hospital). It is reprinted from the *Lancet* (1937), **1**, 1505–9 and **2**, 5–9.

found in the mental deficiency institutions of the L.C.C., others, less systematically collected, were got from various out-patient departments (King's College, The Queen's, Hackney-road, Paddington Green, and the Maudsley Hospitals). The Central Association for Mental Welfare was also approached; they supplied a list of patients, some of whom were available for examination. It was not possible to be sure that one had, by the above means, obtained a good sample of all those in London who have suffered from thyroid deficiency during childhood, but it seemed possible that the collection would include most varieties of course and treatment, as well as of severity of illness. In all, 145 cases were collected of whom 89 were examined. The remainder were either dead (6 cases), or unavailable for physical and psychological examination; in some of these latter, where the diagnosis had been beyond question, details of their family history, personality, etc., were obtained. Ten of the cases examined were rejected because the diagnosis was doubtful or definitely erroneous.

The ages of the cretins tested ranged from 3 to 58: eleven were 12 years old or less, twenty-three were more than 12 and less than 21 years old, fourteen were in the next decade (21–30), seventeen between 31 and 40, twelve between 41 and 50, and two were over 50.

INVESTIGATION

The patients were examined physically; they were inspected, the texture of the skin felt, and measurements, chiefly of height and hand dimensions, made. In 35 cases the impedance angle was measured by Mrs M. A. B. Brazier, Ph.D., at the Maudsley Hospital. A psychological examination was made in detail by one of us (N. S.): the Binet-Simon test was applied; where the degree of deficiency was very great, the Merrill-Palmer and the Gesell methods of assessing intellectual development were used instead. The Goddard form board, the Woodworth-Wells substitution test, and manikin, vocabulary, and reading and writing tests were also employed. The general demeanour of the subject and his attitude towards the examination were recorded and particular note taken of the speed of his performances—e.g., in tying a bow, and carrying out the Goddard form board test. Fuller inquiries were also made by one of us (J. G.), who visited the homes of the patients, and obtained from the relatives a detailed history which, together with the hospital records, gave a fairly complete picture of the patient's personality and development. The family history was also investigated. The condition of the mother in pregnancy, the type of birth, weight at birth, history of fits in infancy and childhood, ages of sitting up, walking, talking, teething, and the attainment of clean habits and of sexual maturity were among the data collected. Details of speech, as regards quality of voice, mispronunciation, and extent of voluntary usage of speech were also noted. Consideration of many of these details must be excluded here for want of space.

PHYSICAL FEATURES

The familiar signs of the condition were found to be present in differing degrees and combinations. Some of the cases were as typical as the illustrations in textbooks; others had a characteristic face, skeleton, and gait, but their skin and hair were normal. Those who presented difficulty in diagnosis were either free from nearly all the recognized physical features of the condition, or might have been cases of mongoloid deficiency. As regards the latter, in only one instance was there still doubt after careful examination; the balance of evidence favoured mongolism. The former, physically negative, cases, however, raised a difficult problem: were they to be included on the history alone? Inasmuch as some other cases, which had been previously diagnosed as 'cretins', were rejected after investigation—e.g., one was found to be a hydrocephalic idiot—it seemed partial to accept all these without present evidence of the condition. On the other hand, to exclude them would be to eliminate any case in which treatment had been entirely effective in clearing up the symptoms. A scrutiny of the hospital records written when the patient was first seen, and a detailed history from the parents, made it possible to include these cases—except a case of adult myxoedema. It may be reasonably concluded that all of the patients upon whom the following report is based had at some time in their childhood shown recognizable symptoms of thyroid deficiency.

The hope of correlating amount of treatment with persistence of physical signs proved vain. Except for skeletal changes, the physical features cannot be measured, and arc difficult even to rank in order of severity. The amount and continuity of treatment with thyroid can rarely be measured. Such data are therefore unsuitable for statistical analysis. There were other difficulties, which are discussed below in connexion with the effect of treatment and mental development. Such crude comparisons as could be made between treatment and disappearance of physical signs are given below, as well as the data concerning stature (see Table, pp. 188–9). It was found easier to compare physical measurements with mental measurements than to compare either with amount of treatment.

MENTAL FEATURES

Textbooks give meagre descriptions of the mental changes due to thyroid deficiency in early childhood. Slowness is the characteristic insisted on. Still says: 'Slowness of the mental processes is the most distinguishing mental feature of the cretin.... In temper he is usually amiable and placid, not to say stolid. He acquires clean habits, and is not destructive.' There is moreover some disagreement as to the effect of adequate treatment on mental development. Fordyce says, for example, that if careful treatment is commenced early and conscientiously continued, the children at the best may become indistinguishable, physically and mentally, from normal children—a view held also by Cockayne and by John Thomson—whereas Still, on this point, says that 'when the educational attainments of even the best of them are inquired into, they are obviously below the normal . . . some cases are reported to have become perfectly normal, but I think this must be very exceptional.' Many authorities agree with Still—e.g., Petterson, and Kimball and Marine. All writers hold that the mental improvement is seldom as satisfactory as the physical; spasticity is regarded as an ominous sign (cf. Rolleston). Some Austrian and Swiss investigators have gone more fully into the mental characteristics of cretins. The endemic form has been the more fully studied and reported in systematic treatises, because of the large material available. De Quervain gives a lively account, tallying with those of other writers. He stresses the slowness of the cretins, their conservatism and need for security, their good memory for places, their tendency to collect and hoard, to imitate others, and to like praise. They dodge trouble, love eating, and show little emotion, except when they have rare and brief outbursts of rage or brood discontentedly. As Maffei pointed out, they are by no means incapable of learning and reasoning, or of utilizing general concepts. But such observations cannot be taken as applying necessarily to the sporadic cases of cretinism under consideration in this paper. De Quervain, though he does not go as far as Zondek, draws a distinction between the two forms, and even describes mental differences between cretins who have a goitre and those who have not; he also thinks that many of the more engaging characteristics of the cretins under his care are those of the Alpine peasants in general, and are independent of the cretinism, though somewhat coloured by the cretin's optimism. In the admirably full description given by Gamper this point is stressed; the torpidity and other features of the cretins may be seen in a mild form throughout the local population. The writers emphasize, moreover, that no specific features can be found in the psychic structure and dynamics of cretins which would make recognition of the thyroid deficiency possible from the mental state alone; there is a torpor which is myxoedematous, and a defect, not accessible to thyroid therapy, which is attributable to arrest of cerebral development and changes in cerebral structure. This is also the view of Wagner-Jauregg.

In the literature of sporadic cretinism, very little is to be found about the details of the mental changes. Kornfeld, and Lazar and Nobel have made investigations, but it is doubtful whether the cretinism in their cases may not have been of the endemic sort. They found a great delay in the development of motor functions, such as grasping, sitting and crawling; to this they attributed much of the apparent mental impairment, since the child had not the usual early mastery of means of getting at grips with the environment by his movements, nor, when he did acquire it, had he the curiosity and other stimuli to use it. Lazar and Nobel say they know no case in which treatment has led to complete mental normality. Kornfeld, who carried out intelligence tests on a small number of cases, did not find parallelism between somatic and psychic effects of treatment, and he emphasized that the deficient auditory attention, poverty of ideas and associations, and few volitional acts of the cretin made special pedagogic training necessary if the best intellectual improvement was to be attained; by such training he was able to get improvement in understanding, reading, and talking. It seems probable, however, that the benefit from special education here is the same as that obtained in other forms of mental defect, whether general or special; it would not be required if hormone therapy had repaired the intellectual defect as well as it does the physical. Bronstein and Brown examined 20 children, and found the intelligence quotient to be below 70 in all but 2. Kimball and Marine considered that with adequate treatment cretins might reach a mental age of eight years.

In the investigation here reported, a description of the personality was first arrived at from direct observation of the patients during examination, and from detailed discussion of their traits with their parents, siblings, or others —e.g., nurses and doctors who knew them well. Often information was obtained from more than one such source.

The following description of one of the patients is a typical account of the more striking features of the personality of these people.

> 'She is exceedingly stubborn. When she is not humoured, or you cross her in any way, she will sit solidly in a chair for hours sulking. She is very slow to understand, or to do what she is told, however simple it is. She has no initiative; you have to tell her to do the same thing day after day. She rarely speaks of her own accord, but will sit mum sooner than ask for anything she wants. She is very particular about being clean and likes to have all her clothes tidy and fresh. She will do whatever you want her to if you promise her a reward. She is very pig-headed, and insists on having her own way in spite of all reason.'

Slowness was the characteristic most often remarked upon: it is recorded as a salient feature in three-quarters of the cases—'painfully slow; no idea of time, you have to prod her all the time'. Nearly a third of them were placid, though this depended somewhat on their circumstances; for example, some who at home had been spiteful and bad-tempered were contented when they got into the routine of an institution. It was noteworthy that only 4 of the 79 patients were reported to be of a depressive temperament: 2 were prone to attacks of excitement, with transient hallucinations when overdosed with thyroid, and many flared up if much provoked ('when I jawed at her she would fire up', as was said by the mother of one girl, who was mostly content 'to sit like a block'). Obstinacy was a frequent trait. Noteworthy, and little remarked upon by any previous writers, was the prominence of traits that are more common in obsessional patients than any others—excessive care about order and cleanliness, with a proneness to repeat their behaviour. This was conspicuous in at least a quarter of the cases and was in contrast to their general indifference and slowness. Thus one apathetic cretin was described as 'most painstaking and thorough and slow over everything she does. She must polish the stairs, although she has been told not to; she polishes an electric switch in a dark cupboard, although it can't be seen. She is always washing herself and her clothes.' A few others showed related attributes: they were thrifty, or given to hoarding trifles.

Half of them were fairly sociable or friendly. Hypochondriacal tendencies and suspiciousness also occurred, but had little or no relationship to the cretinism. Most of the patients showed the foregoing attributes more when they stopped taking their thyroid tablets. Inquiries about personality were made in another 18 patients, who were not available for examination, but whose medical history was that of unequivocal thyroid deficiency in childhood: of these no less than 15 were reported to be placid or apathetic, and 10 showed 'obsessional' traits.

PSYCHOLOGICAL TESTS

The most important feature of the psychological testing was the estimation of mental age by the customary Binet method, confirmed or replaced by the Merrill-Palmer test in those too low in the scale to be suitable for Binet testing: in 2 cases the Gesell method of testing infants was employed. The notorious difficulties in ranking adults by a Binet test would make it desirable

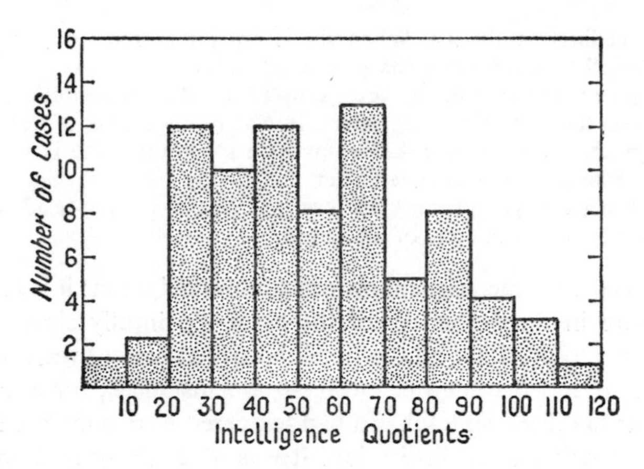

Fig. 1.—Distribution of intelligence, as measured by tests, in 79 cretins.

to give the scores in terms of 'mental age' rather than intelligence quotient, but as 10 of the subjects were less than fourteen years old they could not be included in such a series. It was, therefore, necessary to grade the subjects according to intelligence quotient. Owing to the unrepresentative method of selection, it would not be justifiable to compare the frequency curve of the intelligence quotients in these subjects with that which is obtained when a true sample of the average population is tested. It is, however, clear from Fig. 1 that, although the number of mentally defective people is high, no less than a fifth of the subjects had intelligence quotients which fell within the range of what is usually called 'normal'—i.e., above 80. Somewhat contrary to expectation there was in the individual cases no more scattering of successes over several years than is usually found when these tests are given to an average population. Certain special tests were, however, done better or worse than they might be by non-cretinous subjects.

As slowness seemed so striking a feature in these subjects, various tests were specially employed because speed was a factor taken into account in scoring them. Of these, the chief were the Goddard or Seguin form board, the Woodworth-Wells substitution test, and the numerous Merrill-Palmer tests in which time of performance determines the score—e.g., manikin, matching, cube-pyramid, pink tower, picture puzzles. By scoring these in terms of mental age it was possible to compare the speed of performance with the general level of intelligence (Fig. 2). In spite of the incompleteness

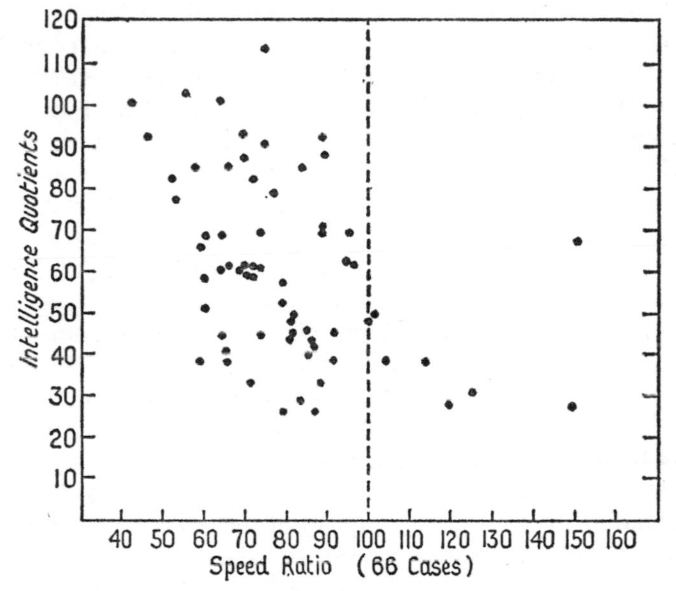

Fig. 2. Relation of speed to intelligence in a group of cretins.

$$\text{Speed ratio} = \frac{\text{mental age in speed tests}}{\text{mental age in intelligence tests}} \times 100.$$

of such a method it gives valuable information, confirming the clinical impression and showing that the slowness may be notable in those whose intelligence quotient is not far below normal or is actually normal; consequently such people may, in school and elsewhere, give an impression of greater deficiency in intelligence than is actually the case (cf. Ziehen). It is also evident that slowness in the performance of intellectual tasks may be greater than that exhibited in ordinary motility. This is in conformity with Kassowitz's observation that there may be remarkable improvement in motility after treatment, but it partly invalidates his view that the improvement in motility supplies a measure of the general psychological improvement.

The apparent lessening or even reversal of the disparity in some of the cases with low intelligence quotient is partly attributable to the preponderance, among intelligence tests at this level, of tests in which speed is an important factor, and to the figures employed in scoring and computing the ratio.

Vocabulary tests were also given to the subjects, and a similar procedure —i.e., comparison between mental age so estimated and mental age measured by the customary Binet tests—indicated that there was a slight superiority in respect of vocabulary over what is customarily found in non-cretinous persons. This is in keeping with the observations of de Quervain. Few of those with an intelligence quotient below 80 could articulate clearly: they slurred their consonants and in many instances used *F* for *Th*, and other childish mispronunciations. This was more common in those with severe defect, who also had, for the most part, husky, gruff voices, and little to say.

The results of the intelligence tests on this sample, which is not necessarily representative, do not in themselves indicate more than that some people who have thyroid deficiency in childhood can become intellectually quite normal, and that in this disease every gradation can occur from normality to idiocy. For fuller use of the findings, it is necessary to compare them with the age of onset of the illness, its severity, the adequacy of treatment (as to dosage, continuity, and promptness of administration after the onset of symptoms), and the other, i.e., physical, evidences of the disorder now evident. On many of these points certitude is unobtainable. Still less can the innate endowment of the affected individuals be assessed; it is not unlikely, for example, that a few of these people might have been of poor intelligence even if they had not had any thyroid deficiency. This last problem can best be met by considering the general level of intelligence in their family, especially among their siblings. The other points as to the illness and its adequate treatment have been settled, as far as was possible, by considering the details of their illness obtainable from hospital records and their parents' recollection, and then grading the cases as to adequacy of treatment on a five-point scale (see Table, pp. 188–9).

FAMILY HISTORY

1. *Familial intelligence.*—In 14 families there were one or, rarely, more members (parents or siblings) who were described as dull or feeble-minded, apart from cretinism. Of these, only six persons were certified defectives or imbeciles: in 4 families one parent was feeble-minded or dull, and in two cases a collateral was recorded as defective. These data are, of course, not complete, and are given mainly to indicate that the general level of intelligence may be assumed to have been average in the majority of the patients, had they not had thyroid deficiency.

2. *Thyroid disorder.*—Of the 'familial' incidence of thyroid disease it is not possible to say more than that, apart from 4 families in which there were two or more cretins, in five cases a sibling also had 'cretinoid' features, and in one case a sibling was hyperthyroid, in another a sister had a goitre; two had

myxoedema. In seven there were subthyroid features in the mother, in four they were present on the father's side: in one the mother had a goitre until the birth of the child, and in another the mother was hyperthyroid and her mother had had myxoedema. Many of the families were of short stature, so that there seems a possibility that a cretinoid constitution may predispose to the illness; the data do not warrant a conclusion.

3. *Familial cretinism.*—One of the 3 families in which several cretin members were examined is of interest (see L. H., F. H., and A. H., in Table, pp. 188–9). In this family there were four cretins, the most severely affected having died when 43 years of age. Eleven other children had died in infancy of causes unknown, and three were normal. The mother, an active woman, was slight in build though not short, but her features were cretinoid (her nose was flat, the eyes far apart, and the skin somewhat flabby). None of the other maternal collaterals nor members of the father's family were cretinoid or short. In another family with a brother and sister mildly affected neither the parents nor any collaterals showed cretinoid features or short stature. The female patient had been born during the war, when the mother was very anxious, and there was a history of fits in the mother's family. In the third family (where two brothers were cretins) the mother had a goitre, which disappeared at the birth of the elder cretin. There were seven other healthy children surviving to adult age, all successful in their work, and of good physique. One is a policeman. The father was also in the Metropolitan Police, and came of very healthy stock. One of the cretin's healthy siblings has, however, a strong facial resemblance to the elder cretin.

4. *Mental disorder.*—In 11 families there was a history of mental disorder (the diagnosis of which cannot now be determined); in 3, one or more siblings had fits; in 2, the siblings were deaf or deaf and dumb.

5. *External factors.* An external factor could seldom be discovered or held responsible for the disease: there had been a difficult or prolonged labour in 20 cases; one patient was syphilitic, another had had meningitis. It is noteworthy that 12 were reported as having had one or more fits, but only 2 of these were reported as having been born asphyxiated or after a difficult labour.

In an additional 18 cases investigated as to familial incidence of abnormality, there were 4 instances of fraternal imbecility, 2 of fraternal goitre, 1 of paternal cretinism. Late menarche in the mother was found occasionally here as in the larger group.

AGE OF ONSET

The age of onset can be determined satisfactorily only by medical records made at the time. Unfortunately, since most of these cases had been seen as out-patients, their records are no longer available, most hospitals destroying their out-patient notes after fifteen years. For those who were in-patients, or whose parents have photographs and other data less deceptive than their memory, some estimate can be made. It seems that definite signs of thyroid deficiency had been noticed by the doctor or parent before the end of the first year in twenty patients, of whom the intelligence quotients were found to be still low, varying between 70 and idiocy which defied measurement. In ten more, signs had been noticed before the end of their second year. The latest recorded ages of onset among the remainder were 8, 9, and 12, the corresponding intelligence quotients being respectively 69, 80, and 102. It looks as though, other things being equal, the earlier the onset the worse the outlook; but the data are, as already pointed out, unsatisfactory, and closer inspection of the details of the early history as recalled by the parents suggests that signs of thyroid deficiency could probably have been noted very much earlier than they had been in the majority of the cases. This is also indicated by a large number of instances in which walking and talking were acquired later than the third year (just two-thirds of the cases). Clean habits were remembered as having been attained before the end of the third year in only a third of the cases; in 31 others there was delay, in the rest it was not recorded.

INTERVAL BEFORE TREATMENT

In ascertaining the interval before treatment began there are much the same difficulties as in regard to the preceding question. In 26 cases treatment had been instituted promptly—i.e., less than a year after symptoms were first noticed. At the cost of anticipating some other points as to adequacy of treatment, it is worth recording here that in one case where treatment had commenced when the patient was only four months old, and had been continued with scarcely any interruption since, the intelligence quotient is now only 34, and that in another whose symptoms appeared at the age of eighteen months and were immediately treated, the intelligence quotient is only 27, though thyroid administration had gone on steadily ever since; moreover, as a paradoxical instance of the opposite kind, a man who showed some symptoms soon after birth had no treatment until he was thirty-one, and yet has an intelligence quotient of 63. There are cases in the series where symptoms had been noticed before the age of three, no treatment had been instituted for ten years or more, but the intelligence quotient is within normal range; the most striking instance being a girl with an intelligence quotient of 101, and typical cretin appearance, whose symptoms began during the first six months of life, yet she had no treatment until she was eleven, and then it was stopped for good after a year. It would be a manifest error to conclude from these cases that treatment is as effective when tardy as when prompt: it is, however, legitimate to suppose that in some cases conspicuous physical evidence of cretinism may not be associated with gross mental deficiency, irrespective of whether treatment has been given at all, or been started late. The relationship of physical to mental retardation of development is discussed below, as is also the adequacy of treatment.

RELATIONSHIP OF MENTAL TO PHYSICAL DEVELOPMENT

Fig. 3 shows the relation of height to intelligence quotient. The individual figures are given in the Table on pp. 188–9.

There was no reason to suppose that the physical and the mental development would in these cases have run parallel, or that standing height is the best criterion of defects of physical development. If it be assumed that thyroid deficiency leads to an arrest of development, the comparable data would be those of children. The correlation here is sometimes made between intelligence quotient and actual height, sometimes between intelligence quotient and the comparable relative measure—i.e., the deviation from the

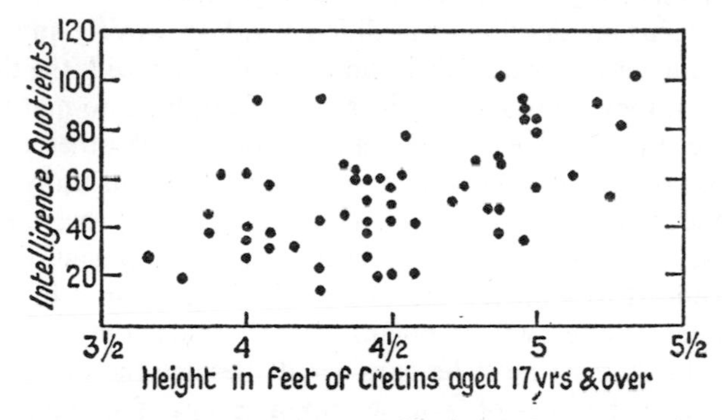

Fig. 3. Relation of intelligence to standing height in a group of cretins.

average height for each age-sex group. There is a slight positive correlation, varying between 0·14 ± 0·03 (Murdock and Sullivan), 0·45 ± 0·026 for boys, 0·3 ± 0·028 for girls (Dawson), and 0·22 ± 0·036 for gifted boys, 0·21 ± 0·38 for gifted girls (Terman). There is, in short, a definite but slight correlation between height and intelligence in children.

It is, however, unsafe to assume that the effect of thyroid deficiency is to arrest development as a whole; it may only retard development and its effect may be selective on different organs and functions. On these matters there is a large body of evidence.

Before attempting to make in cretins a similar comparison to that just quoted for healthy children—viz., between a mental measure of development, such as the intelligence quotient, and a physical one such as height—it is advisable to consider the differential nature of growth in the body, and the distinction between growth and development. Growth cannot be regarded as a unitary process in the organism. It varies in different parts, and the rate of growth of various parts is dependent on that of others. Growth is an aspect of development, the coarse structural expression of it. Growth does not occur in a steady progression; the rate of growth of various organs and groups of organs is not only different but varies for the same organ during different periods of life. Four types of development have been described: neural (brain, cord, eye), lymphoid (intestinal lymph masses, thymus), genital (testes, ovaries, prostate, uterine tubes, seminal vesicles), general (body as a whole, respiratory and digestive organs, kidneys, aorta and pulmonary trunks, blood volume, spleen, musculature and skeleton). There are other heterogenic types among which are the curves of development of the suprarenal glands, the hypophysis, and the thyroid. The hypophysis and the thyroid both show a fairly constant increment from birth to maturity, 'with little indication of more rapid growth in infancy, nor, surprisingly, a parapuberal acceleration' (Scammon). The relative increment of the hypophysis is less in post-natal life than that of the thyroid, but the form of the curve is the same. Although there are the figures of Rössle, Wehefritz, Arndt, and more recently Freeman to show the weight of the adult thyroid gland, no data are available for patients with juvenile myxoedema.

Different organs are developing at different rates; scarcely any do so with a constant increment for age. This is, however, the case with the thyroid and the hypophysis: they show a steady increment from birth to maturity. These glands each exert an influence on the development of other organs. One might suppose that they themselves developed at an intrinsically determined rate, independently of other organs. However this may be, the extent to which these steadily growing glands influence the development of other parts can be determined by studying the effects of ablation. Since in man precise studies of differential growth of organs after thyroidectomy are impossible, the evidence in animals must be considered. Besides the many reports on amphibia, there is the work of Hammett upon groups of albino rats in whom the thyroid was removed at 23, 30, 50, 65, 75, and 100 days respectively and the organ sizes and weights determined and compared with those of unoperated controls. It was found that the relative retardation of growth which ensued increased with the age of the animal; this did not mean that the actual level of development attained was necessarily lower in the animals operated on later than in the earlier ones. Moreover, it was found that the central nervous system and the eyeballs were resistant to the retarding effect of the thyroid loss; their growth was less retarded than that of the body-weight but approximately the same as that of the body length. The reverse was the case with the lungs, heart, liver, kidneys, spleen, adrenals, and pancreas; in some of these there was not merely greater retardation than that of the body as a whole, but even retrogression. The hypophysis showed accelerated growth. It is doubtful whether these observations on the rat can be applied in detail to the phenomena of thyroid insufficiency in man. They indicate, however, that the influence of the thyroid on the growth of other organs is to produce a distortion of differential development; they suggest also that the degree of sensitivity to thyroidectomy in a group of organs is related to their normal growth coefficient. Hammett denies this, but on unconvincing grounds, as Huxley points out.

In these studies it is the increase in size of organs that has been used as the criterion of rate of development. Functional development has not been measured. A parallelism between development of function and size of organs is not easy to establish. In the case of mental functions it is especially difficult to correlate their development with that of the organic substrate.

A structural change in an organ (usually enlargement) during development will be an expression of alteration in the size of its cells, their number, and the proportion of different kinds—i.e., it expresses enlargement, multiplication, and differentiation. Together with this there will be a manifestation of entirely new functions or an alteration of previously manifest function, which may be qualitative or quantitative. In the case of the thyroid gland, for example, only a quantitative development of function need be considered (i.e., more thyroxine is secreted): in the case of the central nervous system, on the other hand, all the possibilities of functional development are realized. In considering the differential growth of organs, it is necessary to take into account their dependence on other organs, and relationship with them, and the fact that integration is itself a feature of development. This is still more necessary if functional development be considered; not only organ systems must be regarded, but the whole organism in relation to its tasks; mental development can only be assessed by considering what the environment requires of the organism, and this is true also, to a great extent, of respiratory, cardiac, alimentary, and other part-functions.

It is therefore irrational to attempt a correlation between level of mental development, which is a measure of function, and level of physical development—e.g., stature—which is a measure of structure, unless one assumes that structure is itself a measure of function, or that some other constant and measurable relationship obtains between all structure and function in the organism. This assumption is impossible at present, as the central nervous system clearly illustrates; even if the most refined methods of histological and chemical investigation be employed, we are still unable to show a constant measurable relationship between the functional capacity and the structure of normal tissue. In the case of abnormal tissues, such a correlation can in some instances be established. It may therefore be permitted, on empirical grounds, to attempt to relate the disordered function of people with thyroid deficiency to their disordered structure.

There is, however, still another difficulty here. The thyroid is not the only influence upon development. There is the pituitary, there are other endocrine glands, there are exogenous factors such as food and vitamins (cf. also Wendt); there are complicated mixtures of endogenous and exogenous factors, as in renal dwarfism; a physically or mentally defective creature may be unable, because of his defect, to get adequate nutrition, and so he becomes stunted. These possible influences are disregarded or taken as constant when one compares subthyroid patients with each other or with normal people; some of the influences, if operative, will have a differential effect on various structures and functions, so that they would complicate the relationship between particular features of cretinism. The growth of the pituitary in thyroidectomized animals (Zeckwer, Davison, Keller, and Livingood) and in subthyroid human beings lends support to the view that the symptoms of myxoedema in childhood are not due solely to the thyroid loss, excluding other endocrine changes; it is not known whether the hypophyseal growth after thyroidectomy mediates or mitigates the effect of the operation. Moreover, the thyroid itself is only a mediator; setting the tempo, rather than supplying the main stimulus. The body tends to develop along certain lines, hereditarily determined, modifiable by the environment, and worked out through variables which may be disturbed artificially (e.g., amputation of an organ or interference with its function causes other organs to develop differently); removal of, say, thyroid secretion causes the whole organism to develop differently, but still not without regard to its genotype, its inherent one of development. Thus it is to be expected that the loss of the same amount of thyroid secretion at the same stage of development would have very different results on the intellectual level of two boys, one of whom had hitherto been an imbecile and the other gifted. One cannot ignore individual differences which are irrespective of thyroid deficiency when assessing the effects of such deficiency.

It is, moreover, false to assume that all the phenomena of subthyroidism or athyroidism are in the nature more or less of complete arrest of development. This is not uncommonly taken for granted in regard to the intellectual disturbance. The phenomena are indicative in part of a perversion of function or degeneration: this is strikingly seen in the myxomatous changes from which the condition derives its name. The changes in the ossification of the bones are another illustration; it is not as if they remained those of a child. The signs of myxoedema, as it occurs in adult life, are by no means entirely the same as those of the condition occurring during the phase of rapid development; they are metabolic and trophic, rather than developmental. It is true that development is a process which does not cease after adolescence, and that decay itself is part of it, but the relative stability of structure and function during adult life, and the relatively very slow tempo of change then, justify the above distinction. The phenomena of adult myxoedema are in part those of juvenile myxoedema or cretinism, and it might be supposed that the differences between them, obtained by subtracting the former from the latter, represented the effects of thyroid deficiency upon development. They may be due to arrest of development, or to a perversion of functions that would not be possible if development had slowed down and stability been reached. The latter changes, there is ground for supposing, are less reversible than the trophic and metabolic changes found also in adult myxoedema: the myxomatous condition of the skin, for example, responds far more to substitution therapy than the skeletal changes. The length of time that there has been thyroid deficiency during childhood is of far more importance as regards response to treatment than in the adult form of the illness. When assessing, in this investigation, the parallelism between different functional or structural effects of the deficiency, it has been impossible to ignore the factor introduced by delay in commencing treatment as well as by long interruptions in treatment (cf. Canelo and Lisser).

Finally, before attempting to compare mental measurements with stature, it is necessary to consider that the chief material substrate of mental function, the central nervous system, is of rapid growth in size, especially during the first few years, and that in this respect it is resistant to interference—e.g., by ablation of the thyroid in animals. Todd, pointing out that the brain reaches approximately full dimensional growth in six years or less, and that mental growth thereafter cannot parallel physical progress, concludes that up to the present no statistical correlation is practicable between physical growth and mental development, but that the course of each can be studied and collateral progress noted. It is, moreover, possible for development in weight to go on without concomitant development in higher functions; the brains of adult imbeciles cannot be differentiated by their weight from those of normal persons. The researches of Scholz and Zingerle, and of Wegelin, do not disclose any difference in weight between the brains of cretins and those of the rest of the population. Microscopic changes have been described but are by no means specific (Lotmar, Kena-Apajalahti). There is consequently a wide gap between the level of mental development, measured by the customary tests, and the level of neural development, measured by weight, size, or architectonics. This is what might be expected; it indicates how difficult it is to compare 'mental' levels with others, as Gesell has emphasized. The general question of our methods of measuring function, especially mental function, is not suitable for examination here. Accepting these methods, the curve of mental development has been found by Richardson and Stokes to correspond to the Gompertz equation, $y = Ca^{b^x}$ where y is the growth at time x; C is the amount of growth at maturity, and b and a are constants; but that the growth curves of the abilities tested by different test-items are distinct from one another, though clustering fairly closely about the mean curve. Since, however, different tests are employed at different ages, and their standardization is attained by working out a mean, a growth curve here is a dubious affair. The same difficulties are met with if mental development in other than intellectual respects be considered. Psychosexual development, for example, cannot be measured, though a rough parallelism between it and the development of the gonads can be recognized.

Any correlation made between the level of mental development, as measured by the Binet-Simon scale, and the standing height of the patients is therefore a statistic that is partly invalidated by the uncertainty and unsuitability of the data from which it is derived.

INFLUENCE OF TREATMENT

Much of what has been said above has a bearing upon the evaluation of treatment. Clinically, however, it is important to know whether patients who are treated promptly, adequately, and continuously, do well, or, if not, what other factors must be considered as having influenced the outcome.

Table showing Patients arranged in order of Intelligence Quotients, with columns after them, showing Height, Degree of Physical Signs, Adequacy of Treatment, and Age of Recognition of Symptoms (in 1st year, 2nd year, or later)

Patients' initials	*Age*	*I.Q.*	*Height*	*Physical signs*	*Adequacy of treatment*	*Symptoms first noted*
			ft. in.			
G. J.	9	116	—	1	A	L.
M. A.	27	103	5 4	1	A	L.
H. P.	38	102	4 10½	3	E	L.
C. L.	16	101	3 10½	2	E	L.
B. A.	13	94	4 3½	2	E	L.
K. E.	26	93	5 2½	1	A	2 yr.
F. H.	50	93	4 0½	3	E	L.
L. I.	17	92	4 11½	1	A	L.
F. T.	22	89	4 11½	3	C	L.
G. M.	17	88	4 11½	1	B	2 yr.
G. T.	11	87	—	2	C	L.
R. J.	16	86	4 4	2	C	L.
W. E.	23	86	5 0	2	B	L.
A. S.	38	83	5 3½	1	C	L.
B. G.	12	83	—	1	A	2 yr.
W. P.	23	80	5 0	1	A	L.
L. S.	43	77	4 6½	3	C	? 2 yr.
H. E.	12	72	—	1	C	L.
J. M.	7	70	—	1	A	L.
S. E.	18	70	4 10½	1	D	1 yr.
C. W.	12	70	—	1	C	1 yr.
Go. A.	11	69	—	3	D	2 yr.
N. C.	26	69	4 10½	2	B	L.
V. E.	32	69	4 9½	1	D	L.
L. H.	53	67	4 4	3	E	L.
R. E.	22	64	4 4½	2	C	2 yr.
H. F.	40	63	4 1	3	C	1 yr.
B. M.	30	62	4 0	3	D	L.
D. F.	40	62	5 1½	2	C	L.
G. G.	42	62	4 5½	3	C	2 yr.
A. H.	47	62	3 11	3	E	L.
M. E.	24	61	4 5½	2	E	?
C. M.	27	61	4 6½	3	E	1 yr.
R. F.	31	60	4 5	1	E	L.
F. C.	47	59	4 6	1	C	2 yr.
T. E.	42	59	5 0	1	C	L.
E. E.	32	58	4 1	3	B	1 yr.
W. G.	34	57	4 9	1	E	L.
R. C.	27	54	5 3	3	C	1 yr.
C. E.	41	52	4 5	2	E	L.
N. B.	31	51	4 8½	1	D	1 yr.
D. J.	21	50	4 6	3	E	L.
M. B.	6	49	—	2	B	1 yr.
R. J.	41	49	4 10½	2	E	L.
B. V.	32	48	4 10	2	C	L.
K. A.	40	46	4 4	3	E	L.
L. H.	28	46	4 11½	2	E	1 yr.
G. M.	20	45	—	3	C	L.

Patients' initials	*Age*	*I.Q.*	*Height*	*Physical signs*	*Adequacy of treatment*	*Symptoms first noted*
			ft. in.			
S. J.	42	45	3 10½	3	E	L.
H. A.	19	44	4 6	3	E	1 yr.
M. G.	24	44	4 3	3	D	? 2 yr.
B. P.	21	42	4 7	2	E	L.
S. L.	32	41	4 5	2	E	1 yr.
E. M.	43	40	4 0	3	D	2 yr.
J. A.	30	39	3 10½	3	E	? 1 yr.
K. D.	20	39	4 5	2	E	1 yr.
S. M.	20	39	—	1	D	L.
B. E.	24	38	4 10½	1	—	L.
T. A.	36	38	4 1	2	E	L.
O. L.	19	34	4 0	1	B	1 yr.
C. N.	3	33	—	1	B	?
G. L.	34	32	4 1	3	E	1 yr.
T. J.	21	32	4 2	1	A	1 yr.
W. H.	16	32	3 0	3	C	L.
M. J.	11	29	3 5	1	E	1 yr.
R. M.	58	29	3 8	3	C	L.
T. B.	14	29	3 7½	2	C	2 yr.
B. F.	33	27	4 0	3	E	? 1 yr.
S. R.	14	27	4 4½	3	C	L.
C. G.	49	24	4 3½	3	E	2 yr.
K. M.	17	22	4 5	3	C	1 yr.
S. A.	24	21	4 6	1	C	L.
K. M.	31	21	4 7	2	E	? 1 yr.
S. R.	16	21	3 11½	3	D	1 yr.
M. F.	40	20	4 5½	1	E	?
R. A.	27	20	3 9½	1	E	1 yr.
C. S.	6	16	—	3	D	2 yr.
B. G.	26	13	4 3	1	E	L.
D. E.	16	—	3 8	3	A	1 yr.

N.B.—Adequacy of treatment is reckoned on a five-point scale of descending efficiency. A–E (see below).—Physical signs of cretinism are reckoned as (1) slight or indefinite; (2) moderate and definite; (3) marked. L. = later, i.e., after second year.

In some of the cases in this series an exact record of their treatment was available, as well as a definite history as to the time when symptoms of the condition had first been noticed. In others the position was less clear. Many of them had been treated in the out-patient departments of hospitals which discard their out-patient records after ten or fifteen years, so that no medical data about the patient had survived; others had taken their tablets off and on, some with intervals of many years between medication, others with a capricious indifference that defied any precise statement as to quantity or duration of treatment. It was often impossible to discover whether the doses were of whole or desiccated gland substance.

With the data available, treatment was rated on a five-point scale:

A: representing prompt, continuous treatment;

B: treatment promptly undertaken and continued with only brief interruptions until adult life;

C: treatment begun a year or more after the first appearance of symptoms, but carried on pretty continuously thereafter, or treatment promptly undertaken, but carried on only at long intervals until adult life;

D: treatment begun a year or more after onset and carried on only at long intervals, until adult life;

E: no treatment at all during the first twenty years of life.

The accompanying Table shows the subjects arranged in order of intelligence quotient, and classified according to adequacy of treatment, age, height, degree of physical signs, and age of recognition of symptoms (in first year, second year, or later).

It is evident that a majority of those with an intelligence quotient of above 70 had had fairly adequate treatment, but that it was by no means impossible for those who were treated promptly and continuously to remain grossly defective. In short, adequacy of treatment is an important, but not always a decisive, factor in determining the mental level attained.

There were five patients who remained grossly defective in spite of prompt and continuous treatment. One of these could not be assessed on any intelligence tests. (The statements about treatment in this case may have been incorrect as the mother had left the home. Little or no history could be obtained about the mother or her collaterals. The birth was instrumental.) In three of the remaining four cases a difficult birth was recorded; in addition, one had a spinal deformity, another had been a difficult feeding problem in infancy, but in all three the possibility of some brain injury at birth must be considered. In the remaining case there was nothing in the family or the clinical history to account for the mental backwardness.

The five patients whose intelligence quotients were good in spite of little or no treatment showed, with one exception, well-marked physical signs of cretinism. One patient (aged 38), who had had no treatment, had an intelligence quotient of 102. He had been diagnosed as juvenile myxoedema at 12 years, but, judging from the history, had shown physical signs of cretinism as an infant, and at the time of this study showed well-marked signs. No family history was available in this case. Another patient (aged 16), with an intelligence quotient of 101, had also shown physical signs from infancy, but had only had one year's treatment, from 11–12 years; the birth was reported to have been difficult; there was nothing of note in the family history. Another patient, with an intelligence quotient of 94, had had no treatment until 13 years, and very little for some years since; his mother had cretinoid features. Familial cretinism and cretinoid features in the mother were present in the fourth case (F. H.), described elsewhere. Her intelligence quotient was 93; she had well-marked signs of cretinism but had had no treatment. The fifth case showed only slight signs of cretinism and had had treatment from 3–11 years continuously; her intelligence quotient was 70.

In the foregoing the possibility of information about treatment being erroneous has to be borne in mind. Moreover, treatment may have been prompt and continuous, yet the doses given inadequate: Nobel lays stress on this point. And, finally, there were doubtless differences in the degree of the hypothyroidism—in some total athyroidism, in others mild deficiency—and differences in age of onset which were important, but which could not be evaluated in this study.

SUMMARY

Seventy-nine patients who had been treated for cretinism were examined. Detailed psychological tests showed that it is possible for cretins to become mentally normal. The occurrence of other psychological features, including traits of personality commonly called 'obsessional', was established. Comparison of present intellectual level with treatment received indicated that promptness and continuity of thyroid administration were not alone decisive in determining whether or to what extent the child would remain backward. A few who had normal intelligence quotients had had inadequate treatment; a few with low intelligence quotients had been treated regularly from the time their symptoms appeared. In the majority, however, there was a rough correspondence between adequacy of treatment and intellectual level attained. The other factors which influence psychological attainment were apparently the stage of development at which symptoms of thyroid deficiency appeared, the degree of this deficiency, the hereditary endowment of the child (as it might be inferred from the intellectual level and other specific features in his family), any cerebral damage either at birth or in infancy, and the environmental influences (including special education). Problems of development, as assessed in the somatic and the psychological spheres, also presented themselves in the inquiry and are discussed.

REFERENCES

BRONSTEIN, I. P. and BROWN, A. W. *Amer. J. Orthopsychiat.*, 1934, **4**, 413.
CANELO, C. and LISSER, H. *Endocrinology*, 1935, **19**, 21.
COCKAYNE, E. A. in Garrod, Batten, Thursfield, and Patterson's *Diseases of Children*, London, 1934.
DAWSON, S. *Spec. Rep. Ser. med. Res. Coun. Lond.*, 1931, No. 162.
FORDYCE, A. D. In L. G. Parsons and S. Barling's *Diseases of Infancy and Childhood*, London, 1933.
FREEMAN, W. *Hum. Biol.*, 1934, **6**, 489.
GAMPER, E. In Bumke's *Handbuch der Geisteskrankheiten*, vol. 10, Berlin, 1928.
GESELL, A. *The Ontogenetic Patterning of Infant Behaviour* (Biology of the Individual), Baltimore, 1934.
HAMMETT, F. S. *Quart. Rev. Biol.*, 1929, **4**, 353.
HARRIS, H. A. *Lancet*, 1931, **1**, 691.
HARRIS, J. A., JACKSON, C. M., PATERSON, D. G. and SCAMMON, R. E. *The Measurement of Man*, Minnesota, 1930, pp. 173–215.
HUXLEY, JULIAN. *Problems of Relative Growth*, London, 1932, p. 186.
KASSOWITZ, M. *Wien. med. Wschr.*, 1902, **22**, 1049.
KENA-APAJALAHTI. *Acta Pediatr., Stockh.*, 1928, **7**, Suppl. 2, 42.
KIMBALL, O. P. and MARINE, D. *Ann. Intern. Med.*, 1930, **14**, 569.

KORNFELD, W. *Über die geistige Entwicklung hypothyreotischer Kinder bei spezifischer Behandlung*, Berlin, 1926. (Quoted by Nobel, Kornfeld, and Ronald.)

LOTMAR, F. *Z. ges. Neurol. Psychiat.*, 1929, **119**, 491.

MAFFEI. *Der Kretinismus in den nordischen Alpen*, Gotha, 1790. (Quoted by de Quervain and Gamper.)

MURDOCK, K. and SULLIVAN, L. R. *Amer. phys. Educ. Rev.*, 1923, **28**, 209, 276, 328 (see Harris, J. A.).

NOBEL, E., KORNFELD, W. and RONALD, A. *Schilddrüsenerkrankungen im Kindesalter*, Vienna, 1935.

PEARL, R., GOOCH, M., MINER, J. R. and FREEMAN, W. *Hum. Biol.*, 1936, **8**, 92.

PETTERSSON, A. S. *Acta Pediatr., Stockh.*, 1932, **14**, 263.

DE QUERVAIN, F. and WEGELIN, C. *Der Endemische Kretinismus*, Berlin, 1936.

RICHARDSON, C. A. and STOKES, C. W. *The Growth and Variability of Intelligence*, London, 1933.

ROLLESTON, H. *The Endocrine Organs in Health and Disease*, London, 1936.

RÖSSLE, R. and ROULET, F. *Mass und Zahl in der Pathologie*, Berlin, 1932, p. 71.

SCHARFETTER, H. In Bumke's *Handbuch der Geisteskrankheiten*, vol. 10, Berlin, 1928.

SCHOLZ, W. and ZINGERLE, H. *Z. Heilk*, 1907, **27**, 57.

STILL, G. F. *Common Disorders and Diseases of Children*, London, 1927.

TERMAN, L. M. *Genetic Studies of Genius*, vol. 2, p. 168, California, 1925.

THOMSON, J. and FINDLAY, L. *Clinical Study and Treatment of Sick Children*, Edinburgh, 1933.

TODD, T. W. *The Progress of Physical Maturity and Mental Expansion in Childhood* (Biology of the Individual), Baltimore, 1934.

TODD, T. W. and WHARTON, R. E. *Amer. J. Anat.*, 1934, **55**, 97.

WAGNER-JAUREGG, J. In *Handbuch der Psychiatrie* ed., *Aschaffenburg*, Leipzig, 1912.

WENDT, H. *Münch med. Wschr.*, 1935, **82**, 1679.

ZECKWER, I. T., DAVISON, L. KELLER, T. B. and LIVINGOOD, C. S. *Amer. J. med. Sci.*, 1935, **190**, 145.

ZIEHEN, T. *Die Geisteskrankheiten des Kindesalters*, Berlin, 1926.

ZONDEK, H. *Die Krankheiten der endokrinen Drüsen*, Berlin, 1926.

9

ASPECTS OF PSYCHOSOMATIC MEDICINE

PLUTARCH BORROWED from an earlier writer the statement 'If the body sued the mind for damages, the mind would be found to have been a ruinous tenant to its landlord'. Psychosomatic studies have been an extended homily on this text, pointing to the bodily havoc which emotional disorder can produce. There is, of course, a counter-accusation, in which the mind arraigns the body for giving rise to deliria, dementia and many more subtle disturbances.

The matters turn on two fundamental questions—the mind–body relationship and the nature of causality. Philosophical theories about these difficult issues would not call for mention here if it were not that many papers on psychosomatic questions show a strong implicit bias towards a particular theory—most commonly towards a Cartesian interactionism, and towards assuming a causal force at work which brings physical and psychical phenomena into regular conjunction or succession. On the problem of causality, little need be said. Hume's famous arguments in favour of relations of time and place from which we can infer a causal relation but cannot directly perceive it, still hold good but when they are applied to psychophysical relations they create great difficulties for those psycho-analytical investigators who work with concepts of mental energy, borrowed from nineteenth-century physics. As so many of the writers on psychosomatic subjects have been psycho-analysts, this is a considerable problem; they try to translate libidinal flux into physiological flux and imply a causal nexus. It is difficult enough (even if one forgets that causes are multiple) to admit the notion that the quantity of energy in a psychic cause must be equivalent to the quantity of energy in the psychic effect which it produces. As Boring says, 'we must dismiss the notion that psychic causality deals with the interrelation of separate substantial mental things. . . . There is no mental energy nor any other all-pervading concept to which everything psychic can be reduced. Therefore we must understand that there is no equivalence intended when we speak of

Reprinted from *Recenti Progressi in Medicina*, (1954), **16**, 434–53.

psychic causality.' How much more necessary to guard against implying or assuming such equivalence in the transition from psychic to physical events and vice versa.

The mind–body problem in psychology and psychiatry has been predominantly a mind–brain problem. The great nineteenth-century controversies were variations on the theme 'Brain as the Organ of Mind'. But where emotion was concerned a mind–viscera relationship occupied attention, especially after William James and Carl Lange had stressed the vasomotor, muscular and visceral changes which may follow simple apprehension and which, as they believed, may bring about the corresponding emotion. James held that the bodily changes 'are so definitely numerous and subtle that the entire organism may be called a sounding board' and he denied any special brain centres for emotion, though he held, of course, that conscious perception of the visceral changes was a cerebral function. Insufficient though the theory was, it had the great merit that it called fresh attention to the widespread bodily accompaniments of emotion, giving force and precision to the epiphenomalist views of Cabanis and Bichat. Descartes had, indeed, also emphasized the role of viscera in emotion, relating the lungs, liver, heart, stomach and intestines specifically to certain passions, though his notions of animal spirits mediating the process of reciprocal interaction between brain and viscus were a moribund relic from Greek speculations. Greek influence in this had been very powerful. From the *Timaeus*, the *Nicomachean Ethics* and the *Enneades* of Plotinus, and right on to the *Summa*, we find the bodily accompaniments of an emotion regarded as its material consequence and expression—a bodily movement secondary to the psychical apprehension.

There is then ample evidence that the connexion between emotion and bodily events had always caught the attention of thoughtful minds and that the degree of specificity in the association, especially between the subjective experience of emotion and its visceral accompaniments, was a matter of special interest from the time of Descartes and Malebranche onwards.

Such interests were closely linked with the acceptance of psychophysical parallelism as a working hypothesis. The strictly dualist point of view has lost so much ground in this century, however, that the 'double aspect' theory may be regarded as the prevalent one; it fits well with the operational point of view, and the old controversies about monism and dualism can be discussed as pseudo-problems. It is of course clear that psychodynamic formulations such as those of Freud, cannot stand up to operational criteria at present. If logical positivists exercised ruthless editorial power over scientific publications, a considerable section of psychosomatic literature would be annihilated. But in spite of philosophical confusion and semantic looseness, the subject has been advanced.

DEFINITION

Stanley Cobb has written, with good reason, that 'the idea of a dichotomy between mind and body has become so ingrained in the thinking of most persons that "psychosomatic" expresses to them what emotions can do to the body, as if emotions were something apart and supernatural. The conception is intellectually sinful, but at present no better word seems to be forthcoming', and he defines psychosomatic medicine as that field of clinical medicine in which psychiatrist and the internist can advantageously work together in the study and treatment of disease. This is an operational definition, to be sure, but on the one hand it depends too much on the outlook of the particular psychiatrists and internists who might co-operate, and on the other hand, it is, as Cobb recognizes, too comprehensive. Moreover, it ignores the essential contributions to be made by the physiologist, the psychologist and the experimental pathologist. It is best to recognize that 'psychosomatic' refers to an ill-defined area of interest, with constantly changing boundaries, in which there are manifest relations between events best studied by psychological methods and events best studied by physiological methods. Many of these events will be such as can be studied by methods of both kinds, according to the aspect from which the events are viewed. Any disease qualifies for psychosomatic study as soon as someone makes out a prima facie case for believing that sustained or violent emotional disturbance play a part in causing, aggravating, or maintaining the localized morbid process that is characteristic of the disease in question. If this view is accepted, the reverse situation does not fall within the psychosomatic range, i.e. tissue changes or metabolic anomalies which cause, aggravate or maintain a psychological disturbance (emotional or otherwise) are not psychosomatic. Such a distinction might justly be dismissed as a verbal quibble, or an attempt at unduly sharp cleavage between complex and interwoven phenomena, if it were not that without this arbitrary separation almost all psychiatry and a large segment of internal medicine would fall to be considered psychosomatic. The difficulty of applying it, however, shows how transitory should be the life of such a vague term as 'psychosomatic' which reflects only a rather muddled phase of specialized ignorance. When all medical students receive as satisfactory a training in psychology as in physiology, and all doctors appreciate fully the psychiatric as well as the physical aspects of illness, the advantages of creating a special 'psychosomatic' division of medicine will be less evident than a present, though research in it may then be more general and more exact.

METHODS

These have been concerned with demonstrating.

(*a*) that a characteristic type of personality and physique is associated with a particular pathological condition of the body;

(*b*) that a conflict, emotional upheaval or environmental 'stress' has closely preceded the onset of a pathological condition;

(*c*) that conflict or emotional stress produces under experimental conditions physiological changes which could, if severe or repeated, contribute to the development of a pathological condition;

(*d*) that a particular organ or function in a particular individual is especially liable to respond to psychological stress by exhibiting pathological changes;

(*e*) that continuous study of the psychological and the somatic happenings in an individual shows such regular concomitance and succession that the somatic happenings can be predicted from knowledge of the psychological happenings at a particular time;

(*f*) that the somatic pathological condition clears up, or improves, when psychological treatment is administered, or emotional strain is otherwise removed;

(*g*) that epidemiological characteristics of the somatic disease (such as its seasonal fluctuation, sex-ratio and age incidence) conform to those of indisputably psychogenic or 'functional' disorder;

(*h*) that the disease co-exists so frequently with a psychiatric disorder that a common cause or nexus may be assumed;

(*i*) that animal studies demonstrate that morbid tissue change can be induced regularly by 'emotional' stress;

(*j*) that no physical causes provide as plausible an explanation of the occurrence of the disease as psychological causes can, though direct evidence of the action of the latter is lacking.

When these lines of approach are scrutinized, it is evident that they are by no means all equally cogent. It is also apparent that without rigorous application and strict control, many of them could lead to a false conclusion.

The most frequently employed methods in the early phases of psychosomatic inquiry were biographical study (to determine personality-type and the timing of emotional crises), anthropological measurement (to determine constitutional somato-type), psycho-analytical study of psychic structure and conflict, and observations on the effect of psychotherapy. During this phase of inquiry it was not uncommon for a disease to be suspected of being 'psychosomatic' because a clinical picture of almost identical form could be presented by patients in whom no pathological tissue change could be found and the evidence for psychogenesis was strong: bronchial asthma, migraine and peptic ulcer were examples of this mode of approach. It represented the reverse side of a coin, on the obverse of which was the search for a physical cause and an organic pathology for such illnesses as effort syndrome.

During this earlier phase of psychosomatic studies, extremists went to great lengths in claiming that physical diseases were psychogenic; George Groddeck was probably the boldest of these. In justice to such adventurous thinkers it must be remembered that they were out-and-out monists who did not attach to the ill-defined word 'psychogenesis' the narrower meaning it commonly bears. The danger in their speculations lay in the belief that by psychotherapy many physical diseases could be prevented or cured—a standpoint close to that of Mrs Mary Baker Eddy. In the customary dualist view of the world, as understood in the 'double-aspect' theory, the somatic changes of disease must be described in physical language; the unbridgeable transition between physically and mentally viewed phenomena may well be recognized in some distances, just as it remains most obscure or practically irrelevant in others. The pragmatic strength—and the metaphysical weakness—of the 'double-aspect' manner of describing and relating phenomena lies in its ready acceptance of the interplay and sequence of physically viewed and mentally viewed processes in the individual, the physical or mental view being allowed to predominate according to the adequacy of our physical or mental theoretical formulations and concept language. The error of the extremists lay in their insistence on one all-embracing aspect—the psychodynamic—which could not be used to describe such sequences as the histologist and the biochemist know. Nor could it reveal that morbid biological processes, e.g. in a neoplasm, are changed and corrected if the patient is psycho-analysed.

In the more recent phase of psychosomatic study, work has been more exact on the physiological processes and psychosomatic correlations have been more critically reviewed. Instead of the numerous reports that were published stating the psycho-analytical findings in patients with supposedly psychosomatic disease and assuming without further evidence that a *possible* psychogenesis of symptoms connoted a *certain* psychogenesis of the disease the more valuable psycho-analytical studies now distinguish what is plausible from what is probable, and seek to relate physical to psychological happenings in a significant way that can be checked. Coincidence in single cases is no longer confounded with correlation in a series of cases, nor are the over-schematized distinctions made by Alexander between neuro-vegetative mechanisms and voluntary neuro-muscular and sensory mechanism accepted without question. For the assessment of personality not only the clinical biographical method and the psycho-analytical but also the refined devices of the psychologist are employed. It is now seen to be necessary that a control series should be compared with the group exhibiting the disease under study, and that statistical methods of analysis should be used on appropriate data. Instead of making psychogenesis the touchstone—the unreliable touchstone—of psychosomatic illness, and psychopathology the major object of research in such disorder, the emphasis is placed on the varieties of associated somatic and mental responses that the human organism may offer to life-situations. This change of outlook was well indicated in the Symposium on Life Stress and Bodily Disease (1950).

Peptic Ulcers

It is convenient to begin with this condition since it has received the closest attention and exemplifies the different approaches.

The 'ulcer diathesis' was a widely held assumption; whether this diathesis could be recognized by physical habitus, psychological constitution or lowered threshold for localized disturbance of gastric function, was not as a rule clearly stated. Julius Bauer and Draper were two noted champions of this constitutional biological inferiority of the stomach and duodenum as the central prerequisite and inferred that there is also a 'neuropathic constitution' involving an abnormally excitable autonomic nervous system; Draper, like Viola and Pende, paid much regard to anthropometric features—the 'Linear type'—and proceeded to a detailed study of the personality, hoping to find correlations between the physical and the mental constitution that predisposed to ulcer. His examination of a group of patients showed that almost all feared to lose the affection of their mother or some substitute for her, that a majority (84%) felt insecure and inferior, were jealous and aggressive (65%), and (in about half the cases) were worried about problems of sex. Moreover, half the subjects compensated by extra effort for their sense of inferiority. Draper speculated about the psychosexual constitution of the patients, whom he supposed to be showing a masculine protest against female components in their make-up. The conspicuous weakness of this study (apart from the unwarranted assumptions about sexuality) lay in its failure to demonstrate that these findings were necessarily connected with peptic ulcer; they might be equally often found in groups of people with other diseases or no disease. The same objection could be made to Alexander's psycho-analytic investigations, based on a smaller number of patients, and without a control series.

Alexander, after psycho-analytical study of three patients with gastric neurosis, and six selected because they had duodenal ulcer and were suitable for his method of investigation (presumably eager for psychotherapy), concluded that gastric symptoms are connected with 'intense oral-receptive tendencies' and a more or less repressed wish to be loved. The oral tendencies were opposed to the desire for activity and independence so that a conflict was generated. Alexander was no longer concerned with the constitutional features in the patient's personality, but with the conflict within his personality which appeared to determine his ulcer. Alexander referred to a single patient who lacked the drive and ambition often found in people with peptic ulcer, and added, 'This one example shows that it is the thwarting of receptive cravings and not a certain personality-type that is of primary importance.' Reliance upon a single patient or a few patients is a characteristic weakness of psycho-analytic investigators. The symbolic value of an ulcer is brought out in Alexander's assumption that the oral-receptive traits betoken a regressive tendency, which leads the patient back to his infantile wish to be fed, and so puts his stomach constantly into the state of readiness for food.

There have been similar studies of patients with peptic ulcer which were held to confirm Alexander's view; thus Kapp, Rosenbaum and Romano found intense parasitic dependent desires, with resultant conflict, in every one of twenty patients with peptic ulcer whom they examined. These studies, however, are open to the same objection as Alexander's own. Alexander, however, adheres to his formulation, though in his most recent exposition of his views he conceded that 'similar emotional conflicts involving dependant receptive urges are found in individuals who do not suffer from any disorder of gastro-intestinal functions. Still unknown co-existing local physiological or anatomical factors must be assumed to explain pathological developments as a result of this type of emotional conflict situation.' One of his pupils, Szasz, assumed a concomitant disturbance of the activity of the salivary glands and of the lower bowel, but his tendency to slip backwards and forwards between psycho-analytical and anatomical language makes it difficult to give his findings much weight.

Alexander's contribution, which may be regarded as an outstanding example of the psycho-analytical approach to the problem, made a bold bid for a specific psychodynamic constellation which should account for the site and nature of the tissue change. It cannot be said that his effort has been successful; he has not demonstrated that his conflict-situation is specifically related to peptic ulcer (he has merely shown that it could be, if psycho-analytical theory is accepted) and he has had to recognize that other causal factors may be of as much or more importance than these which he stresses. Neither in respect of another, more general feature of his psychosomatic theory has he been wholly fortunate. He insists that there are two fundamentally different types of (somatic) symptom-formation, viz. conversion as in hysteria, and vegetative neurosis (of which peptic ulcer is a salient example). The hysterical conversion symptom he maintains is an attempt to relieve an emotional tension by some symbolic expression, whereas the vegetative neurosis is not a substitute expression but a physiological concomitant of emotion, which becomes chronically established when the conflict remains unresolved. But conversion symptoms may be exhibited in damaged or inferior locomotor and other systems under voluntary control; they may pass from the voluntary to the involuntary expression (as when an hysterical girl over-breathes and so develops tetany with convulsions as her patterns of behaviour in given situations); and they may fail, even on thorough investigation, to reveal a symbolic content, as was often observed in the hysterical symptoms of soldiers in the late war; conversely, Alexander's own formulation of the mechanism whereby peptic ulcer can develop reveals it as a displaced expression of desire to be fed and loved, and suggests that the visceral symptoms have a psychic content, so to speak.

Another line of inquiry was concerned with demonstrating that some disturbing experience had occurred so shortly before the onset of ulcer symptoms that it should be assumed that the stress had precipitated the pathological changes in the stomach or duodenum. Here there were many isolated observations and clinical impressions, but a systematic inquiry with a control series was called for. This was provided by Davies and Wilson who compared 205 patients who had peptic ulcer with 100 who had hernia. Whereas 84% of the ulcer patients reported a recent emotional stress, only 22% of the hernia patients did so. Stress had taken the form of a threat to the patient's security. When the patients were followed up five years later, 52 recurrences were recorded, and of these 42 had been preceded by some distressing experience. When every allowance was made for the introspective tendency, the greater co-operation and the cause-seeking rationalizations which might be met in a group of people with peptic ulcer, these findings point strongly to a stress-precipitated illness. But here again caution proved necessary. When Emery and Monroe carried out a similar inquiry on a much larger population, they found that great emotional stress had preceded a recurrent attack of ulcer in only 258 of their 1,279 patients. Strong and Spencer discovered sufficient evidence of preceding stress in only 33 out of 189 patients; Slater and Gainsborough in only 10 out of 130 males (though in females the percentage who reported recent stress was 37%). It is therefore by no means certain that a close time relation between stress and ulcer is so frequently found that it can be considered to show a causal relation. The discrepancies between different investigations possibly depend on different methods of eliciting and checking the information about stresses, as well as on varying social factors, such as are likely to have influenced the war-time figures of incidence. It was shown by Harris and Titmuss and others that the incidence of ulcer varies with population density, social class and occupation, and that it would be unsafe to attribute the rise in the number of perforating ulcers among males in London during the heavy air-raid period to stress, since many other possible factors were also at work, and a similar rise was observed in Scotland and Sweden where there were no raids or comparable experiences. The most one can infer from existing studies of this type is that social and emotional stresses very likely precipitate or aggravate, but do not alone suffice to evoke peptic ulcer activity. The interesting study by Doll and Avery Jones illustrates the contingent and suggestive nature of the evidence. They found that peptic ulcer occurs significantly more frequently among foremen, managers and executives in industry than if they were no more prone than people in other occupations; the added burden of responsibility which they carry seems the most probable common factor explaining this, though the qualities of personality which lead to their promotion may also be concerned.

The studies so far considered have pretty well taken the somatic process for granted, and have concentrated on evidence pointing to psychological conflict and stress. But much of the stimulus for modern psychosomatic research has come from the physiologists—notably from Pavlov and Cannon. These men worked with laboratory animals, and demonstrated that situations involving a response in the animals which could best be described in the language we use for human emotions—fear, rage, pain—were accompanied or followed by visceral responses which if long sustained could conceivably be expected to lead to a morbid tissue change. Since Alexis St Martin had been studied by Beaumont, no one had made detailed and regular observations on a human subject, though relevant information had been accumulated by test meals, radiography, gastroscopy, and direct observation of fistulous subjects. It remained for H. G. Wolff to seize the opportunity and thereby provide a model for the experimental study of psychosomatic diseases; or rather to put it more correctly, for the experimental study of the visceral concomitants of emotion in human beings, which might provide a basis for postulating the pathogenesis of certain 'psychosomatic' diseases.

The study of fistulous subjects enables the gastric functions to be observed almost as easily as the skin or tongue. Beaumont had noted that fear, anger and other passions dulled the gastric mucosa and made it sometimes go red and dry, sometimes pale and moist, while inhibiting gastric secretion. Schrottenbach likewise observed in two subjects with gastric fistula that latent unpleasant affect would reduce or abolish secretion, and that pleasant affect had the opposite effect. Bogen conducted in 1907 a conditioning experiment on a child three and a half years old who had a fistula following oesophageal stenosis, and he observed that when the child was disappointed and angry because she was given no meat, the normal flow of her gastric juice did not occur even if she was then given meat to appease her. Hornberg made kindred observations on a boy five years old who had a gastric fistula. By means of hypnosis Heyer and others obtained like data by passing an oesophageal tube into the stomach, and Wingate Todd in the course of extensive radiographic examination of medical students demonstrated that severe disappointment, fear and worry reduced gastric motility, whereas long-continued anxiety provoked hyperactivity. H. G. Wolff's studies of Tom are now classical. In this man life situations and the consequent emotion could be utilized rather than the pale artefacts of emotion which the experimenter usually had to be content with in his human subjects. Fright, shame and gloom were accompanied by pallor of the gastric mucosa and decreased activity; anger, anxiety and hostility, on the contrary, were associated with humid, reddened mucosa, very active secretion and increased motility. Experiments carried out in the same laboratories on other patients, some normal, some with duodenal ulcer, indicated that unpleasant affect was mostly associated with a rise in acidity and in motility which lasted longer and was larger in the ulcer patients than in the normal subjects. These phenomena could no longer be produced by emotion in one patient, after he had had a bilateral vagotomy, though his stomach still responded with hyperaemia to food. Szasz, Kirsner, Levin and Palmer (1947) made similar observations, suggesting that it is through impulses conducted by the vagus that the reactions of the stomach to emotion are mediated.

Since Harvey Cushing revived Rokitansky's suggestion about the cerebral causation of gastric ulcer, the pathways connecting brain and stomach have been assumed to convey impulses of emotional provenance, which may betoken, as V. Bergmann suggested, a disturbance of autonomic balance, though as Gellhorn has lately emphasized, there is evidence indicating that in aggressive or defensive reactions, predominantly sympathetic impulses are sent out from the posterior hypothalamus. Recent work has shown 'how much more complex the downward discharge is than Cannon assumed it to be. Indeed there are few physiological—i.e. reversible—reactions of the organism which involve as many organs and systems and as profound changes as are seen in emotion. No wonder that repeated exposures to these effects are apt to alter the reactivity of the person (neurosis, etc.) and even induce permanent anatomical damage in various organs.'

The last clause of this passage contains the Achilles heel of the explanation. We have no experimental evidence in animals, and only suggestive evidence, or plausible hints, in man to bear out the statement that repeated emotional disturbance produces not only reversible changes in particular organs but also lasting tissue damage. Wener and Hoff have reviewed the relevant data, and it is plain from their account that acute damage to the diencephalon can produce acute disturbance and anatomical lesions in the stomach and duodenum, just as Fulton and Davey have demonstrated that in dogs and monkeys there is an area in the frontal lobe cortex which, upon stimulation, can elicit increased gastric secretion. There are evidently intracerebral pathways which are as important as the vagus in mediating this effect.

Mahl produced a state of inert terror in dogs and monkeys by daily electrical shocks, and found that whereas acute fright did not raise the hydrochloric acid output in the stomach, chronic terror did do so; he rightly pointed out that Cannon's emergency theory could not be extended to apply to a chronic emotional state.

An intermediate study of the protracted effect of anxiety was recently published by Heller, Levine and Schler, who induced mild anxiety in ten patients and showed that the free and total gastric acid secretion remained elevated for a period of twelve hours: as soon as the anxiety was relieved, the acid fell to normal values. The finding, of course, does not throw any light upon the development of a chronic ulcer.

More informative was the study of Margolin, carried out intensively over a period of two years. The subject was a woman with gastric fistula, whose gastric secretion was inhibited by anger or fright. In contrast to the behaviour of the male patient studied by Wolff, Margolin distinguished between conscious emotion (felt by the patient and inferred by observers from her expression and utterances) and unconscious mental content, especially in so far as it was aroused by the physiological observations regularly made upon her. He found that anger produced different gastric patterns of activity according to the psychic (libidinal) origin and aim of the anger. Much depends on the reliability of his psycho-analytical observations; a check was afforded by the association between gastric pattern and unconscious mental pattern which Margolin reports to have been close, repetitive and predictable.

A well-designed experiment was carried out by Poser, to determine by means of objective psychological tests whether patients with duodenal ulcer exhibit the specific personality traits attributed to them by Alexander and others. Thirty patients with duodenal ulcer, thirty with ulcerative colitis, and thirty healthy control subjects were examined; they had been matched in respect of age, sex, intelligence and educational status. Tests of neuroticism, level of aspiration, suggestibility, persistence, sensitivity to pain, reaction time under conditions of stress (motor conflict), galvanic skin response, Rorschach and Thematic Apperception tests were given. Careful statistical analysis showed that the duodenal ulcer patients differed significantly in several respects from the patients with ulcerative colitis, the latter showing more neurotic features, less tolerance for pain, greater sympathetic response to psychological stimuli, more suggestibility, compliance with authority, whereas the patients with ulcer resembled the normal subjects in degree of suggestibility, threshold for pain and sympathetic response; they had rather rigid emotional control, were preoccupied with success, and had difficulty in establishing social relations.

Hamilton applied statistical procedure to a number of characteristics found in four groups of 50 male patients suffering from respectively, duodenal ulcer, gastric ulcer, non-ulcer dyspepsia, and no alimentary disorder. The only dimension of personality which was found to differentiate one group from another was concerned with anxiety traits: and this distinguished, not so much between ulcer patients and controls, as between patients with gastric ulcer and patients with duodenal ulcer, the latter showing more anxiety, as did also the non-ulcer dyspeptics. The interest of this inquiry was methodological, since Hamilton used refined statistical methods for analysis of variance. Hecht, taking account of the ambitious striving personality attributed to ulcer patients, gave a level of aspiration test to thirty subjects with this disease and to thirty others with ulcerative colitis. The ulcer patients obtained higher scores than those with colitis. The finding would be more impressive and convincing if an adequate sample of healthy persons had also been studied. Marquis, Sinnett and Winter used projective tests (the Blacky Pictures, Rorschach, T.A.T.) as well as the Goodenough Draw-a-person and the Guilford-Martin Gamin tests. Interpreting these according to the slightly intuitive methods usually employed for projective tests, they found common features—oral fixation, feelings of inferiority, sexual maladjustment, dependency and tension—and two types of reaction—a 'primary' type in patients who accepted and recognized their needs and dependency, and a 'secondary' type in patients who denied or repressed these needs. A more cautious and critical study has been made in Sweden by Wretmark. In this survey of 164 patients (130 with duodenal ulcer, 34 with gastric ulcer) checked by an adequate control series, he found that those with duodenal ulcer were more intelligent, more syntonic, more energy-saving (reserved, conservative, relentlessly diligent but easily fatigued) and more unsteady than the controls; when the conservative tendencies came into conflict with unsteady, impulsive trends, autonomic imbalance was more common. Duodenal ulcer more often ran a serious course when the patients were of non-syntonic personality; in such patients it also appeared at an earlier age and their relatives had a higher incidence of peptic ulcer. Wretmark infers a heredity determinant of duodenal ulcer in these non-syntonic subjects.

There remain to be considered the social factors which vary from culture to culture, and are different in their impact upon men and women, children and adults, rich and poor. The findings of Morris and Titmuss, already referred to, represent a recent development of epidemiological and sociological inquiries, to which Halliday has given a considerable impetus. The best-documented study of the social history and background of patients with duodenal ulcer is that of Ruesch. He concludes that ulcer is a disorder of modern civilization, occurs primarily in the middle class and especially among those who are trying to climb into a higher social class; they belong to the semi-skilled, clerical, professional and executive occupational groups, they have a longing to conform, to achieve success, and to be liked; they live in small groups keeping to themselves; and their attacks are precipitated by situations in which the patients are changing from one culture pattern to another, are separated from someone on whom they depend, or are frustrated.

It is very common to assume that if an illness has been shown to depend largely on psychological causes, it will respond to psychological treatment. This fallacy is often evident in statements about psychosomatic illness: either it is urged that extensive psychotherapeutic facilities should be set up in general hospitals to provide for the needs of the psychosomatically ill, or it is argued that the beneficial results of psychotherapy in such conditions have proved their psychogenic nature. It is easy to show dialectically that this line of thought is a naïve product of that dualistic thinking which the enthusiasts of psychosomatic medicine usually repudiate, and equally easy to show empiricially that in the familiar neurotic disorders demonstrable psychopathology by no means connotes demonstrable psychotherapeutic accessibility. As to the need for psychotherapeutic facilities in general hospitals, the arguments in favour of this are very strong: but they depend not on the psychogenesis of the psychosomatic disorders but on the co-existence of neurosis with many physical diseases—whether psychosomatic or not—and on the inevitable psychological problems that arise in all sickness and may call for more or less expert attention. The argument from psychotherapeutic responsiveness deserves closer attention. If, for example, patients with peptic ulcer recover while receiving psychotherapy, it may be impossible to prove that the psychotherapy was chiefly or solely responsible, since dietary, medicinal, social and inadvertent psychological influences were also likely at work on the patient at the same time. But if it can be safely inferred that the psychological treatment was the main factor producing recovery, it lends much force to the argument that in studying and treating this disease, we do well to forget Morgagni and Virchow returning instead to the Hippocratic ways of regarding the whole man instead of his affected organ, and in fact confining ourselves pretty much to the psychological aspect of his history and treatment. It is therefore important to discover how much benefit in fact can be attributed to psychotherapy in peptic ulcer. A. C. Ivy has recently looked closely into the matter. Accepting the view, very widespread in the United States, that psycho-analysis is the most effective method of psychological treatment, he addressed a questionnaire to American psycho-analysts asking what their experience had been in the treatment of peptic ulcer. It emerged that 80% had not treated any such patients, that those who had were dealing with patients who had overt neurotic symptoms (such as are usually found in no more than a fifth of any large sample of patients with ulcer), and that of the twenty-seven patients treated, some had failed to persist with their treatment, others were not indisputable cases of ulcer, and that after all, only three patients could be discovered who were free from symptoms eighteen months after the conclusion of psychotherapy. This inquiry, it is important to recall, was concerned only with treatment by psycho-analysts; the number of patients who received supportive, suggestive and other varieties of psychological treatment would be much larger. But *a fortiori* it must be admitted that the benefits of psychological treatment in peptic ulcer are still open to question: it may well be that environmental adjustment, e.g. at work and at home, may be more efficacious than intensive psychotherapy, or that alterations in smoking, drinking alcohol and dietary habits, are of greater consequence—or, perhaps that there is a small minority of persons with peptic ulcer who need intensive psychotherapy, the indication for which may be overt neurotic symptoms or personality traits such as Alexander has stressed. At all events, the arguments for psychogenesis cannot yet be made to depend on good response to intensive psychotherapy, since evidence of the latter is restricted to a very few isolated cases.

It is scarcely necessary to cite many other papers that have been written on this problem. From the foregoing it is clear that the subject is lively but unsettled. The most vigorously present psychodynamic views—those of Alexander and his colleagues—are not universally accepted, and they are open to the objection that they are based on study of a small number of subjects and at best true only of a proportion of all ulcer patients; moreover there is not yet sufficient evidence for the corollary, viz. that these patients can be cured by intensive psychotherapy. The best known investigation—that of H. G. Wolff and his associates on the fistulous subject, Tom—demonstrates that emotion can, and perhaps always must, be accompanied by visible physiological and anatomical changes in the stomach; but it did not demonstrate that these could proceed to become chronic morbid changes, nor did it indicate why, if they could so proceed, it should happen in some people and not in others. The vexed questions of organ-inferiority, choice of viscus for somatizing expression, and specificity of emotional state or typical conflict situation, are still unanswered. As to pathways, we have good reason to suppose that discharges pass from frontal cortex to thalamus and hypothalmus; thence to posterior pituitary, vagus centres in the brain stem, and sympathetic centres in the cord, and so to the viscus and to the adrenal medulla.

It is a field of inquiry as stimulating and exacting as can be found anywhere in medicine. It offers problems not only to the medical investigator—whether he be internist, psychiatrist, pathologist or physiologist—but also to the sociologist, geneticist and psychologist. The discoveries and the lacunae, the hints and the mistakes in the study of peptic ulcer can be taken as telling examples of what has been going on in other fields of psychosomatic inquiry, which will therefore be more cursorily dealt with here. In all of them the basic problems recur, ranging from epistemological and other philosophical issues, through the biological question of protective reactions to stress, homeostasis and adaptation, to the minute analysis of mental and bodily processes, both normal and morbid.

Arterial Hypertension

The lability of blood pressure and its prompt response to emotional stimuli are matters of everyday clinical observation. Inevitably, therefore, it was surmised that sustained emotion might bring about sustained hypertension. Many investigations were made into the personality and psychodynamic conflicts of people with essential hypertension; and a few investigations were made into the physiological accompaniments of induced emotion in such patients.

The psychological studies seemed to show that inhibited hostility was a common feature of hypertensive patients. This was taken to conform to Cannon's observation of the effect of rage in his laboratory animals, and an output of adrenalin was assumed to be held responsible for the rise in blood pressure. But recent work (Alf) has suggested that noradrenalin as well as adrenalin is released from the adrenal medulla during anxiety, and has in physiological concentrations opposite effects on heart rate and peripheral vessels from those of adrenalin. However there is a considerable difference between overt rage, such as Cannon induced in his animals, and the frustrated rage observed in the hypertensive subjects, many of whom seem unable to give vent to their energy impulses. Binger's studies are of particular interest because of his cautious attitude to the findings. He ascertained that hypertensive subjects are tense, prone to depression and anxiety, with inhibited aggressive impulses, insecurity and dependence on a threatening parent. But he does not conclude that this disturbed personality is the cause of hypertension. It may be an independent characteristic, or, as Binger suspects, both may be the outcome of a common, unknown cause. 'At present no adequate proof is at hand to establish the fact of psychogenesis or that commonly observed disturbances of personality are more than frequently occurring associated phenomena. . . . The fact that acute emotional excitement may result in transitory elevations of blood pressure should not be used as a basis for the inference that long-lasting emotional states or conflictive situations can act as precipitants in chronic vasomotor constriction.' That such a warning should be necessary or worth uttering testifies to the loose thinking that sometimes creeps into psychosomatic discussions.

Binger is also cautious in stating the case for psychotherapy of this condition: 'there is as yet no evidence that psycho-analysis or any psychotherapeutic procedure can reverse the psychological process or change the destiny of this disease'. Following Binger's lead, many writers have stressed that the personality associated with hypertension is often found in people who have no hypertension, and that it may be only when an inherited somatic predisposition exists that the disease can develop. This mode of reasoning is not so often applied to other psychosomatic disorders, though it well might be with equal justification.

Reiser and Ferris investigated between 1945 and 1950, 230 unselected hypertensive patients with regard to psychiatric, physiological and pathological findings. They concluded that 'emotionally stressful life situations influence adversely the course of hypertension in terms of its onset, associated symptoms and complications, and that emotionally relaxing situations such as the doctor-patient relationship may improve the patients'. This relationship they regard as a potent influence, even when it is unrecognized: in other words, the fact that a doctor is taking a responsible interest in the patient does him good, no matter what the treatment. The same group of workers were unable to relate 'specific dynamic constellations in the patients' total personality' to the onset of benign hypertension, fluctuations in blood pressure and exacerbations, but 'the data do not reveal any specificity of personality structure or conflict for the group (hypertensive patients) as a whole and thus do not explain the selection of this organ system'. They are prepared to believe that there may be an additional causal factor such as a predisposing renal lesion.

On this crucial question of what determines the choice of the present organ-system, long-term studies seem called for, since no patients have so far been observed before their essential hypertension was manifest: inferences about the genesis of the disorder, and even about the patient's personality before the disorder had become established, are therefore retrospective and for the most part speculative. The studies of Lacey and Van Lehm in children, and of Jost in adult hypertensive subject may prove valuable, as indicating that the individual's profile of autonomic response to a stress such as the cold pressor test reveals a constitutional pattern peculiar to himself or characteristic of proneness to a disease in some organ controlled by autonomic impulses.

Another illness closely associated with the circulatory apparatus is '*effort syndrome*'. Sir Thomas Lewis demonstrated that this is not accompanied by any consistent, morbid tissue change, and during the Second World War close parallel studies were made of the psychological and physical features of this condition. But effort syndrome is like headache, benign arterial hypertension and many other disorders which have been studied on the same lines as psychosomatic diseases; it has no lasting somatic correlate, and is therefore best excluded, in any formal grouping, from the psychosomatic disorders and classified with the familiar neuroses. It need hardly be stressed at this point that formal classification, useful though it is, does not presuppose any real biological distinction between 'functional' neuroses (which obviously have structural and metabolic correlates) and the partly 'psychogenic' 'organic' disorders which we call psychosomatic. The transitions between 'functional' and 'organic' are numerous; the distinctions now current often rest on differences in degree rather than in kind, or on inadequacies in our methods of investigating part-functions during life.

As a rather startling reminder of the need to check psychiatric and clinical observations, Storment's treatment of some of Flanders Dunbar's findings deserves attention. Dunbar, unlike Alexander, relates personality types to diseases; thus according to her the hypertensive patient is shy, introversive, aggressive but with conflict between active and passive tendencies, and so forth, whereas the patient with rheumatic heart disease typically has a different set of personality traits and the patient with coronary occlusion yet another personality pattern. Storment put these assertions to the test by taking five groups of male patients in hospital—25 with hypertensive disease, 25 with rheumatic heart disease, 8 with coronary occlusion, 19 with arteriosclerotic heart disease, and 13 with infectious and other non-cardiac disease. All these subjects were tested in the same way to determine their personality by means of the well-known Guilford-Martin inventories. Not all patients could or would co-operate in the inquiry but the statistical treatment of the data was rigorous, and it leaves no room for doubt that, by this method of investigation, no significant differences were found between the personality of any of the groups with circulatory disease, or between any of these and the non-cardiac groups. Storment points out that the Null Hypothesis was confirmed at the 5% criterion of significance, but that if a still less exigent criterion is applied, trends or probable differences can be discerned which, however, are scarcely in the direction to be expected if Dunbar's findings were correct. Storment puts his finger on an undoubted defect when he says of clinical observations such as hers, 'There is an especially serious weakness in the usual qualitative methods of analysing data. The analysts are at all times fully aware of the disease categories into which the patients fall and of the general personality pictures which have been presumed to prevail in these entities.' Undoubtedly it would be a great step forward if the psychiatric assessment of patients with psychosomatic disease could be made by investigators who were kept unaware of the nature of the patient's physical disease: it is, however, hard to see how this could be achieved, and it is therefore all the more necessary to supplement and check clinical findings by the more detached measurements and findings of the psychologist, using inventories, projective tests and other more or less objective procedures.

Asthma

The methods of investigation applied to the psychosomatic problem of bronchial asthma during the last twenty years are so like those used for the preceding conditions, and indeed so largely influenced by the same energetic and prolific investigators, that it would seem repetitive to describe them. A nuclear psychodynamic factor is believed to be specific: it is a conflict on excessive dependence upon a parent. This was believed also to be specific to peptic ulcer; but whereas in ulcer the dependence connoted an oral wish to be fed, here it connotes a wish to be encircled and protected as in the uterus, and is often associated with a history of unconscious maternal seduction and overt maternal rejection. The allergic features of the asthma obviously present a difficulty for any psychodynamic interpretation: this difficulty has not been resolved. The suggestion is put forward that sensitiveness to being separated from one's mother and sensitiveness to allergens may be 'Parallel manifestations of the same basic constitutional factor'—a somewhat similar proposal to that made in the case of arterial hypertension.

Some of the most recent writers are critical of these views. Gendrot observed, during the course of four years, a hundred male and female adult asthmatics. Impressed by the rapid improvement which ensued in many recent cases after the patient had told the doctor freely about themselves he concluded that the asthmatic attack is a visceral and humoral equivalent of anxiety, relieved by the cathartic confession. He found little support for the narrow psychodynamic theory which would make the attack a response to some effective conflictual constellation, and he went so far as to say, 'Nous pensons avoir montré que l'étude psychologique de l'asthme et son traitement psychothérapeutique gagnent à se dégager de la méthode psycho-analytique.' This challenge to a widely spread prevalent way of studying and explaining psychosomatic phenomena is echoed, on quite different grounds by Beach, who after reviewing 'psychosomatic phenomena' in animals, argued against postulating a 'psyche' and unconscious dynamic forces and conflicts: 'repeated use of the terms "conscious", "unconscious", "preconscious", "subconscious", "psychic stress", and so forth makes me feel as though we were surrounded by ghosts. . . . The best insurance against fuzzy-headed thinking is to restrict our discussion to words and phrases that have been carefully and objectively defined.' Leigh, in his critical review, is also sceptical about the value of observations which may be coloured by the observer's preconceptions and bias.

Autonomic studies have been carried out, naturally, in asthmatics. The findings of Funkenstein are among the most recent. In six asthmatic patients he obtained blood pressure responses to adrenalin and to mecholyl which varied with the patient's mental state, being of parasympathetic type when the mental state was comparatively healthy, but of sympathetic type when the patient showed psychotic symptoms (as most of them did). Clearly these six patients were not typical sufferers from bronchial asthma, and it would be unsafe to draw conclusions from the findings quoted. The patients bring up, however, another question often debated in the psychosomatic literature, viz.: are the somatic symptoms of the psychosomatic disorders a defence against gross mental disorders, and is there consequently a risk that if the somatic symptoms are removed by drugs or other means a psychosis may take their place? In a wide range of disorders this relationship has been suspected or postulated, and with the advent of Cortisone and A.C.T.H., which will temporarily abolish the symptoms of many supposedly psychosomatic disorders (e.g. rheumatoid arthritis, atopic dermatitis), it was possible to test the correctness of the assumption. On the whole the evidence has been decidedly against the assumptions (which are chiefly based on psychoanalytical evidence) that the physical symptoms are a defence which it might be dangerous to remove. However this is a territory now difficult to survey, because the work of Selye and his colleagues has opened up much debatable ground regarding the physical processes of adaptation—alarm, resistance and exhaustion.

Normally it would be necessary to consider seriatim all the other organs and diseases which have been regarded as psychosomatic. But, apart from the inevitable restriction of space, there is no need to attempt this extended review, for two reasons, first, there is a remarkable sameness, on the whole, about the methods, the findings and the weaknesses of psychosomatic research into various diseases, and, secondly, there are a number of excellent and comprehensive reviews.

There is hardly any part of the body which has not received psychosomatic attention—the skin, the endocrine glands, the metabolic processes, the joints and skeletal muscles, the urogenital apparatus, and, as already shown, the alimentary, the respiratory, the cardiovascular apparatus. And this is as it should be. For psychosomatic medicine and psychosomatic research have no other justification than that they are part of that systematic study of normal and morbid processes of the body which takes full account of both the physical and the psychological aspects:

> nam communibus inter se radicibus haerent,
> nec sine pernicie divelli posse videntur.

Any method that is reliable, any set of concepts that fits the phenomena, any theory that provides fruitful hypotheses, any function, any disease, might properly be employed or studied in so wide and difficult an undertaking: any critical procedure that can detect premature or misleading inferences needs also to be used to the full.

REFERENCES

ALEXANDER, F. *Psychosomatic Medicine; Its Principles and Application*, London, Allen & Unwin, 1952.

ALEXANDER, F. *Psychosom. Med.*, 1939, **1**, 173.

ALF, L. *Acta Physiol. Scand.*, 1951, **25**, 55.

BAUER, J. *Constitution and Disease*, London, Heinemann, 1945.

BEACH, F. A. *Psychosom. Med.*, 1952, **14**, 261.

BEAUMONT, W. *The Physiology of Digestion*, Edinburgh, 1913.

BERGMANN, G. VON. *Berl. klin. Wschr.*, 1913, **50**, 2374.

BICHAT, M. F. X. *Recherches physiologiques sur la vie et la mort*, Paris, 1805.

BINGER, C. A. L. *Psychosom. Med.*, 1951, **13**, 273.

BINGER, C. A. L., ACKERMAN, N. W., COLM, A. E., SCHROEDER, H. A. and STEELE, M. J. *Personality in Arterial Hypertension*, American Society for Research in Psychosomatic Problems, New York, 1945.

BOGEN, E. *Pflügers Arch. f. d. ges. Physiol.*, 1907, **117**, 150.

BORING, E. G. *History of Experimental Psychology*, Appleton Century, New York, 1950.

CABANIS, F. J. G. *Rapports du physique et du moral de l'homme*, Paris, 1799.

CANNON, W. B. *Bodily Changes in Pain, Hunger, Fear and Rages*, New York, Appleton Century, 1915.

COBB, S. *Emotions and Clinical Medicine*, New York, Norton, 1950.

COBB, S., MILES, H. H. W. and SHANDS, H. C. *Case Histories in Pyschosomatic Medicine*, New York, Norton, 1952.

CUSHING, H. *Surg. Gynaec. and Obst.*, 1932, **55**, 1.

DAVEY, L. M., KAADA, B. R. and FULTON, J. F. In *Life Stress and Bodily Disease—Res. Pub. Ass. Res. Nerv. and Ment. Dis.*, vol. 29, ch. 4, Baltimore, Williams & Wilkins, 1950.

DAVIES, D. T. and WILSON, A. T. M. *Lancet*, 1937, **2**, 1353.

DEUTSCH, F. *Acta Med. Orient.*, 1951, **10**, 67.

DOLL, R. and JONES, A. *Occupational Factors in the Aetiology of Gastric and Duodenal Ulcers—Medical Research Council Report N.* 276, London, 1951.

DRAPER, G. *Ann. Int. Med.*, 1942, **16**, 633.

DUNBAR, H. F. *Emotions and Bodily Changes*, New York, Columbia University Press, 1935.

DUNBAR, H. F. *Psychosomatic Diagnosis*, New York, Hoeber, 1948.

EMERY, E. S. and MONROE, R. T. *Arch. Int. Med.*, 1935, **55**, 271.

FALCONER, W. *Dissertation on the Influence of the Passions upon Disorders of the Body*, London, Dilly, 1796.

FUNKENSTEIN, D. H. In *Life Stress and Bodily Disease—Res. Pub. Ass. Res. Nerv. and Ment. Dis.*, vol. 29, Baltimore, Williams & Wilkins, 1950.

GAINSBOROUGH, H. and SLATER, E. *Brit. Med. J.*, 1946, **2**, 253.

GARDINER, H. M., METCALF, R. C. and BEEBE-CENTER, J. G. *Feeling and Emotion*, New York, American Book Co., 1937.

GELLHORN, E. *Physiological Foundations of Neurology and Psychiatry*, Minneapolis (Minn.), University of Minnesota Press, 1953.

GENDROT, J. A. *Evol. Psych.*, 1953, **3**, 493.

GRACE, W. J., WOLF, S. and WOLFF, H. G. *The Human Colon*, New York, Hoeber, 1951.

GRODDECK, G. *Das Buch vom Es*, Vienna, Psychoanalytischer Verlag, 1923.

GROEN, J. *Med. Tijd. v. Geneesk*, 1951, **95**, 2336.

HALLIDAY, J. L., *Psychosocial Medicine*, London, Heinemann, 1948.

HAMBLING, J. *Brit. J. Med. Psychol.*, 1951, **24**, 242.

HAMBLING, J. *Brit. J. Med. Psychol.*, 1952, **25**, 39.

HAMILTON, M. *Brit. J. Med. Psychol.*, 1950, **23**, 182.

HECHT, I. *J. Clin. Psychol.*, 1952, **8**, 262.

HELLER, M. H., LEVINE, J. and SCHLER, T. P. *Psychosom. Med.*, 1953, **15**, 509.

HEYER, R. In Schwartz, D., *Psychogenese und Psychotherapie körperlicher Symptome*, Vienna, Springer, 1925.

HOLMES, T. H., GOODALL, H., WOLF, S. and WOLFF, H. G. *The Nose—An Experimental Study of Reactions within the Nose in Human Subjects during Varying Life Experiences*, Springfield, Ill., Thomas, 1950.

HORNBORG, G. *Berl. klin. Wschr.*, 1905, **3**, 86.

HUME, D. *Treatise of Human Nature*, London, 1739.

IVY, A. C. *Gastroenterology*, 1952, **21**, 185.

JAMES, W. *Psychol. Rev.* 1894, **1**, 516.

JONES, M. S. and SCARISBRICK, R., *Lancet*, 1943, **2**, 331.

JOST, H., RUILMAN, C. J., HILL, T. S. and GULO, M. J. *J. Nerv. and Ment. Dis.*, 1952, **115**, 33.

KAPP, F. T., ROSENBAUM, M. and ROMANO, J. *Am. J. Psych.*, 1947, **103**, 700.

LACEY, J. I. and VAN LEHN, R. *Psychosom. Med.*, 1952, **14**, 71.

LANGE, C. *Über Gemütsbewegungen*, Lipsia, 1887.

LEIGH, A. D. *Arch. Allergy and Appl. Immunol.*, 1953, **4**, 227.

LEIGH, A. D. and LOVETT-DOUST, J. W. *J. Ment. Sci.*, 1953, **99**, 489.

LEWIS, A. and JONES, M. *Lancet*, 1941, **1**, 813.

LEWIS, A. *Brit. J. Sociol.*, 1953, **4**, 109. (See also 'The State of Psychiatry 1967'.)

LEWIS, T. *Medical Research Council Special Report No. 8*, London, 1917.

LEWIS, T. In *Life Stress and Bodily Disease—Res. Pub. Ass. Res. Nerv. and Ment. Dis.*, vol. 29, Baltimore, Williams & Wilkins, 1950.
MAHL, G. F. *Psychosom. Med.*, 1949, **11**, 30.
MAHL, G. F. *Psychosom. Med.*, 1952, **14**, 182.
MARGOLIN, S. G. *Psychoanal. Quart. J.*, 1951, **20**, 349.
MARQUIS, D. P., SINNETT, E. R. and WINTER, W. D. *J. Clin. Psychol.*, 1952, **8**, 266.
MINKOWSKI, E. *Evol. Psych.*, 1953, **3**, 345.
MITSCHERLICH, A. *Internat. Arch. Allergy*, 1950, **1**, 79.
MORRIS, J. N. and TITMUSS, R. M. *Lancet*, 1944, **2**, 841.
MURRAY, J. B. *Some Common Psychosomatic Manifestations*, London, Oxford University Press, 1949.
O'NEILL, D. *Modern Trends in Gastroenterology*, London, Butterworth, 1952.
POLI, E. *Sett. Med. (Firenze)*, 1949, **37**, 381.
POSER, E. G. *Personality Tests in Psychosomatic Research*, University of London, 1952.
REISER, M. F., BRUST, A. A. and FERRIS, E. B. *Psychosom. Med.*, 1951, **13**, 133.
REISER, M. F., ROSENBAUM, M. and FERRIS, E. B. *Psychosom. Med.*, 1951, **13**, 147.
REYMERT, M. L. *Feelings and Emotions*, New York, McGraw-Hill, 1950.
ROKITANSKY, C. *Handbuch der speziellen pathologischen Anatomie*, vol. III, Vienna, Braunmüller & Seidd, 1842.
RUESCH, J. *Duodenal Ulcer*, Los Angeles, California University Press, 1948.
SCHOU, H. I. *Physiology of Emotions*, London, Oxford University Press, 1937.
SCHROTTENBACH, H. *Z. f. d. ges. Neurol. u. Psych.*, 1921, **69**, 254.
SCHWARTZ, D. *Psychogenese und Psychotherapie körperlicher Symptome*, Vienna, Springer, 1925.
SELYE, H. *J. Clin. Endocrinol.*, 1946, **6**, 117.
SELYE, H. *Physiology and Pathology of Exposure to Stress*, Montreal, Acta Inc., 1950.
STORMENT, C. T. *Psychosom. Med.*, 1951, **13**, 304.
STRANG, C. and SPENCER, J. O. B. *Brit. Med. J.*, 1950, **1**, 873.
SZASZ, T. S. *Psychosom. Med.*, 1949, **11**, 300.
SZASZ, T. S., KIRSNER, J. B., LEVIN, E. and PALMER, W. L. *Psychosom. Med.*, 1947, **9**, 331.
TODD, W. *Behaviour Patterns of the Alimentary Tract*, Baltimore, Williams & Wilkins, 1930.
WEIZSÄCKER, V. VON. *Der kranke Mensch*, Stoccarda, 1951.
WENER, J. and HOFF, H. E. *Canad. Med. Ass. J.*, 1948, **59**, 115.
WEST, R. *Lancet*, 1946, **2**, 899.
WEST, R. *Lancet*, 1950, **1**, 1025.
WITTKOWER, E. In *Modern Practice in Psychological Medicine*, London, Butterworth, 1948.
WITTKOWER, E. *J. Ment. Sci.*, 1935, **81**, 533.
WOLF, S. and WOLFF, H. G. *Human Gastric Function—An Experimental Study of a Man and his Stomach*, London, Oxford University Press, 1947.
WRETMARK, G. *The Peptic Ulcer Individual*, Copenhagen, Munksgaard, 1953.

SOCIAL PSYCHIATRY

IO

NEUROSIS AND UNEMPLOYMENT

MUCH HAS been written about the 'industrial neuroses' that follow accidents for which compensation can be claimed, and about the 'war neuroses' in which pensions play a part. The effects of unemployment upon the mental state have also been much spoken of in the last few years. There are, in short, generally recognized conditions in which social influences seem to play an indispensable part in provoking mental illness and so maintaining social incapacity. But since these social influences act upon many more than the few who respond with neurosis, it is important to see what other predisposing factors are at work in these few, as well as the social and clinical consequences of the adverse circumstances.

A special group was available for such inquiry. A series of patients on out-relief had been seen in whom presumptive mental disorder, generally of a mild chronic kind, was associated with long periods of unemployment. They were referred to the Mile End Psychiatric Clinic by the local public assistance committees (P.A.C.) for an opinion as to diagnosis and treatment. Fifty-two successive male cases, so referred between May, 1931, and June, 1932, have been taken for study. They do not form a representative group of people on out-relief, nor perhaps even of those on out-relief who had been diagnosed as neurasthenic, for the process of referral was not a routine one but depended on selection of appropriate cases by the various district subcommittees of the P.A.C. In age they ranged from 20 to 67: seven were between 50 and 65, thirty-two between 35 and 50, thirteen between 20 and 35. The information about them was obtained by the following inquiries:

1. A social history was obtained from a relative of each patient, prior to his attendance at the psychiatric clinic, by a psychiatric social worker.
2. The P.A.C. supplied details of medical history in most cases.
3. The psychiatrist examined the patients on one or more occasions and recorded the findings.
4. The case papers of the P.A.C. giving the whole history of the patient's relations with the administrators of out-relief, under the guardians' regime and that of the present P.A.C., were put at the disposal of the psychiatric social worker. The relieving officer who dealt with each case was interviewed in person.

This paper is reprinted from the *Lancet* (August 1935), **2**, 293–7.

5. In 49 of the 52 cases the psychiatric social worker visited the patient's home at a later date, saw him, his wife or a relative, and ascertained the subsequent happenings.

Only a brief account of the voluminous data accumulated can be given here. For them I am indebted to Miss M. A. Lane, the psychiatric social worker attached to the clinic, and to Miss Janet Galloway, who as research social worker at the Maudsley Hospital has studied the social aspects of this matter fully; her findings are being published elsewhere.

THE CLINICAL FEATURES

The clinical pattern was remarkably uniform. It was that of a chronic neurosis in which hysteria predominated. Various combinations of anxiety, irritability, hypochondria, depression, querulousness or resentment, and (hysterical) conversion symptoms were found; often all of these would be discoverable, and seldom less than four. Outstanding features were a preoccupation with discomforts, whether expressed in physical, mental, or social terms, a feeling of dissatisfaction or resentment in regard to them, and various expressions of anxiety; trembling was frequent. The complaints were commonly vague, but expressed with great earnestness, often also with rich prolixity and as though learnt off by heart. Sometimes these complaints verged on the bizarre—e.g. 'when I eat the food it gets just here and it keeps on boiling and wind, and after my food this right leg of mine goes dead. . . . Like an acid it keeps on fermenting in my mouth. And the wind works round me here. And it goes dead, I got no feeling. And this fluid seems to work all through my body, this acid boiling up: all my food seems to go to it. . . . White stuff dries in my socks. . . . Then when the doctor stroked the soles of my feet, he struck the delicate spot and it ran all up my leg. . . .'

A majority had a grievance against the pension authorities, the public assistance committee, medical boards, or society at large—'the capitalist system'. This was not expressed as a delusion but as a general attitude of touchiness and resentment, which would perhaps be evoked in a previously friendly and deferential patient when one asked him what standard he had been in when he left school, whether he had a pension, what work he had been able to do in the last two years, whether he had used any form of contraception, and so on. In 17 of the patients this attitude was very evident, and had at some time led to more or less severe outbursts of rage or violence. Convinced assertions of victimization, made in apparent calmness, were never obtained, and the patients showed, to express it in psychiatric terms, a paranoiac reactive development of personality, rather than a paranoid delusional formation.

Irritability was commonly complained of, or was reported by the patient's wife; it was always associated with some depression. Depression was observed and reported in 30 of the patients, but (like all the other symptoms mentioned) may well have been present, though at the time of examination unobtrusive, in many more. It rarely was extreme and in no instance was it associated with self-reproach or delusions. It is remarkable that in a few of the men it was apparently not the case that they were depressed; they were cheerful, in spite of the shaking and other discomforts, they slept and ate well, and their general manner suggested that they were content. It would of course be unwise to assume that these patients were happy or that their general mood differed greatly from that of many others who were said to be, or professed themselves, depressed, and who wept or looked glum—though unconvincingly —while reciting a catalogue of queer feelings and tremors.

The doubtless complicated and equivocally shown attitude of these men towards their situation and their symptoms cannot easily be expressed in simple affective terms, such as 'depressed', and their affect was not so sweeping and unvarying as in the familiar psychiatric disorders of mood; it corresponded more to the instabilities of psychopathic personality. Anxiety was a common feature among the patients; in 28 it was conspicuous, and in almost all demonstrable. The modes of its manifestation varied; clear-cut anxiety attacks, not obviously occurring in terrifying situations, in which the somatic expressions were brief, widespread, and 'classical'; or sweating, trembling, and dread before medical examination and other more or less important occasions; or constant restlessness and ill-defined apprehension occurred, as well as localized anxiety in which the activity of the heart or other organ was the centre of anxious preoccupation. Phobias—e.g., against crossing the street or riding on a bus—were not infrequent. Tremor was one of the most common findings; it was striking in 23 of the patients and was observed in most of the remainder; it was in many cases obvious to the casual glance—coarse, uneven, with jerkings or twitchings of the head and trunk as well as of the extremities; and in a large number it was the chief symptom complained of. Where it was a fine tremor other evidence of anxiety was present: where coarse or odd, less of general anxiety and more of interest in the symptom was the rule.

Three of the patients showed a mild pseudo-dementia, professing not to understand questions or giving inappropriate answers; they were unintelligent men who resented questioning, and their behaviour may perhaps be regarded as an intentional effort to mislead the examining physician. One patient had had a fugue, and he fell about when he walked: two others had a gross, anomalous stammer. These were all hysterical phenomena. Five of the patients were chronic schizophrenics, and 3 of these had been in mental hospitals: in none of them were the symptoms recent, the onset had been at least 7 years before: it is unnecessary to describe the symptoms they showed, which included affective incongruence, characteristic thought-disorder and paranoid hallucinations. There was one epileptic patient, and 6 in whom arteriosclerotic changes were present and seemed contributory to some of the 'mental' symptoms—e.g., lacrimose expressions of anxiety. In one patient a diagnosis of cortical degeneration, possibly of vascular origin or conforming to Pick's disease, was made.

CAUSAL FACTORS

On a careful survey of the history of each of these patients, one could understand how the present illness had developed. This way of thought, however, can be deceptive since it ignores the alternative modes of response to those taken by the patient and is willing to leap over unknowns: it may be no more than fitting the data into one's preferred scheme of mechanisms and consequences. It is however the most satisfying and profitable way of regarding the individual case clinically. In distrust of this clinical approach, one may look for the common occurrence in these patients of presumptive causal factors, or to put it more correctly, for biographical data which characterize this group, and to some extent differentiate them from people with other illness, or from healthy people. Unfortunately, on many of the points investigated in this series, comparable data for the rest of the population are not at hand.

In this group, therefore, it was not so much the 'causal' factors but rather the common peculiarities that were examined—these were concerned with social and medical facts and extended over more than the individual history of the patients.

THE FAMILY

The fathers of the patients had in 26 of the 45 known cases been unskilled workers; in these 26 the size of the family to which the patient belonged was nine children, whereas it was seven children in the 19 cases where the father had done skilled work. There were 7 instances in which a parent or sibling of the patient had been for years in a mental hospital: in these relatives schizophrenia, involutional melancholia, and mental defect were the diagnoses, while in all of these 7 patients themselves there was some departure from the clinical picture presented by the majority: in 1 there was extreme hypochondria of a bizarre sort, in another a paranoid psychosis, 2 were schizophrenic, 3 were mentally defective. It is very probable that the details obtained about the family history were incomplete, so that an appraisal of the findings might be misleading. The further information under this head is as follows: in 5 of the cases 'nervousness' in one form or another (mostly anxiety states) was reported in parents or siblings: alcoholism in 7, in 3 asthma, in 4 epilepsy. In 8 patients, tuberculosis occurred in other members of the family. All these facts are probably underestimates. The parents of 4 of the patients had lived apart; 3 patients were brought up in an orphanage, and 1 who was illegitimate had been brought up by a foster mother; one of their parents had died during the childhood of 8 of the patients. The places of the patients in the order of births did not appear significant, collectively.

PREVIOUS EVIDENCE OF NEUROSIS

In 12 cases there had been in childhood neurotic traits, such as shyness, extreme sensitiveness, restlessness, somnambulism and day-wandering, unmanageableness, nail-biting, incontinence of urine and faeces, facial tic, and fits. During adolescence one had been delinquent, another had had fits. Serious ill-health in childhood appeared to have had a considerable influence on development in 3 cases. In 23 of the patients there had at some time been overt evidence of mental illness. Thus half the patients who had been in the army during the war were discharged with the diagnosis of shellshock, neurasthenia, or D.A.H.: almost all of these received pensions, for a time at least. Ten of the 25 non-army cases had shown some anomaly (epilepsy in 2 cases, delinquency in 2, neurosis after trauma in 3, and single instances of other disturbances). The physical health of the patients during adult life is considered below. In the work record and war service of these patients significant hints or plain evidence of neurosis appear.

OCCUPATIONAL HISTORY

Two-thirds of the men were unskilled workers, a higher proportion than was found among claimants for unemployment benefit by the Ministry of Labour in 1925 (51%). In 11 of the cases the father had been skilled, the son was unskilled; in only 5 did the reverse hold true; in 7 both father and son were skilled.

Owing to the varied ages of the group, the facts about working life and duration of unemployment could not easily be compared. For various reasons it seemed best to estimate first the individual efficiency of each patient prior to his first post-war application for relief: 14 of the patients could not be so treated because of their youthfulness and brief period of industrial life. Of the remaining 38 there were 26 with satisfactory work records—i.e., they had held one job for seven years at least, or had not changed their jobs frequently without improvement of status. Seven of the 12 men who had unsatisfactory records in this respect had previously applied for out-relief (i.e., before the war), and the other 5 had aimlessly changed from job to job and might be called 'feckless' or unsettled.

As there was a rapid increase in unemployment and dependence on out-relief in London between January 1920 and January 1923, with its peak in 1922, it might be supposed that extraneous factors had played a large part in bringing about the unemployment of the group under consideration. Actually the highest number of them applying in any one year did so in 1920, before the difficulties had reached their maximum. Of the total 52, 36 had applied for relief a year before the height of the out-relief figures for East Londoners as a whole had been reached.

In each case the reason for the application for out-relief had been inability to support the family because of inadequate or no earnings. Actual illness and particularly neurosis had not been given as the reason for loss of occupation. It must however be remarked that 36 of these 52 men had on one count or another previously shown some inadequacy: they had been diagnosed as neurotic (24 cases) or as mentally defective (3 cases) or had experienced the 'pension situation'—i.e., had had some income, which was not current earnings, in the form of war pension or pre-war out-relief. Nineteen of them during their unemployment received National Health Insurance benefit for varying periods.

The amount of employment since the first application for out-relief is very little. Ten of these men have been unemployed for ten or more years, 34 of them have done no work lasting more than two weeks for the last five years or more. Half of them had been completely idle for the four years before their referral to the clinic, and only 6 had had more than a year's work during that time. One who showed mental defect, has never been employed at all. Eleven of the men have done no work for years except hop-picking in the autumn. The wives of 8 of them, incidentally, worked while their husbands were unemployed, but in only one instance was the work full time.

WAR SERVICE

Just over half of these patients had been in the Army. Of the remainder, 10 were exempt because of their age, 4 were rejected as unfit, and 10 were either exempted or rejected on indefinite grounds. Of the 27 who were in the Army, 8 did not go overseas at all; 4 of them were discharged unfit soon after enlistment, and the rest were not called up until towards the end of the war. Nineteen saw active service; only 4 were discharged from the Army without any disability. Of the 19 on active service, 12 were awarded pensions, and so were 2 of the eight who were never sent abroad. Of the 14 pensions, 10 were for nervous disability, and 3 other men who did not receive pensions were similarly diagnosed neurotic on discharge from the Army.

It is evident that a large number of these men eligible for war service were either initially recognized as unfit to meet the stresses of war or later proved so.

PHYSICAL ILLNESSES

Physical illness had been recognized in 13 of these patients before their first post-war application for out-relief. In the individual cases the influence of this on general development seemed clear. Two of them had heart disease; in one case it was first diagnosed in adolescence, and in the other it has since brought about the patient's death. Two had had attacks alleged to be epileptic; others were tuberculous or had sustained injuries or were defective in some respect—e.g., crippled.

As the pension or compensation situation has so many analogies with out-relief in its possible deleterious effects upon personality and mental health, it is worth noting that besides those with Army pensions, 6 of these men have received compensation for injuries sustained since the war. Machine accidents to their hands and accidental falls had resulted in the receipt of a lump sum: in all these men neurotic symptoms had been evident before the happening, and probably they were more prone to accidents than is usual. Another patient injured one eye so that it had to be removed in 1930, at the age of 48: impaired vision in the remaining eye made work impossible. It is only since then that he has shown definite neurotic symptoms; he claimed but did not receive any compensation or insurance. Two other patients received compensation for injuries sustained by their children.

One of the patients when examined at the psychiatric clinic showed a presenile cortical degeneration; in 7 circulatory disorder (arterio-sclerosis in 5) was found responsible for some of their incapacity. Dental caries, pyorrhoea, and arthritis were recorded in isolated instances.

It has often been said that the repeated medical examination of hysterical patients fosters symptoms. No clear connexion between previous examination and any particular symptom could be demonstrated in this group, though 4 of them quoted gloomy prognostications by consultants who had seen them, and many recited their symptoms with a readiness and uniformity of iteration that bespoke practice, and perhaps also iatrogenic acceptance of their incapacity.

INTELLIGENCE

Careful psychological tests were not practicable: information was drawn from the alleged standard reached at school and from the psychiatric observations made at the clinic. The school record could not be verified, unfortunately, as the necessary official documents had not been preserved except for special schools. The following numbers may therefore be taken as minimal. Of the 52, 3 had attended special schools for the mentally defective, 13 others had had not reached Standard 5 at school. On psychiatric examination 8 men were recognized as definitely defective in some degree: they had none of them been to school in the period subsequent to the passing of the 1913 Act, as had the 3 who were certified defective; if they had, several of them would probably have been certified. At the other end of the scale, 3 of the men were said to have won scholarships at the elementary school; none of them, however, had continued at school till sixteen; they had all done skilled work prior to the loss of their employment (engineer, grocer, petty officer). Only 12 men however had definitely reached Standard 7 or Ex. 7 by the age of fourteen. The proportion of people of poor intelligence here is higher than for the average population: the figures are, however, too small and incomplete.

MARITAL STATE AND CHILDREN

All but 9 of the men are married. Their average age on marrying was 25½ years—i.e., two years less than Beveridge's figure for the general population.

Eight were married before twenty, 18 between twenty and twenty-five, 10 between twenty-five and thirty. In 4, the marriage was definitely a failure (desertion, cruelty, separation by consent). One could not be sure whether others got on well together: in the majority it appeared to be tolerably so: many of the wives showed loyalty and affection, sometimes against heavy odds. The offspring of the 43 marriages numbered 221, of whom 182 survived. Well over a third of the children had been born since the first post-war application for out-relief. Of all the marriages, in only 16 cases had there been no addition to the family since going on out-relief. There were 8 instances where four or more children had been born after the patient had gone on out-relief; objections to contraception here played a large part, as 4 of the men in question were Roman Catholics and others expressed their dislike of any precautions. The average number of children was six for men over forty, and four for men under forty. The unskilled had larger families than the skilled. The proportion is the same as was found for the previous generation of these families and shows also the fall in the birth-rate: the average figures for size of sibship to which the patient belonged were 6·8 for the skilled, 9·3 for the unskilled: the corresponding figures for his own progeny were 4 and 5·7. An eighth of the surviving children, belonging to sixteen families, have abnormalities, thus 7 are certified as mentally defective, 7 have neurotic habits (e.g., enuresis), 4 have chorea, and 2 are tuberculous. On the other hand 9 children, belonging to seven families, have won L.C.C. scholarships for secondary or central schools.

Of the 43 married men 40 have dependent children. This figure has been compared with those given in the New Survey of London Life and Labour, and with others specially collected for this purpose from 150 married men, depending on public assistance, who were attending an East London non-residential training centre in the spring of 1933. Making necessary allowances for differences in age distribution (for the majority of the non-neurotic married unemployed were ten years younger than the married neurotic men under consideration) it appeared that the number of dependent children was higher for the neurotic group than for other unemployed. (The figures are given in Miss Galloway's paper.)

SOCIAL CONDITIONS: HOUSING, FOOD

It is not difficult in individual cases to see how neurosis and unsatisfactory housing conditions may interact, aggravating or maintaining each other. To generalize would, however, be unjustified. The general facts as to housing are that the men formerly in skilled trades now live in poorer quarters than they would if working. The overcrowding among these patients is greater than for the average population in these districts: the comparable figures were obtained from the London Survey (Eastern Area) and for details Miss Galloway's paper may be consulted. The conditions under which they live seemed in many instances conducive to ill-health. As regards food, the outstanding observation was that the standards varied over a wide range among families with comparable allowances, the determining factor being apparently the care and intelligence with which the family money was laid out on food and other necessities.

TREATMENT AND OUTCOME

Psychotherapy, treatment directed mainly at physical illness, and occupation were the measures employed. They were recommended according to individual needs, on grounds which need not be particularized except as regards occupation. The mentally defective patients, the schizophrenic and epileptic were dealt with appropriately. Of the various therapeutic recommendations none was so frequently made as that of occupation. In 41 of the patients it seemed to the psychiatrist that regular occupation, such as might be obtained at a non-residential training centre, would be of benefit. This rested mainly on two assumptions: (1) that most of their present symptoms were responses to lack of occupation, and (2) that appropriate occupation is beneficial for most varieties of mental disorder, including that which these men showed. It was recognized, however, that there were practical as well as theoretical objections. Training centres are intended in the first instance for the more promising and healthy man, who has a greater claim upon them than the weakling who has inherent deficiencies of personality and adaptation. The opportunities for the neurotic men were therefore fewer, even if they were eager to avail themselves of them. But they had in the course of years come to have an overtly or subtly hostile attitude towards occupation in general and towards the training centres in particular which could more easily be understood on psychological lines than reversed by psychological treatment. It was therefore impossible to ensure that one's recommendations about occupation would in all cases be carried out: actually they were in more than a third of the cases.

It is difficult to estimate the benefit derived from the various forms of treatment, which were in many cases combined in the one patient. The most satisfactory criterion of improvement seemed the subsequent work-record. It was found on inquiry a year later that just over a third of the men had ceased to be recipients of out-relief, mostly because they had obtained work, and of the others, 5 had had intervals of remunerative work. It must be remembered that the remainder who had not been working included mentally defective, epileptic, insane, elderly, and physically unfit persons. It is of importance also to bear in mind the persistently adverse factors against employment. Many of these men are such as in the London Survey are designated 'on the fringe of unemployability' and are held likely to get continuous work only in times of prosperity or expanding trade in their particular line. It was impossible to get from the patients or their wives useful indications of whether or not there had been improvement in symptoms and well-being.

CONCLUSIONS

These men are as much social as medical problems. The majority of them are evidently unable to support themselves; the grounds for this are not to be found only in the economic circumstances which are responsible for unemployment in the country as a whole. Their previous history and present state are evidence of inherent deficiencies of adaptation to their environment. In their present circumstances may be seen a continuation of the external factors which for the greater part of their lives have interacted with inherited predispositions to make them in various ways unsatisfactory. It is not from them that one can judge what effect long continued unemployment has on mental health: a series of men previously stable and well adapted must be examined if one would test and amplify the almost universal impression as to the harm it does. The group here dealt with had been selected because of mental deficiency or disorder of some sort which was associated with unemployment, and often indeed its chief cause. Their disability could usually be interpreted along the customary psychological lines, if one assumed a constitutional bias towards neurosis. As far as psychopathology was concerned, there was nothing to distinguish them from other patients, in every class and walk of life, who showed hysterical symptoms, anxiety, and irritability. The group was not quite homogeneous as to clinical picture, but if one excepted the few defective, epileptic, and insane patients, there was a considerable uniformity in it, and a close likeness to the syndrome of the chronic 'compensation or pension-neurosis'. It would seem that just as in mental hospitals where there was little occupation schizophrenic patients would tend to lose individual differences and outwardly approximate to a few common types, so persons with hysterical or other types of inadequacy tend, when long unemployed, to exhibit tremors, giddiness, anxiety, hypochondria, resentment, and depression as a fairly characteristic syndrome. They cannot by any means be taken as representative of the unemployed population. Whereas in the latter extraneous factors are mainly responsible for the unemployment, in the group here reported the prevailing economic difficulties seemed only contributory and, in some cases, negligible causes of their lack of work.

Deliberate prophylaxis of such disorders, whether it be genetic or individual, must wait on a better knowledge than we have at present of the essential factors in the causation of neurosis: very likely this end is served to some extent by the now widely available treatment of disorders of behaviour in children, and would be served also by measures of negative eugenics inculcated into, and observed by, psychopathic persons. However this may be, when one is confronted with such patients as these, treatment must be undertaken. It is almost impossible, when seeing these men or studying their individual histories, not to be impressed by the need for early recognition and treatment of their difficulties, before they have become inveterate, and by the need for controlled occupational therapy. Regular occupation with trained supervisors seems the most important requirement for their recovery: if conjoined with psychotherapy it is much more effective, but psychotherapy without regular occupation achieves little. Such a requirement may seem ideal, but it is already available for similar cases at the colony conducted by the Ex-Service Welfare Association, where its value has been proved. The problem of unemployment through neurosis is of course much larger than this, in which one has been considering only men on out-relief; the cost—and the gain—of providing adequate treatment cannot be assessed. But for such men as are here considered, the situation is narrower and simpler. The earlier they are given occupational therapy, with some measure of psychotherapy, the less unfit will they be to cope with their circumstances and the more likely to become socially self-sufficient.

II

SOCIAL CAUSES OF ADMISSIONS TO A MENTAL HOSPITAL FOR THE AGED

THE INCREASING number of old people in the population is reflected in the rising total of elderly persons admitted to mental hospitals. Whereas in 1931 2,918 people aged 65 and over were admitted directly to mental hospitals in England and Wales, there were 3,850 such people admitted in 1938 (constituting 12% of all direct admissions) and the number admitted has since then increased further. Moreover, approximately 54 persons of all ages per 100,000 of the total population of England and Wales were in 1938 admitted to mental hospitals, but the proportion of those admitted who were over 65 years of age was much higher—approximately 94 per 100,000 of the aged population. When it is considered that the people of pensionable age (65 years in men and 60 in women) have increased from $2\frac{1}{4}$ millions in 1900 (6% of the population) to $4\frac{1}{4}$ millions (10%) in 1931, and that by 1961 they will probably amount to more than 8 millions (16% of the population), the future dimensions of the mental hospital problem of the elderly appears formidable.

The social aspects of this problem are by no means of secondary importance. It might be urged that senile psychoses and senility depend on irreparable changes in the body, and especially in the brain, which will occur no matter what the social conditions. But there is convincing evidence that the organic cerebral changes incident to old age are not so directly related to senile dementia that the number of old persons admitted to mental hospitals will depend simply on the prevalence of those changes in the brain. Among the other factors will be social influences, which may cause a rapid increase in the number of persons admitted at a time of social upheaval, such as the outbreak of war. These social influences, however, operate also in ordinary times, and throw light on some of the problems of 'normal' old age.

It was decided, therefore, to examine the social factors which had produced disturbances in old age necessitating admission to Tooting Bec Mental

This paper was written with the assistance of Miss H. Goldschmidt, and is reprinted from the *Sociological Review* (1943), **35**, 86–98.

Hospital. This hospital is for old people only, and has accommodation for over 2,000 patients.

A group of 50 was selected, 25 men and 25 women, who were consecutively admitted to the hospital in the period between 11th November and 16th December 1943. This sample is likely to be representative of the hospital population as a whole. With the exception of one man, the male patients' ages ranged from 65 to 87 and those of the females from 68 to 91 years. Two further patients, although admitted in this period, were not included because of their comparative youth, and because their symptoms were clearly the result of a cerebral ictus.

Visits were made to the patients' husband or wife, other relatives, friends, landlords. Contact was established with a large number of institutions, especially hospitals, and information obtained from them. In all, 75 visits were paid and 97 relatives and others acquainted with the patient before admission to Tooting Bec were interviewed; in some instances patients themselves gave much information. The investigation was begun almost immediately after admission to the hospital, and the patient's progress was followed up for four months. With the exception of 5 men and 5 women who came direct from general hospitals or Public Assistance institutions, all patients had been referred to the hospital via mental observation wards. In all but 6 patients this was the first admission to a mental hospital.

The diagnoses on admission to hospital were: senile dementia (uncomplicated), 15; senile dementia (complicated), 15; arteriosclerosis or hypertension, 13; 'confusional state', 6; pellagra, 1. Twenty of the men had evidence of generalized arteriosclerosis, but only 12 of the women.

SOCIAL INTEGRATION

When normal human contacts are reduced, and the individual has less and less ground for feeling himself a member of a social community, one of the necessities for healthy living has been struck away. Many of the Tooting Bec patients had suffered severe deprivations of this kind before coming to hospital.

In the female group of patients, 9 had remained single living rather solitary lives, and of the 16 who had married, only 2 were still living with their husbands; 12 had been widowed for periods ranging from 2 months to 54 years, and 2 were living apart from their husbands. In the male group, 5 had remained single, another one probably single, and of the 16 who had been married, only 7 were living with their wives at the time when their mental illness began; 11 had been widowed for periods ranging from 8 months to 36 years, and 3 had been separated for from 7 to 24 years.

Only 5 of the female patients (2 married, 2 widowed, and 1 single) could be regarded as socially integrated, viz. 2 married women living with their husbands, 2 widows living with their children, and an unmarried woman who for forty years had worked for one family, continued to live there when she was no longer able to work, and was virtually a member of that family. Seven of the male patients could be so regarded; 6 of these were living with their wives, and 1, a widower, with his daughter.

There were 6 more patients, 3 men and 3 women, who were to a limited extent integrated into the life of the community. Although living under the same roof with children or other members of their family, they did not enter into their activities and were 'put up with' rather than accepted.

E. J., aged 78, was an example of this. Once his children were grown up and set up homes of their own, he remained aloof from them. He lived in fairly comfortable circumstances, never visited them, and placed the onus for maintaining social contact on his children. He remarried after the death of his first wife, but none of his children ever met his second wife, who was killed during a raid. In the same raid E. J. was injured. He had already been deaf for a long time, and now was blinded as well. It was only then that he seemed to remember his children. There were no ties of affection on either side. E. J. had been a domineering type of man, and although the children did not refuse to take him into their home, they felt his presence there to be a burden. He lived in semi-isolation in a room on a different floor from the one where the family foregathered.

Another patient, M. D., a widow of long standing, aged 78, who had no children, rented a room in a house where the landlady encouraged social intercourse between her lodgers and herself. The patient, a reserved but kindly person, became part of the landlady's household, but when she began to show symptoms of mental disturbance this seeming integration proved unsubstantial.

The wife of T. G., aged 68, had deserted him while he was serving abroad in the first world war. He went back to his mother, and after her death went to live in a sister's flat, but remained essentially alone, taking his meals in a cheap café nearby and was never invited to share the meagre amenities of the household.

C. H., aged 79, had always been a dictatorial man, with his wife at his beck and call. Then she had a stroke and became entirely bedridden for twelve months prior to the patient's illness. He was thrown on his own resources, which were inadequate.

Among the remaining patients, 17 women and 15 men were living alone or in Public Assistance and similar institutions just before admission to this hospital; social integration was to a large extent lacking. Fourteen of them were single, and it did not seem that their solitary way of life was of their own choosing. The women were resigned to an inevitable situation; the men tended to be solitary and were unable to make satisfactory contacts.

J. G., aged 70, had lost touch with his family after his mother's death. He, like her, had always suffered from feelings of inferiority. He changed his work whenever he had to make a decision, always evaded arguments, and preferred change of lodgings to a discussion of difficulties with his landladies. He stated that he had never had the courage to face the responsibilities of married life. When later he was forced to enter a Public Assistance institution, he developed delusions regarding the intentions of other inmates.

The propriety of including in this category patients in Public Assistance institutions might be disputed. It might be argued that living in a Public Assistance institution involves contact with people of similar age and interests. But people still enter such institutions for the most part against their own will and only as a last resort. The inmates have rarely anything in common, apart from their inability to remain socially integrated outside the institution. Their attitude to the institution is largely based on traditional prejudice, but it may also be due to a realization that the institutions, as they mostly exist today, mean restricted possibilities of social and vocational life for the aged who live in them.

K. B., aged 74, is a single woman, with some talent for sketching and designing. She never worked regularly, changing her places of employment frequently owing to an erratic temperament which precluded any normal relationship. She was disliked by her relatives. At the time of her mother's death the patient was fifty years old, and had given up work. She became destitute. Her brother made her an allowance, but when it was discovered that she spent this largely on drink, he arranged for her admission to an institution. She had forfeited his sympathy and never heard of him again. She remained in the institution for twenty-two years, but always rebelled against her life there, and as time went on she became more and more unsociable.

Four of the women had been in Public Assistance institutions for periods varying up to twenty-two years before admission to Tooting Bec; 3 others had been in another hospital for 1 to 5 years. Three male patients had made their homes in men's lodging-houses of the Rowton House, Seamen's Hostel, and Salvation Army variety. Of 6 other 'non-integrated' patients, 5 had lived in Public Assistance institutions from 2 months to 15 years.

A man, P. L., aged 65, had been staying in a home for bombed-out people for 2½ years (this is the only case among male patients which demonstrates a direct influence of the war on integration). His wife was evacuated, leaving him in London on his own. His physical condition had been weakened considerably through inadequate care. In an air-raid he sustained an injury which precipitated his mental illness.

There was also only 1 female in whom the effect of the war on integration was noticeable. L. W., aged 77, an unmarried woman, who was going blind, had been staying with a niece until the war broke out. The niece had to go out to work to supplement her soldier-husband's income. L. W., always a quarrelsome person, developed increasing irritability, possibly as a result of her progressive blindness, and could not be left to be looked after by neighbours in the niece's absence. Placement in an institution became necessary.

There remains the group of those who lived in a room by themselves, despite the fact that they had children who might have made more satisfactory provision for them. Eight women and 7 men come into this category. In most of them the children did not consider it their duty to take the elderly patient into their home, mainly on the grounds that they were only working-class people. This attitude suggests a decreasing tendency for the dependent aged to be supported by their own children and grandchildren; also, higher standards of living are recognized as necessary for subsistence. This raises the question whether the care offered by the community can compensate or be a substitute for the close and intangible bond of family relationships. [1]

Another important factor—temperament and character—affects social integration. Out of the 15 men who were living alone or in institutions, 10 had shown personality difficulties, and out of 17 such women, 12 had shown similar defects of personality. There are grounds for holding that abnormalities of personality indicate a predisposition to senile psychoses. [4] They also make it less likely that relatives will have the aged person to live with them.

E. S., aged 87, was a widow, with four sons, only one of whom remained in touch with her. He described her as a bad-tempered person who had had difficulty in earning her living as a nurse because she lost her temper with her patients. She was intensely interested in religion and suspected the good faith of anyone who did not share her beliefs. It never occurred to her son to invite her to live with his family, even when she was in need of care.

In other instances the patient's excessive consumption of alcohol made children or relatives ashamed and therefore reluctant to have anything to do with her.

M. C., aged 75, had always neglected her household duties in favour of drinking in public houses. The children left home and, after the death of her husband, none of them volunteered to have her with them. They felt the indignity of her conduct and wished to spare the feelings of their respective wives or husbands. The patient eventually was admitted to hospital after an accident due to drunkenness.

Five of the women were estranged from their family because of drunkenness, and in another it had caused repeated dismissal from work; in a further case it was indirectly responsible for the patient's admission to an institution.

Among the male patients excessive consumption of alcohol was recorded in 11 cases, but in only 3 was there evidence that it had had a bad effect on family ties.

J. G., aged 66, had a record of persistent drunkenness and cruel treatment of his wife arising out of this. His numerous children resented it bitterly. Only one showed any interest in him, and even he spoke with great bitterness of the unhappy home atmosphere which the patient had created.

Relatives and friends showed close and continuing interest in 7 of the women; in 7 others there was spasmodic but not sustained interest, and in 10 of the women the relatives and friends showed no concern at all.

Of the men patients, 6 were without friends or relatives. In 8 cases the relatives had submitted to a great deal of stress, and even suffering, to provide care at home for them; in 4 others there was occasional interest, and in 7 no trace of any concern about them. Those relatives who had felt themselves to be actively responsible for the patient's care were extremely hesitant about agreeing to his entry into any institution.

PREVIOUS OCCUPATION

The 25 male patients had pursued occupations mainly in the lower wage class. Nine were employed in unskilled work as carmen, warehousemen, dustmen, navvies, stevedores, etc., 12 at semi-skilled work as draper's assistant, publican, baker, etc., and 4 were skilled, e.g. engineer, clerk, foreman in factory, photographer. The opinion is generally held (Folsom, 1940) [2] that physical disability due to age comes on sooner in manual workers than in more privileged classes of the population and that their work causes this to happen. In this sample 17 patients (including 7 manual workers) carried on work up to the age of 65 or later. Of the remaining 8, only 1 was directly incapacitated through his work (an accident while driving a lorry).

Taking the group of male patients as a whole, the following were the reasons for discontinuing work: loss of sight (4), epilepsy (1), accidents (3), legacy (1), forced out of employment owing to inability to compete in speed of performance with younger applicants (4). Four others worked until just before their admission to Tooting Bec Hospital. The findings in these patients, therefore, do not support the above-mentioned belief about the relationship between type of work and age of ceasing to work.

Although it can be assumed that the termination of active work often leads to impaired mental and physical functions, it was difficult to trace an obvious connexion between the cessation of work and the onset of mental illness, except in three cases. In these the patients yielded to a sense of frustration at having to make room for younger people and became very upset.

A striking example of this is J. D., aged 72, a carpenter, who was anxious to continue work, but could not secure a job because he was considered too old and too slow at his work. He was not eligible for old-age pension as he had not spent the requisite number of consecutive years in this country after his return from Australia. His wife had to become the breadwinner. This, combined with his enforced leisure, evidently resulted in mental disturbance in which preoccupation with his former work was the recurrent theme.

The extent to which the patients remained active after having given up their regular work was determined by their 'normal' personality, by their dependence on others for the satisfaction of their needs, and by their infirmities. Only 5 patients had insisted on performing certain duties; 4 of these were socially integrated, 1 lived on his own.

W. S., aged 72, for example, had been anxious to do something in return for the hospitality of his son and daughter-in-law, and asked to be allowed to do the errands, although his poor eyesight made this dangerous. The shopping expeditions, however, afforded an opportunity for social contact with other people of his age and satisfied a need.

None of the men had belonged to any club or taken part in social or religious activities; they were content to spend their time strolling, sitting in the park, and reading the daily papers. Only 1 was known to have gone to the cinema regularly.

Among the 25 female patients all but 6 (2 nurses, 3 dressmakers, 1 shop assistant) had been employed in domestic work (14 of them in the employ of other people as housekeepers, cooks, charwomen, or maids). There did not seem to be a relationship between the type of work performed and the onset of the mental illness, nor had the cessation of regular work had an immediate effect on the mental health of the patients. Except 2 who lived in institutions before their admission to Tooting Bec Hospital, all the women had remained active in their own homes or their children's. Three of them had been interested in Church activities.

FINANCIAL SECURITY

Patients were judged to have been insecure in this respect when their income or resources at the beginning of their mental illness had been much smaller than during the previous decade, or when they had been irksomely dependent on some other person's economic support.

All the patients were within the lower income group. Therefore the difference between their working income and their old-age pension and supplementary pension was comparatively small. But the transition from earned to unearned income constituted a problem, offset probably only by the fact that the old-age and supplementary pensions were theirs by right and would be available under any circumstances.

Five of the women patients had been financially insecure, and 10 had no other income than from old-age and supplementary pensions. Four who received old-age and supplementary pensions while living in their children's or friends' houses were no doubt able to manage more comfortably than those who had to live on the same income, but alone. Two others received a special disability pension in addition to their old-age pension. There were 2 patients in receipt of old-age and supplementary pensions who had apparently been in financial straits.

One of them, E. R., a woman of 73, had always worked as a housekeeper, usually 'living in'. Owing to her old age and an accident which incapacitated her, she was no longer acceptable as a worker and was forced to live on her own. This coincided with the war, when higher cost of living and rationing made demands on her ingenuity to manipulate her small income successfully. She failed to do so, neglected her food, and became ill.

Nine of the male patients were financially insecure. Four of them had felt keenly their dependence on others for their maintenance.

J. G., aged 77, who had made a satisfactory living as a bricklayer working for one firm for 25 years, could not secure further employment when his employer had to close down. This coincided with domestic difficulties which resulted in separation from his wife. He had to go to live in Rowton House. He did not look after himself properly on his allowance from Public Assistance and became ill through prolonged under-nourishment.

Only 3 of the women and 5 of the men had made some financial provision (savings, legacies, annuities, small investments) for their old age, apart from those who had been in pensionable employment.

A substantial legacy had been left to one patient, J. G., aged 70, so that he retired from work at the age of 50 and lived on his capital, which he estimated would cover the remaining years of his life. Because of the war with its rising cost of living, he found his money dwindling fast. He allowed himself an astonishingly small weekly sum, with the result that he finally collapsed in the streets from starvation. He was contemplating suicide at the time.

DIET

Six of the male patients are known to have had a deficient diet over a prolonged period, 4 because of allegedly insufficient income, and 2 as a result of general mental deterioration and lack of energy to provide food for themselves. Two women showed signs of malnutrition.

A. W., a woman of 70, had always been of unstable temperament and unable to face responsibilities. She could not cope with rationing restrictions and neglected her diet. Her relatives suggested that she should take her meals in a communal restaurant, but she could not bring herself to do this.

W. A., aged 68, a reserved and unassuming man, had lived alone in a room after his wife's death three years earlier. He was one of a large family, but owing to some differences of many years' standing he felt he could not approach them for help of any kind. He even told them that he had a grown-up daughter, in order to appear self-sufficient. He took to drink, neglected his meals completely, and developed signs of vitamin deficiency. He had to be certified, but was restored to normal health and mental balance after a few weeks of treatment in Tooting Bec Hospital.

INFIRMITIES

Three of the women were totally blind, and 4 others had progressive loss of sight. As 5 of them were not integrated socially, the impact of this infirmity on their lives was overwhelming.

M. B., a single woman aged 68, formerly a nurse, lived in a rented room on the top floor of a house. The landlord would not cater for the needs of this exacting patient, who had become nearly blind, and refused an operation for cataract. She became severely hypochondriacal and difficult to look after.

Three of the women had had a hemiplegia, 2 were epileptics, 4 were severely handicapped by deafness, and 2 by arthritis. All but 2 of these 11 patients lived on their own and their infirmities had contributed to their mental breakdown. Five of the male patients were blind, or nearly blind, but 3 of these had been adequately cared for in their homes; and the same applied to 3 out of the 7 who had had a hemiplegia. Only 1 of the 3 men who had become deaf had no one to look after him. One patient who had epileptic fits had been the centre of interest in his home for many years, and it was not this infirmity that had brought about his transfer to hospital. Bronchitis and emphysema were common among the male patients. Gout, osteoarthritis, paralysis agitans, and enlarged prostate also occurred.

NATIONALITY

To be a foreigner can be tantamount to an infirmity for the aged, especially when it makes conversation as difficult as would dysphasia or deafness. This was true of a Greek patient who could hardly make himself understood. More important, however, than language was the incomplete acceptance of the foreigner by the English community. There were 2 male and 3 female patients in whom this factor had been at work, though not always prominently. It is a natural tendency for foreign-born people to gravitate towards those who speak their own language and have similar cultural patterns; and this applies to all the non-British patients, except a Spanish woman, married to an Englishman, who had lived most of her life in this country. Their acceptance by the English community had been therefore of secondary importance until they were forced out of their familiar setting.

A Polish woman patient, aged 76, had until her admission to Tooting Bec Hospital lived for years in a Public Assistance institution. She had a pronounced foreign accent, typical of the Jewish emigrant from Eastern European countries. The inmates of the institution made no secret of their objection to her presence there. She was sufficiently intelligent and sensitive to realize this.

EFFECT OF WAR CONDITIONS

It is reasonable to suppose that this sample, studied in the fifth year of the war, at a time of comparative freedom from raids, shows fewer traces of conditions specifically due to the war than would have been apparent earlier, e.g. at the end of 1940.

The effect of raids was noticeable in 3 men and 3 women. All three women had previously in their lives been treated in mental hospitals.

In one, A. B., aged 71, the fear of raids had played a large part in precipitating the mental illness on this occasion. She became excited during raids and ran about the house shouting and crying, so that at times the police had to be called in.

Another patient, R. W., aged 76, who was preoccupied with religious themes, became very upset during raids and identified the enemy planes as devils.

Injuries sustained during bombing had indirectly led to admission to the hospital in three instances.

One extremely obstinate old man, A. B., aged 83, always refused to take shelter during a raid. One night the raid became particularly fierce and he started to go to a shelter but fell on the way, his eyesight being very bad. He remained in an institution thenceforward until his admission to Tooting Bec Hospital.

In another patient, G. P., aged 74, the fright caused by the falling of a landmine nearby is said to have marked the onset of overt mental disturbance.

ENFORCED CHANGE OF HABITS

The dislocation due to loss of home and other changes caused by bombing was a disturbing factor in 6 cases.

A single women, E. P., aged 83, was financially secure, lived alone in her own house, and managed all her own affairs completely. Then her house was badly damaged during a raid, and a succession of changes followed. From a Red Cross

Hospice she was transferred to a Rest Centre and then to a Rest Home. There she became restless and made various attempts to return to her former home, and finally was found wandering in its vicinity. In 1939 she had become similarly confused on being taken to hospital with a fractured humerus, but the condition had cleared up.

Other 'critical occurrences' had included change of accommodation, loss of spouse or of close friends of similar age.

E. G., aged 76, always a highly-strung woman, had become deaf and very suspicious. The district in which she had been living was badly damaged during raids, so she went to the country. There she continually fretted about her home and finally returned to London. Shortly afterwards her husband died; she was left alone in the flat and became upset and hallucinated.

Another patient, W. S., aged 72, hearing of the sudden death by suicide of two friends with whom he had been living for some years, became profoundly disturbed.

Another woman, E. R., aged 73, was acutely distressed when she had to leave the house in which she had lived happily for years. She referred constantly to her former accommodation, and could not adapt herself to the new conditions.

PREVIOUS MENTAL HEALTH

Two male patients and 3 women had previously been treated in a mental hospital. More striking than this was the frequency with which relatives reported defects of personality. These fell mainly into two groups—the domineering and the timid. Nine of the men and 5 women were said to have been always overbearing, quarrelsome, interfering, hard to live with; 4 men and 9 women had been retiring, weak, helpless, over-sensitive people. Besides these there were patients described as of a crafty, whining, unreliable personality, or abrupt, moody, and violent-tempered. Six had been conspicuously jealous and suspicious. Much care was taken to ensure that these descriptions applied to the patient before the advent of the psychosis, but it is possible that in some cases the early symptoms of senile dementia or the 'halo' due to the psychosis biased the description of the patient's usual personality. Nevertheless, it is plain that the majority of these patients had been ill-adjusted and difficult people. Rothschild and Sharp (1941) [3] have lately emphasized that persons with peculiar or inadequate personality are more vulnerable to cerebral damage than others; they break down in the face of cerebral changes which people mentally more robust could deal with. Meggendorfer (1926) [4] made much the same point in his restrospective study of senile patients.

ULTIMATE SOCIAL FAILURE

Lapses of conduct which make admission to a mental hospital imperative are usually severe, though the illness of which they are the evidence may not be: social criteria of the severity of morbid behaviour are sometimes very different from medical ones. It is a mistake to infer that because the patients admitted to Tooting Bec are senile, their illness must be a progressive dementia and the outlook for improvement dark. It is a social quite as often as a medical breakdown that compels their admission, and a social improvement sometimes makes it possible for them to leave hospital again and resume their normal way of life—a restricted way of life, but not an unhealthy one necessarily.

Many of the patients studied had been of a distorted and psychopathic personality for the greater part of their lives. As they grew older their relatives had noticed the usual signs: their memory was poorer, they grew garrulous and reminiscent, more fixed in their opinions and limited in their ideas, irritable when crossed, suspicious, emotionally uncontrolled. But these failings did not oblige anyone to intervene in the patient's affairs until some overt action or gross omission revealed that the old man was helpless, a social responsibility, or an intolerable anomaly in ordinary society. The social lapses which disclosed or underlined the mental illness and necessitated admission to Tooting Bec Hospital had been varied.

Among those who had been in a hospital or institution before coming to Tooting Bec Hospital, it was interference with others that drew attention to their mental state. Thus 4 women and 2 men had become a nuisance because they kept getting into other people's beds. Eleven other patients (9 women and 2 men) who were living at home had caused annoyance to neighbours (by accusations that they were murdering someone, damage to walls and property, shouting or moving furniture about at night).

One old man, G. P., aged 74, had been brought before the Court, fined, and served with an eviction notice.

Wandering, often coupled with restlessness at night, had been common: 8 of the men and 8 women had had to be admitted because of this.

J. D., aged 72, would frequently leave the house at night, in spite of his wife's watchfulness, and wander the streets for hours.

A. T., a woman aged 71, on removal from the district where she had lived for nearly 50 years, could not settle down in her new milieu and, although she was nearly blind, would frequently disappear, to be found perhaps days later in her old home.

Another patient, aged 66, would knock at people's doors in the middle of the night, asking to be taken home by taxi.

Four patients (3 men, 1 woman) had attempted or seriously threatened suicide; in two instances this was associated with homicidal inclinations. Two men and 2 women had got into trouble for indecent behaviour (stripping themselves, micturating in public). Five of the men had become violent (often in a mild delirium), and another, who had been punished several times for trespassing, was on remand for having bilked the railway company of his fare, when his mental deterioration was observed and a diagnosis of cerebral arteriosclerosis made.

After admission to Tooting Bec Hospital 7 male patients died within 6 to 25 days, and 3 women within 3 to 46 days. Of the 8 male patients whose condition improved greatly, 5 had been living by themselves before their admission, as had the 3 women whose condition improved appreciably. Six men improved slightly (5 of whom had been living alone) and 10 women (4 of whom had not been socially integrated). The condition of 4 men and 9 women remained stationary or deteriorated.

As this paper deals with the social aspects of senile deterioration, the clinical features of the patients' illnesses will not be described: they conformed to the familiar picture of organic disease in the aged (Diethelm and Rockwell, 1943) [5]. It is, of course, true that some of the social factors discussed (especially 'social integration') have been inseparably linked with either the patient's personality or his developing dementia: if he had not been cantankerous, for instance, he would have had more friends; if he had had more friends he would not have become so embittered; and so on (Rothschild and Sharp, 1941) [3]. It is, however, useful to consider the social aspects in isolation, so far as that is possible; and indeed nothing but the bare pathetic records themselves could convey the tangle of medical and social threads that constitutes the latter history of these wrecks.

COMMENT

The social study of a small sample of old people admitted to a mental hospital cannot be the basis for conclusions about old people generally; but neither can it be regarded as yielding information only about the consequences of gross cerebral deterioration. If the group studied is much narrower than the ageing and aged population, it is also broader than the population of senile dements. The Tooting Bec patients, as this study has shown, could in many instances have remained in the ordinary community if social circumstances had been more favourable; and many of them could (and do) improve and return to the community when social circumstances are favourable. It is not a group of hopeless dotards but of people showing various degrees of mental and physical old age that has been studied; in a large number of them social factors have played the main part in making admission to a mental hospital necessary.

Failure to retain a place in the community, to be a member of a family, to have an appreciated share in the life of some household or working group, has been common in the patients studied: this defect of social integration is powerfully adverse to mental health—it could hardly be otherwise. It has in some of these cases been the outcome of a wayward and difficult personality; but more often it has been an unavoidable consequence of the narrowed circle, the bereavement, and the incapacity for forming new habits and associations which often characterize old age. Its effects on mental health are plain in these patients who have had to seek the care of a mental hospital, but the effects are not all irremediable; the patients might not only have remained in tolerable mental health if their social conditions (not only in the material sense) had been bettered, but having once broken down they can still in many cases improve in hospital (largely because of the social care and nursing) and become capable again of living in the community, provided always that the milieu will then be favourable to their social reintegration. It would not be difficult to list such requirements as suitable recreational opportunities and housing; but these clearly depend on individual tastes and habits, and are in any case subordinate to the intimate needs for affection and other human contacts, especially within the family. There has been a distinct development towards the separation of ages. A closer association of age and youth within larger households might well be a move in the right direction. To make this a practical possibility both the older and younger generations will need to reorientate themselves regarding the place of old age within the community. No general formula can do justice to the variety of the individual problems in this regard, as they were brought out in our study. It was, however, striking how often it appeared that timely investigation by a skilled social worker could have indicated steps that would avert or delay the mental breakdown (particularly in glaring cases such as those who seemed unaware of possibilities for financial assistance). This may have been wisdom after the event and cannot be put to the proof: the restoration of patients who appear capable, after treatment, of living again in the community is a field of work which could be extended; its results in bringing about the mental health and happiness of some of the aged would be more important than its financial and economic advantages, significant though the latter are at a time when the cost of hospital care for the aged is a mounting burden upon health authorities.

The investigation indicated the need for non-residential advisory centres for the ageing and aged. These should be staffed by doctors, psychologists, and social workers familiar with the problem of this period of life, very much on the lines of a child guidance clinic. The success of such centres will be bound up with the wider measures the community takes to cater for the special needs of the elderly. Old age need not be, as Socrates thought it, 'the sink into which all distresses flow, unrelieved by any joy'.

Although the group of people studied cannot, of course, be taken as an average sample of the aged population, they show many of the social problems familiar to those working among the aged, and it is legitimate to infer that such problems are seen in this group in their most pressing and insistent form. Loneliness, infirmities, disease, idleness, under-nourishment, and poverty were more conspicuous here because these patients represent utter failure to adjust to the social and psychological as well as material privations of old age, and because their deteriorating mental health has made them especially prone to such privations. They are therefore the extreme cases; what is seen in them in high relief is evident less conspicuously in the social contour map of old people generally, showing their needs and troubles; but the picture of well-adjusted old age, making the best of its handicaps, cannot be guessed at from any study of these failures. It is as an indication of the social causes and effects of unhelped old age that this study of breakdown has been designed, and as a pointer towards social means of prevention and treatment.

REFERENCES

1 WILLIAMS, H. W., QUENSEL, E., FISH, V. W. and GOODMAN, L. *Am. J. Psychiat.*, 1942, **98,** 712.
2 FOLSOM, J. K. 'Old age as a sociological problem', *Am. J. Neuropsychiat.*, Jan. 1940, **10,** 30.
3 ROTHSCHILD, D. and SHARP, M. L. *Dis. of Nerv. System*, Feb. 1941, **2,** 49.
4 MEGGENDORFER, F. *Z. Neur. u. Psych.*, 1926, **101,** 387.
5 DIETHELM, O. and ROCKWELL, F. V. *Am. J. Pyschiat.*, 1943, **99,** 553.

12

VOCATIONAL ASPECTS OF NEUROSIS IN SOLDIERS

NEUROTIC SYMPTOMS and the ability to do good work sometimes go together; but the neurotic illnesses which occur in some uprooted men and women in the Armed Forces are seldom compatible with good military work. The work may have been at first poorly done because it was uncongenial, unsuited to the soldier's capacities and previous training, not of his own choosing, tedious and flat, or onerous: and his neurotic illness may have sprung from this failure in occupational adjustment, to which the neurosis will then further contribute. Or the man's military employment may be well enough suited to his abilities and normal interests, but extraneous causes (such as quarrels with his companions, marital troubles, dread or hate of a superior) may lead to a neurotic illness which clogs his work. Some causes and some effects of neurotic illness have no doubt little to do with a man's work; but when every aspect, including the constitutional, has been given its proper emphasis and perspective in the picture of military neurosis, it is plain that unfitness of the man for his present job or of the job for the man is frequently and impressively in the foreground.

This had become so clear by February 1941 that an array of instances and some statistics could be put before the Director of Organization at the War Office who then instituted a procedure for altering the military employment of suitable soldiers with neurotic illness. Many other measures have been introduced, of a thorough and far-reaching kind, to ensure the best use of man-power in the Services and consequently to employ men and women from the outset in the military work suited to their abilities and conducive to their mental stability. The procedure just mentioned, however (often called the 'annexure' system), has remained a valuable means of utilizing the judgment of the psychiatrist in placing soldiers who had broken down, so that after treatment their services might be used to military advantage.

This paper was written in association with Miss K. Goodyear (late administrative sister, Mill Hill Emergency Hospital) and is reprinted from the *Lancet* (1944), **2**, 105–9.

RESULTS OF ANNEXURE

In Mill Hill Hospital more than 1,500 soldiers and 170 women of the A.T.S. had been dealt with through the annexure system by December 1943. In certain groups of patients the proportion dealt with by 'annexure' has been particularly high: thus 35% of all patients admitted with effort syndrome during 1942 were dealt with by annexure, 24% were returned to their former unit and 41% discharged from the Army.

The results of the annexure procedure have been more satisfying than those obtained before it was instituted or without its aid since.

Of those who returned to Army duties from this hospital during the twelve months May 1940 to April 1941 (i.e., before the annexure system), 160 (23%) were doing full duty satisfactorily twelve months later (provided that the 68% sample of men returning to unit whose subsequent history was ascertained can be taken as representative). Of those who were placed by the annexure method between June 1941, and May 1942, 215 (46%) were doing full duty satisfactorily a year later (if a similar assumption be made). Since only those men might be dealt with by annexure who would otherwise have had to be discharged from the Army, it evidently salved men who would otherwise have been lost. During the six months before the annexure scheme, of all admissions here 330 men (36%) were returned to military duty, whereas during the ensuing twelve months July 1941 to June 1942, in which the annexure scheme was available, 58% of all admissions were returned to military duty. Since then the relative percentages have fluctuated considerably. During the 5 successive six-monthly periods following the institution of the scheme (i.e., from 1 July 1941 to 31 December 1943) the percentage of all admissions dealt with by annexure was 38, 41, 23, 30, 17, the percentage of admissions who had to be discharged here unfit from the Army being 41, 42, 60, 50, 54 during the same periods; and 21%, 17%, 17%, 20% and 29% were returned to their former units without benefit of annexure.

It is evident that an opportunity for the psychiatrist effectively to recommend suitable placement in a military occupation has good results. Not only the psychiatrist is concerned in bringing these results about; those with special knowledge and experience of the application of vocational criteria for healthy men in the Army must play a part in it, as has in various ways been the case from the time the scheme was begun. The psychiatrist, however, must take the chief step in making the recommendation. It is instructive to consider on what his judgment has been based, apart from medical considerations in the narrower sense.

REPORTS FROM INSTRUCTORS

It might be assumed that there can be no better guide to suitability for an occupation, other things being equal, than the opinion of a skilled instructor who has lately seen the candidate working at the occupation in question. As part of occupational treatment for the patients here, and as a guide to their suitability for training or employment, the regular staff of the Hendon Technical College have since May 1941, with the generous approval of the Middlesex County Council and of the Principal, conducted classes which were (and are) attended by a maximum of 60 patients at a time, 20 in each class. These have proved extremely valuable, and have advantages over the customary range of hospital occupations. The subjects are of the clerical type (typewriting, bookkeeping, records), and mechanical or engineering (benchwork, elementary electricity, working from blueprints). Each course lasts only 4 weeks, is not intended to provide an adequate training in itself, and is conducted away from the hospital, at the college, in 2-hourly sessions on 4 afternoons a week. Individual reports are sent in every case by each instructor who had the patient in his class; 7 instructors take part in the two courses.

It was anticipated that the instructors' grading would correspond in some degree to the psychiatrist's decision about disposal, and that those men who had done well, say in the mechanical course, would be posted to a mechanical job. A close correspondence however could not be expected, since clinical considerations would also enter into the decision. Actually, of those posted to a mechanical job, after attendance at the course, none had been graded A by the instructors, 19% had been graded B, 71% C and 10% D. The corresponding figures for those posted to clerical duties were 28% A, 27% B, 38% C and 7% D. Of all the patients who attended mechanical classes during two years, 5% were graded A, 33% B, 55% C, 7% D; of all those attending the clerical course, 30% A, 30% B, 32% C, 8% D. Evidently the mechanical classes had less promising patients sent to them or perhaps were judged by a higher standard than the clerical. In order to decide whether the patients sent to the mechanical classes were less promising the two groups were compared in respect of (*a*) their distribution of intelligence levels, and (*b*) the respective proportion of persons discharged as medically unsuitable for further service.

The intelligence level, as measured by the progressive matrices test, showed that among those attending the mechanical classes 8% scored grade 1 (which in the conventional scale corresponds to the top 5% in the average population), 30% grade 2 (the next 20% in the average population), 48% grade 3 (the middle 50%), 13% grade 4 (20% in the average population) and 1% grade 5, whereas the corresponding figures for intelligence among the clerical group were 17% in grade 1, 33% grade 2, 38% grade 3, 10% grade 4 and 2% grade 5. The samples on which this comparison was made numbered 233 for the mechanical class, 198 for the clerical. For the whole group of patients attending the technical college the level of intelligence was higher than for all Army patients admitted to the hospital, among whom the grades were represented by: 7% in grade 1, 19% grade 2, 41% grade 3, 25% grade 4, 8% grade 5 (obtained from a sample numbering 2,650 patients).

The patients selected for the special courses are therefore to some extent an élite.

Using as a second criterion the percentage who have to be discharged from hospital unfit for further military service (category E), the patients taking these courses are found to be somewhat superior to the remainder of the hospital patients; 38% of them had to be discharged unfit, category E, whereas for all admissions to the neurosis centre the percentage was 55.

It is clear that the patients sent to these courses were intellectually and in potential fitness for duty somewhat superior to the general run of the neurotic patients admitted to hospital. Moreover the clerical group included more intelligent people than the mechanical, and the instructors rated the clerical group higher (because they did better or because the standards were less severe) than the mechanical group. The proportion of people discharged from hospital unfit for further service was 34% in the clerical group, 44% in the mechanical.

It is not easy to tell whether the information provided by the instructors led the doctors to form sound conclusions as to the patient's fitness for a particular Army employment or for any Army employment. In many cases this information was an important factor in the decision to discharge the patient from the Army (Table 1); but there is no means of telling whether such a decision has been the right one. The men who are sent back, either by special posting or without the aid of the annexure, to military duty, might be expected to provide a reliable means of judging the usefulness of the instructors' reports. This would be easier if the psychiatrist were guided in his recommendation entirely by the report, but he is of course influenced by many other considerations, medical and military, as may be inferred from Table 1, and

Table 1. Instructors' Grading

	*Mechanical**					*Clerical†*				
	Grade				*Total cases*	*Grade*				*Total cases*
	A	B	C	D		A	B	C	D	
Discharged from hospital unfit, category E	6	31	85	12	134	15	33	31	9	88
Returned to duty (annexure or to former unfit)	8	70	84	9	171	62	44	51	12	169

* $\chi^2 = 11{\cdot}4$, n = 3, P = 0·01.
† $\chi^2 = 11{\cdot}1$, n = 3, P = 0·01.

from the occupational estimate under workshop conditions. The association between the instructor's grade and the doctor's decision is nevertheless significant.

It is, however, possible that if the doctors had paid more attention to the instructors' grading their recommendations for return to duty, whether by special posting or otherwise, would have been more far-sighted; conceivably some of the men they returned to military duty who had to be discharged during the next 12 months might have been better placed or should have been discharged as unfit here. This can be partly tested by seeing whether men with a high instructor's grading did better on return to duty than men with a low grading. In Table 2, 61 of the 'mechanical course' men who are known to have been discharged from the Army within 12 months of their return are compared with 91 of the same group who are known to have been doing full duty efficiently and willingly (in the Home Command) at the end of 12 months after return.

Table 2. Instructors' grading of men known to have been discharged from the Army within 12 months, compared with gradings of men known to be doing well in home command after 12 months

	Mechanical					*Clerical*				
	Grade				*Total cases*	*Grade*				*Total cases*
	A	B	C	D		A	B	C	D	
Discharged, category E, subsequently	3	25	29	4	61	17	16	18	10	61
Doing full duty satisfactorily	6	38	44	3	91	40	30	26	3	99

For the mechanical group there is no significant relationship between the instructors' grading and the subsequent outcome: for the clerical group there is a significant relationship (fusing columns A and B and C and D, $X^2 = 4{\cdot}5$ and P is less than 0·05). It may be concluded from the association between grading and outcome that rather more weight might have been given to the instructors' grading of patients in the clerical course, but there is no evidence that paying more regard to the performance of those attending the mechanical course would have been advantageous.

Some of those, graded D by the instructors, who are now doing full duty, were returned to military employments in which clerical or mechanical ability is not required; the doctor's action was in part based on the adverse judgment passed by the instructors. Without this advice he might have formed a mistaken opinion about the man's untried and sometimes self-proclaimed abilities. 'Il est plus facile,' said la Rochefoucauld, 'de paraître digne des emplois qu'on n'a pas que de ceux que l'on exerce.'

CIVILIAN EXPERIENCE AS A GUIDE

Other questions relevant to vocational advice for neurotic soldiers can be studied on this material. Of those patients who attended the mechanical classes 41% had done work of the mechanical type in civil life: and of those among them who were specially posted to a military employment of the mechanical kind (riveter, driver, fitter in R.E.M.E., etc.), the proportion of men with relevant civilian experience was only slightly higher (47%). Similarly, in the clerical group there were 59% who had done clerical work as civilians: and among those specially posted to clerical Army employment, 63% had civilian clerical experience. An analysis of the data to see whether previous hobbies and bent towards work of the relevant kind had a bearing on the decision reached within the group attending these courses gave equally negative conclusions. The patient's interests, hobbies and civilian occupation had, however, largely determined whether he should attend one of the courses at the Technical College. When the analysis was extended to those hospital patients who had not been posted by annexure and had not attended the special courses, it was found that clerical work or interests in civilian life were reported in only 18% of these, and mechanical or engineering activities in 15%. These figures (derived from 200 consecutive such cases admitted during part of the same period as the men who attended the special courses) and those given above point to an association between a soldier's pre-Service work and inclinations and the doctor's decision about special posting by annexure.

Selection for special posting evidently does not turn only on previous training, experience and interests, but on a due assessment of these along with other relevant considerations chiefly clinical.

THE OPINION OF THE PATIENT

There is a further possible influence. It is sometimes feared that psychiatrists are unduly swayed by the patient's assertions and wishes; and in particular are too ready to recommend, at the patient's suggestion, his discharge from the Army or his transfer to an easier Army employment. Competent psychiatrists are scarcely as pliant and ingenuous as this; it may even be doubted whether they are more pliant and ingenuous in these matters than other doctors or sensible laymen. But it is true that they are alive to the importance

Table 3. Opinions of patients about Army job, related to disposal

	A	B	C	D	E	*Total*
Discharged, category E	31	11	31	26	59	158
Returned to Unit	16	8	24	16	23	87
Posted by annexure	38	18	22	41	62	181
Total	85	37	77	83	144	426

$\chi^2 = 12{\cdot}946$, n = 8, P is more than 0·1.
A = like very much, B = quite like, C = don't mind,
D = not very keen on, E = dislike very much.

of motives and feelings, and take them into account along with other, and perhaps overriding, considerations. In order to find out how far the soldier's overt attitude to his last Army job had influenced the mode of disposal, the men's replies to a written questionnaire, filled out soon after their admission to hospital, were analysed. After various other questions of a non-committal sort, the man had been asked to answer, 'Is your present job in the Army one that you (*a*) like very much, (*b*) quite like, (*c*) don't mind, (*d*) are not very keen on, (*e*) dislike very much,' by underlining the appropriate entry. The findings are shown in Table 3. There is no more relationship between their answers and the doctor's recommendation than chance could account for. It does not appear therefore that in this group of men their initially stated liking or dislike for their Army employment had materially influenced disposal.

INTELLIGENCE LEVELS

It has already been indicated that there were more intelligent men, judged by the progressive matrices score, among those who attended the special courses than in the average neurotic population of the hospital. It is possible that a man's intelligence level influences the doctor's recommendation for disposal. Table 4 (from which 6 men are omitted who scored so low that they were in grade 5 only) shows that there is no such association in this group of men who had been attending the special courses. It cannot, however, be assumed that because there is no evidence of association between intelligence

Table 4. Intelligence of men attending special courses related to disposal, compared with findings in whole neurotic population

	A.*—*Special course men*					B.†—*Whole neurotic population*					
	Progressive matrices grade				*Total*	*Progressive matrices grade*					*Total*
	1	2	3	4		1	2	3	4	5	
Discharged, category E	22	40	81	18	161	57	177	444	275	102	1,055
Returned to unit	10	24	40	9	83	33	121	227	140	27	548
Posted by annexure	20	71	68	22	181	31	118	166	70	12	397
Total	52	135	189	49	425	121	416	837	485	141	2,000

* $\chi^2 = 9{\cdot}822$, n = 6. † $\chi^2 = 44$, n = 3.
P is more than 0·1. P is less than 0·001.

score on the matrices test and disposal in this group, there is no such association for the whole neurotic population of the hospital; this group had, as pointed out above, already been sorted partly on criteria related to intelligence. For the whole neurotic population admitted during a 12 months period, the corresponding figures showing a significant association between matrices grade and Army retention or discharge were as in Table 4. Evidently the less intelligent men are more likely to be discharged than retained.

Not all those who are specially posted by annexure have attended one of the special courses; valuable as the latter are for judging whether certain factors appear to influence the doctor's recommendation about posting, it is misleading to conclude that everything which applies to them applies to others specially posted. A special posting as cook, for example, would depend on different factors from those at work in the bulk of the men here under discussion. Moreover, although the men who are referred to the special course are, in intelligence level and potential fitness for duty, superior to the general run of men admitted to the neurosis centre, this is not true to an equal degree of all men specially posted by annexure.

Thus among 393 men consecutively posted by annexure in 1943, the intelligence grades (measured by the progressive matrices test) were distributed as follows: grade 1, 8%; grade 2, 30%; grade 3, 42%; grade 4, 17%; grade 5, 3%. The corresponding percentages for 1929 men discharged category E in 1943 were: 5%, 17%, 41%, 27%, 10%. The annexure cases as a whole fall midway in intelligence scores between the men discharged unfit and the men attending the special classes.

LATE RESULTS

A follow-up inquiry about 436 men who had attended the special courses and had continued with military duties after leaving hospital yielded information, covering the ensuing 12 months, in 368 (84%), of whom 122 had been discharged unfit category E, 190 were doing full duty efficiently and 56 were doing either light duty or were inefficient though still serving. It is difficult to use such figures for comparison when the replies do not cover the whole sample inquired about. In order to check this, advantage was taken of a special follow-up inquiry made by the War Office and kindly made available by the Directorate of Army Psychiatry. They had investigated the subsequent history of a large number of men posted by annexure from E.M.S. and military hospitals. Adequate replies had been received and analysed in 88% of all cases.

Among those reported on and analysed were 473 patients from this hospital; 186 of them had been discharged category E, 219 were doing full duty efficiently and 68 others were still serving. The hospital follow-up records showed that adequate information had been received independently about 280 of these—of whom 101 had been discharged category E, 148 were doing full duty efficiently and 31 others were still serving. There is no significant divergence between the proportion of the War Office's analysed replies which show number discharged and number doing full duty, and the corresponding proportions in the smaller series here.

It may therefore be assumed that there is no selective factor, concerned with discharge or retention in the Army, invalidating the replies obtained by the follow-up inquiries here; and that in the replies on men who continued in the Army after having attended the special courses, the percentage who had been discharged unfit during the ensuing 12 months was approximately 33, and 52% were still doing full duty efficiently at the end of the year. Comparison of the figures with those of the War Office follow-up of all annexure cases from this hospital during approximately the same period shows a possibly significant difference (P is slightly larger than 0·05) to the advantage of the men attending the special courses. It is of some interest that 3 of the men have since attained commissioned rank.

COMMENT

The method of posting neurotic soldiers on a psychiatrist's recommendation, which was introduced in May 1941, has proved valuable in retaining men in useful service who would otherwise have been discharged unfit. The psychiatrist's recommendations have apparently been influenced by skilled instructors' reports on the men's work during their stay in hospital, and more attention paid to such reports on patients with clerical training or interests would have been advantageous. Other demonstrable influences were the soldier's previous occupation and experience, and his intelligence level. But his professed attitude, soon after admission, towards the last Army occupation he had had before coming into hospital did not seem to have affected the recommendation as to whether he should be discharged as unfit, returned to former unit or specially posted by annexure. The outcome of recommendations made about men who had attended the practical courses in clerical and engineering subjects while in hospital suggested that the psychiatrist's judgment about the fitness of these men for further military service was better than for the whole group of persons posted by annexure; either these men were selected for the special course in the first place by criteria relevant to their future military fitness or the guidance afforded the doctor by the instructor's reports, and the salutary effects of these occupations may have been responsible. Their therapeutic aspect has not been referred to because it could not be measured or judged separately from other methods of treatment, but the testimony of the patients, as well as of those treating them, bears strongly in support of such an influence.

Two matters have been examined here—the value of a scheme of psychiatric recommendations for vocational placement of neurotic men in the Army, and the value of an appropriate occupational scheme at the hospital for guidance in making such recommendations; the criterion of both has been the subsequent Army record of the men who on leaving the hospital continued with Army duties. It is, however, obvious that since the annexure system was only invoked for men who would otherwise have had to be discharged unfit and who were judged to have been unsuitably employed in the Army before admission to hospital, it cannot be regarded independently of other Army procedures, nor compared directly with the results of return to unit without change of occupation. Nor can these difficulties be wholly avoided by comparing the follow-up results of all men who returned to duty after the annexure scheme had been introduced, with the follow-up results of those who returned during the 12 months before it was available. The criteria of suitability for retention in the Army had changed during the two periods in question, in accordance with the man-power situation and other influences; the Army machinery for allocating recruits suitably also improved progressively. Even the criteria of suitability for admission to this hospital changed somewhat during the period. Consequently it is a suggestive rather than a conclusive observation on the value of the annexure scheme that 13% of the 1,782 men admitted to this neurosis centre during the year before its introduction were estimated to be still doing full duty efficiently in the Army 12 months later, as against 19% of all those admitted during the first year of its operation.

To use the success or failure of those who returned to Army duties as the only criterion of the value of the special courses is to ignore their effect on the men who were discharged from hospital unfit for military duties. In many of these, besides the therapeutic value of the occupation, the instructors' reports had provided evidence bearing on the man's unsuitability for any practical military occupation, and helped in the arrangements for rehabilitating him in civilian life; the recommendations made under the interim scheme of the Ministry of Labour reflect this.

It is also to be stressed that ability to perform military duties efficiently need not connote mental health; symptoms may be compatible with working efficiency. It is, however, a more objective indication of their mental health than any other available on those men who returned to military duties. In the follow-up of the men posted by annexure, there were 18, among 287 still serving, who were stated to report sick frequently; and of these 18, 6 were also inefficient. As for the men in the various series here analysed who were discharged unfit from the Army, they were thereafter inaccessible to trustworthy investigation, except in numbers too small to be useful for this purpose.

If any certain conclusion has emerged from the analysis of these data—a deliberately planned experiment would have yielded surer answers, but that was not possible in the circumstances of a war-time neurosis centre for soldiers—it is that the vocational problems of the neurotic cannot be isolated; nor can they safely be left to look after themselves. Decisions about disposal based on a narrow view of occupational background and suitability will be the worse for ignoring other issues, clinically and psychologically important; and a course of treatment in hospital, or a decision about disposal on leaving hospital, will be incomplete if the doctor does not offer the best advice he can about future occupation. There seems no reason to suppose that this is less true of civilians in normal times than of soldiers now. Civilians, moreover, will be able to choose whether they will follow the advice—a salutary liberty, not without value for mental health.

SUMMARY

The results are examined of a scheme whereby hospital psychiatrists can recommend special posting for neurotic soldiers who would otherwise have to be discharged from the Army.

Engineering and clerical courses, specially arranged at a technical college, permitted a closer study of the patients' occupational suitability, of the factors which influenced the psychiatrists' recommendations about disposal and Army employment, and of the success of such recommendations.

The reports of experienced instructors, the previous bent and civilian training of the soldier and his intelligence level proved to have a significant assocation with his disposal and subsequent Army career.

13

SOCIAL PSYCHIATRY

PSYCHIATRY IS mostly thought of as being concerned with the individual. Research has been concentrated on how individual patients behave, the intricate psychological mechanisms in each individual, and the metabolic anomalies or tissue changes that accompany and underlie his disturbed conduct. In this, psychiatry has of course been following the main stream of medicine. Pathology, whether it be psychopathology or cellular and chemical pathology, has been looked for inside the patient's body and mind.

Alongside this traditional and necessary approach to the study of mental disorder, however, there has been a tentative, less explicit awareness of extraneous forces. In primitive societies, and indeed in Western Europe until a couple of centuries ago, this was expressed chiefly in crude animistic superstitions about witchcraft and possession by evil spirits. As we became more sophisticated and critical, such beliefs were of course given up, but the impact of outside forces upon the mind of each individual was still plain enough. The causes of drug addiction provide a glaring example.

The converse was also plain. Every insane person, every unstable neurotic, had an effect upon others which showed his inability to conform, in one way or another, to the customary requirements of ordered society: his failure in this regard was one of the main reasons for considering him mentally ill.

The social causes of mental disturbance, and its social effects, were therefore perceptible to everybody who reflected on the matter. At certain periods of history the evidence was so dramatic that it forced itself even on the unreflecting. There were the epidemics of flagellation and of crazy dancing which broke out in many German cities in the twelfth, thirteenth and fourteenth centuries, disrupting the regular life of the community, and bespeaking grossly disorganized social conditions. A later example is the affair of the Salem witches, at the end of the seventeenth century. A number of adolescent girls, evidently hysterical, declared that they were being harried by the devil at the instance of various people whom they named. In the course of one

---

This paper was delivered to the British Postgraduate Medical Federation in January 1957. It was first published in *Lectures on the Scientific Basis of Medicine*, Vol. 6, 1956–7, published by the Athlone Press in 1958, pp. 116–42.

year (1691–2) two hundred and fifty members of the small New England community where this occurred were arrested and tried: twenty of these innocent people were judicially murdered or tortured to death and the colony was distracted by the fear and dissension engendered (Starkey, 1952).

There was another powerful reminder of how social influences worked upon psychiatry. A revolution was effected in the care of the insane at the end of the eighteenth century: instead of shackling them in cells, beating and whipping them into submission, Pinel in France and Tuke in England introduced the humane and compassionate regime which has ever since been the practice in civilized countries. The reform was of course a manifest product of the immense social forces then at work, which released humanitarian impulses of many kinds.

It is hardly necessary to recall the ways in which the study of mental illness must be incomplete if social factors are not taken fully into account (Simmons and Wolff, 1944). The truth is, however, that until lately social factors were not studied, or even properly allowed for, in the clinical assessment of prognosis and treatment of mental illness. The main reasons for this comparative neglect were the bias in medical education and the lack of a well-developed science of sociology, with appropriate techniques, concepts and theoretical foundations. The claims of psycho-analysis to explain all human behaviour likewise diverted attention from the social causes, and effects, of mental abnormality. All this has changed in the last decade or two, and I shall attempt in this lecture to outline the methods of social investigation that have been used to illuminate psychiatry in the last twenty years. I shall begin with the Hutterite study, carried out in 1950 and 1951 (Eaton and Weil, 1955).

THE HUTTERITES

The Hutterites are a Protestant sect that originated in Switzerland early in the sixteenth century. From the beginning they were persecuted, and had to flee from one country to another, at first from Moravia, then from Hungary, later from Carinthia and Turkey. In 1774 they emigrated to the Ukraine and then, just a century later, moved in a body to the United States. A large section of the Hutterites continued to live in colonies, which have been virtually closed communities for the last seventy years. Only about 2·5% of the colony population have left for the outside world in that period. Some of the colonies are in Canada, in Alberta and Manitoba: others in Montana and Dakota, in the United States.

The religion of the Hutterites forbids marriage outside the sect, and they believe in the common ownership of all property. The community carries the responsibility for its members; it provides them with their clothing, pocket money and food and looks after them when they are ill. They have no wages, no birth-control, practically no celibacy (except for some of the mentally disturbed and defective) and no divorce. The average size of family is eleven or twelve children. The reproduction and survival rates are fairly uniform throughout the population, showing none of the variations with class or educational level which are familiar in other modern populations. It is a stable, but far from stationary, society, with a fairly constant distribution of persons by age and sex. It tends to double its size every sixteen years.

These are almost unique features, suggestive of some ideal pastoral community of earlier times; but there are also, in dramatic contrast, many of the familiar features of present-day Western society. The Hutterites use tractors and refrigerators and up-to-date machinery; they avail themselves of the resources of modern medicine, and schooling is on the usual American or Canadian pattern.

In this seeming Utopia crime and insanity were said by credible witnesses to be almost unknown. Doctors and sociologists agreed that this was so, and the Hutterites' immunity from mental ills was credited to the freedom from tension and conflict inherent in their way of life—a way of life remote from the financial stresses, family dissension and competitive struggles for prestige and power and enjoyment which are evident in most other societies.

Now it was of considerable importance to preventive medicine to determine whether, in fact, the mental health of the Hutterite community is so notably good as all these observers reported. It would illuminate, it might even settle, a long-standing controversy about the effect of competitive Western civilization upon the incidence of mental disorder. This controversy is typified, on the one hand, by gloomy prophets who declare that mental disorder is steadily on the increase in our troubled times, and, on the other hand, by psycho-analysts who regard the experiences of early life within the family as far more decisive for mental health than the trials of daily life and the vicissitudes of the social order. I shall again touch on this question briefly later.

A field survey was therefore made of the Hutterite colonies. It revealed that of the entire community alive at the time of the survey (1951), amounting to 8,542 persons, fifty-three had at some time had a psychotic breakdown, sixty-nine had had a neurotic illness, and fifty-one were mentally defective; there were also twenty epileptics, and six people with psychopathic personality, making 199 in all who had had some psychiatric disability, that is, about 2·3% of the whole community. More than half of these were exhibiting the mental disability at the time of the inquiry, and another quarter had recovered by this time.

This disposed of the hitherto well-attested reputation of the Hutterites for almost complete freedom from mental troubles. It was in keeping with a similar finding on the Navaho Indians, who had been repeatedly described as stolid and contented, but were found on systematic examination to be anxious and emotionally unstable. Its moral was that a consensus of informed opinion is not to be trusted in a matter of this kind: only competent surveys will do. But the study raised a number of questions which have to be answered in nearly all social and epidemiological investigations, especially psychiatric ones.

Was the method of ascertainment trustworthy and fully effective? Is it permissible to lump together diverse conditions—in this case psychoses and neuroses and mental defect? If not, how reliable are the diagnoses which serve to designate the separate classes of illness investigated? And can one compare the attack rates and prevalence rates in one community with those in another whose social characteristics are also known, and so draw conclusions about the relative effect of social variables?

It was only after these questions had been answered that it was found that although the Hutterites were not collectively blessed with the perfect mental health attributed to them, they were better off in this respect than most others of whom we have detailed knowledge, and that sociological factors are indeed significant in promoting mental well-being.

But this broad conclusion has to be qualified: for example it does not apply equally well to psychoses and to neurotic disorders as conventionally distinguished. It is necessary to look at the question more closely.

First, the method of ascertainment. It is not uncommon to take admission to a mental hospital as the criterion of mental disorder, or, more strictly, of psychotic disorder. But the number of people who go into a mental hospital depends, in appreciable measure, on the number of beds available, the administrative arrangements, and the attitude of doctors and the public towards these hospitals—which may be feared, or trusted. The ascertainment of neuroses is a still more difficult undertaking, since there is room for much difference of opinion about marginal cases—which are numerous—and the fullness of the information available may greatly affect the count. Thus, in the Hutterite study the colonies were dealt with in three ways—nineteen of them were investigated intensively; sixty-five were investigated less closely, with brief interviews; and the remaining nine colonies were assessed on the basis of information provided by doctors and by members of the other colonies, including preachers who travelled about to the colonies in question. In the intensively studied population (1,671 persons), 13·8 per 1,000 were judged neurotic; in the less intensively studied (6,123 persons), 7·2 per 1,000 were so diagnosed; and in the population studied through information supplied by others, 2·7 per 1,000. It is most unlikely that these striking differences reflect any real difference in incidence of neuroses.

This problem of ascertainment is the most serious that waylays the investigator of comparative incidence of mental disorder. It is obviously crucial. Compared with the epidemiological study of physical diseases like pulmonary tuberculosis, psychiatric work in this field is beset with diagnostic uncertainties. To overcome them, there has to be much preliminary work. This is aimed at gaining the confidence of the people studied, so that they will give full information, and at developing uniform, operational criteria of 'a case' which will be applied consistently by all those engaged in the work of ascertainment. Though the difficulties inherent in this do not preclude one from comparing the findings in one study, say in Scandinavia, with those in another, say in America or England, they do enforce caution in doing so. In the Hutterite study, for instance, the amount of psychotic illness found would give an expectancy of nearly three times as much psychosis among them as among the rural inhabitants of Thuringia and Bavaria who had been studied earlier by a German psychiatrist (Brugger, 1931, 1938). But scrutiny of the German investigations indicates that patients who had recovered or were for other reasons outside a mental hospital at the time of the inquiry were likely to have been missed, and the diagnostic criteria used were evidently different. In regard to neuroses, firm operational definitions have to be formulated and adhered to steadily. This is even more necessary with psychopathic personality—a notoriously unsatisfactory diagnostic category (Lewis, 1953). Anti-social conduct, however (which of course may be the outcome and evidence of psychopathic personality), is a less ambiguous term, in a given community, and its amount can be measured. Among the 8,542 Hutterites it was practically unknown. There were none who had committed major crimes such as murder or violent assault or had been involved in a sexual offence; only twelve had been found guilty of theft, usually on only one occasion, and there was no juvenile delinquency (apart from one youth who had been trapping animals for their fur without a licence). Alcoholism and other drug addiction was almost non-existent.

The Hutterites, then—that idyllic community—have slightly less psychotic illness than other rural groups in Europe and North America (though depressive disorder is in higher proportion than usual, as against schizophrenia). They have probably the same amount, or perhaps less, neurotic and related psychogenic illness than others do, though this is hard to estimate; they do not engage at all in anti-social activities or violence; and their children do not become disturbed enough to require special action on the part of parents or doctors.

In the light of these findings, should one conclude that the Hutterites are a particularly healthy society? The question is a deceptive one. An individual's mental health can be determined; but not that of a society, unless the term 'mental health' is to be given a different meaning. It can, however, be concluded that the Hutterite community is more peaceable and law-abiding than most, and that this is achieved at the cost of an austere conformity which restricts inventiveness and enterprise.

From the study of this interesting community, so strikingly different from its neighbours, much knowledge was expected, but in the event it cast less light on the effect of cultural and social influences upon mental health than had been hoped for. Eaton and Weil, the very able investigators who carried it out and reported it, sum it up: 'Our findings do not confirm the hypothesis that a simple and relatively uncomplicated way of life provides virtual immunity from mental disorders. . . . Psychoses and other forms of mental disorder were found to occur with regularity in the Hutterite population. Their existence in so secure and stable a social order suggests that there are genetic, organic and constitutional elements which predispose a few individuals to mental breakdown in any social system, no matter how protective and well-integrated it may be. . . . A mental health Utopia is probably impossible.'

CLASS INCIDENCE

If the close scrutiny of the Hutterites yielded so little evidence which would reflect social and cultural influences upon the amount of mental illness or health, it is perhaps hardly to be supposed that differences in incidence would be found between people more uniformly exposed to one culture. But it has frequently been noted that there is a disparity between the urban and rural rates of mental illness and between the rates for different occupations in the same county. Thus in 1953 in Canada urban residents entered mental hospitals as first admissions at approximately a four to three rate over rural dwellers: in several provinces the urban rate was twice the rural rate (Marshall, 1953). Much of the disparity here depends, it is true, on the differing accessibility of services for ascertaining and treating mental disorder. But such an explanation could hardly account for the much more dramatic discrepancy in admission rates between people of different occupation and social class. Thus in England and Wales in the year 1951 admission rates for males in social class 5 were more than twice those for any other class (Registrar-General, 1955). In Canada the first admission rate for labourers was three times that for professional workers. When the individual diseases are looked at, the figures are even more striking. Schizophrenia shows an immense class difference. Whereas 164 men per million of social classes 1 and 2 over 20 years of age were admitted to mental hospitals in England and Wales in 1951 with a diagnosis of schizophrenia, for class 5 the corresponding number was 803 —about five times as high a rate.

This remarkable class difference has been noted elsewhere. A classical study bearing on the matter was carried out in 1937 (Faris and Dunham, 1939) upon patients admitted for the first time to psychiatric hospitals; they found the schizophrenics came to a large extent from homes in densely populated areas of low economic status and 'social disorganization'. A finding of this kind can be interpreted in two main ways: that the conflicts and privations in crowded urban slums favour the development of schizophrenia, or that schizophrenics as they deteriorate drift into these areas.

If the latter explanation were correct, the schizophrenics of social class 5 should include many who had been descending in the social scale or who had been born elsewhere. This was looked into in another ecological study (Hollingshead and Redlich, 1954). The proportion of schizophrenics who had been born elsewhere and 'drifted' into the area where the diagnosis was made was estimated; it did not confirm the 'drift' hypothesis. Neither did a survey of the social class of the patients' families support the 'deterioration' hypothesis. Ninety-one per cent of the patients were still in the same social class as their families; and as to those who had moved socially, more had moved into a higher than into a lower social class. On these New Haven figures (which are, however, at variance with another American study (Gerard and Huston, 1953)) it could be asserted that drift and social mobility do not account for the predominance of social class 5 among schizophrenics.

But before accepting the alternative explanation, viz. that the stresses of poverty-stricken urban life promote schizophrenia, a further social possibility has to be considered. It may be that the schizophrenic from social class 5 is more likely to be referred to a mental hospital though his illness is not severe; or it may even be that people with a mental disorder coming from such a background are more likely to be diagnosed as having schizophrenia. It would lead us rather far to go into these possibilities. No studies that have so far been made have settled the issue; and the class disparities are so great, on the available statistics, that several factors may be at work. The subject is now being studied by at least two groups of investigators in this country, as well as by people in the United States, where most of the work has hitherto been done.

So far we have considered two kinds of inquiry: one comparing the amount of mental disorder in the simple religious people of a rural enclave with that in the competitive communities surrounding them, and the other comparing the amount of schizophrenic mental disorder in the lowest social classes 1 and 2. Neither of these types of inquiry has given a clear answer to the etiological questions which obviously arise, but both stimulate our curiosity further about the possible social causes of mental disorder, and both indicate that the problems are complex, that summary conclusions and unconfirmed opinions are misleading, and that systematic methods are essential.

All the studies of social causation in psychiatry depend on two requirements: adequate detection and measurement of mental disorder in a specified population, and adequate measurement or description of social characteristics in that population. Unless these requirements are met, systematic study is impossible. If they are met, we can make correlation studies within the population, or we can compare populations to see how far and in what way social differences are associated with psychiatric differences. It is, of course, impossible to measure all the psychiatric phenomena that might be relevant, or all the social phenomena; investigations therefore deal with selected variables, chosen to test a hypothesis. The hypotheses have come to a considerable extent from psychiatry and psycho-analysis; but some of the most brilliant ideas have come from sociologists like Dürkheim, and most stimulating investigations have been made by social ecologists like Faris and Dunham.

MARITAL STATUS, EXILE, EMIGRATION

None of these studies, of course, can do much more than point to an association between psychiatric and social variables. How the association comes about, and in what sequence, has to be studied through rather different inquiries, of a more individual and clinical character. Examples of this may be seen in studies of marital status, and of exile or emigration.

Everyone has observed that at every age and in every diagnostic group the hospital admission rate for single persons is appreciably higher than for the married. This is especially the case with schizophrenia and manic-depressive psychosis, and it is much more striking in schizophrenia than in manic-depressive psychosis. In other words, a strong association can be demonstrated between the incidence of major psychoses and the social fact of marriage. This can be extended on the social side, to determine where the widowed stand in this regard, how sex and economic and class status affect the relation, how the proportions differ between countries in which early marriage is the rule or divorce is common, whether the rate among people who are necessarily celibate, like Roman Catholic priests and nuns (Moore, 1936) varies from that of other single people, and so forth. But the three main explanations put forward (Ødegaard, 1946; Norris, 1956) are (1) that a single person is more readily admitted to a mental hospital than a married person; or (2) that those who develop mental disease present pre-morbid personality traits which militate against marriage, so that the married are a positively selected group; or (3) that in married life there are factors which protect against mental diseases. Now in order to look for support or rebuttal of these possible explanations, an intensive study of individuals became necessary. Ødegaard found that in the single patients before their breakdown, unfavourable features of personality (especially schizoid traits) were twice as common as among the married, and that the sexual outlook of the single patients had been passive and cold, especially in the patients with schizoid personality. The second explanation was therefore supported. There are other findings of this kind reported in the study, which was conducted in two stages—the first, an epidemiological analysis of first admissions between 1926 and 1939, altogether 14,231 patients; and the second, an intensive clinical study of 707 patients personally examined by the investigator.

Sainsbury, as I shall mention in a moment, followed a somewhat similar procedure in studying suicide. There is no opposition between the study of individuals (by clinical or psychological methods) and the study of populations—on the contrary, they complement and reinforce one another.

The same combination of extensive and intensive methods has been employed in comparing the mental health of immigrants with that of the population they spring from. Thus Norwegians who migrated to Minnesota had a higher admission rate to mental hospitals than Norwegians in Norway; this was especially so in respect of schizophrenia. To discover whether this should be attributed to the stresses of adapting to a new country, or rather, to the migrants containing a higher proportion of persons predisposed to mental illness, a careful study (Ødegaard, 1932) was made of the personal history and clinical state of each psychotic migrant in the sample, and then, when it appeared that schizoid features, or insidiously developing schizophrenia, had been already evident in the migrants at the time of their leaving Norway, a further scrutiny was made of the course and pattern of illness in the schizophrenic immigrants, to see whether the content of their delusions and similar clinical features testified to the stresses of adapting to their new environment. This was not the case: their clinical picture was in almost all respects identical with that seen in Norwegian mental hospitals. The outcome of these detailed extensions of the study was to support the view that factors in the personality which predispose to schizophrenic breakdown may also conduce to making a man decide to emigrate.

Broadly we may say that the methods used in socio-psychiatric studies thus derive from epidemiology and ecology; from anthropology, sociology and social psychology; and from clinical psychiatry.

The epidemiological method we have already considered. As ascertainment must be effective, it cannot depend wholly on hospital admissions, nor on incomplete volunteer populations, nor on detection of cases by inexpert persons or by doctors with diverse criteria of illness. But because findings open to these objections are obviously subject to error, they are not without value as sources of stimulating hypotheses and as pointers towards further more detailed and dependable studies.

INCOMPLETE DATA

An example of the usefulness of incomplete data is to be seen in an inquiry by Goldhamer and Marshall (1953). It has long been customary to assert that mental disorder is on the increase, because of the more and more complex strains which society imposes on its members. A hundred and thirty years ago the psychiatrist Esquirol read a paper in Paris on the question: 'Are there more madmen today than there were forty years ago?' There was then widespread alarm at 'the rightful increase of insanity', which people said menaced France with calamity. In his admirably critical review Esquirol showed that the alleged increase was spurious; more people had come into hospitals, it was true, but there had been tremendous advances in the facilities for treatment of mental illness, and the reputation of the asylums had changed from that of cruel prisons to humanely conducted hospitals. Many quiet patients who would not formerly have been sent to these institutions were now admitted, and came willingly. Hence the apparent increase. Esquirol, in his well-reasoned article, disposed of the lament about the increase in insanity—but only for a short time: the same cry has often been raised since.

Goldhamer and Marshall decided to check the truth of this assertion. They surveyed the first admissions to Massachusetts mental hospitals for the hundred years beginning 1840. They found, at first blush, a great increase. The crude admission rate per 100,000 at risk in 1840–5 was less than half what it had become in 1940. But when age-specific figures were calculated, the increase was seen to be wholly due to the large number of admissions nowadays of persons over the age of fifty. For the other age groups there had been no increase, although the hospital facilities were of course more plentiful, the public attitude was more favourable, and the hospitals were now admitting neurotic disorders also. The changes that had occurred in the structure of New England society and the large Irish immigration had not made any appreciable difference in the first admission rate for people under fifty (though there had been fluctuations in the proportions in which the various diseases were represented). The increase in admissions over the age of fifty was evidently, as in Esquirol's day, an indication not of increased incidence but of changing social habits; in the last century families were large and accustomed to look after their elderly members even when demented, unless their conduct was intolerable. We cannot, therefore, attribute an increase in mental disorder to the conditions of modern society, with all its struggles and insecurity, so long as we have no convincing evidence that there has in fact been any increase. But the main point here is that Goldhamer and Marshall's study showed how useful conclusions can be drawn from necessarily incomplete data, provided that the limitations of the data are fully recognized.

SUICIDE

Another instance of how incomplete data can be pressed into service is to be seen in Sainsbury's study of suicide (Sainsbury, 1955). We have had, for two thousand years or so, assertions about the morality of suicide, the motives that may prompt or justify it, and the ways to stamp it out. Then people became more interested in its causes, and in the nineteenth century it was well recognized that besides the special circumstances that affected each individual, factors of more general and lasting force were at work. As Buckle put it, in 1857: 'All the evidence we possess respecting it . . . can leave no doubt in our minds that suicide is merely the product of the general condition of society.' Although there are still many who conceive of every suicide as a response to individual misery, and who are dumbfounded when no evident cause can be discerned, it is now plain to anyone who looks into the statistics that social forces operate to determine the gross amount of suicide in a community. What the social forces are, and how the victims are selected, has, however, been obscure.

To inquire into these problems by intensive clinical study of individuals is made almost impossible by the mournful fact that the man who commits suicide has put himself beyond our reach. Those who attempt suicide and survive won't do, because they differ in some essential respects from those who die (Stengel, 1958). Even when we have had ample data about individuals, we have lacked the clue that would guide us safely to the social influences; for about the strength and nature of these influences different psychiatrists expressed divergent opinions, based on their clinical experience.

Sainsbury decided to use the ecological method. He assumed that in a city like London, 'it is possible to differentiate neighbourhoods with particular social characteristics related to the degree of social mobility and social isolation that prevail within them', and he proposed to 'test the hypothesis that where social mobility and social isolation are pronounced, community life will be unstable, without order or purpose, and that this will be reflected to a greater or less degree in the suicide rates because men and women are more prone to suicide when they live in, but apart from, a social group which neither acknowledges nor provides means for satisfying their needs'. He therefore correlated suicide rates in the twenty eight metropolitan boroughs and the City of London with selected social indices, and, as a more intensive and narrow check, he analysed the social and medical information available about 409 persons whose suicide had been reported to the North London coroner during a three-year period.

Sainsbury found that the London boroughs differed significantly from one another in their suicide rates, and showed the same rank order consistently over three decades, although there had in that time been considerable changes in the composition of the resident population. The suicide rates correlated significantly with the indices of social isolation (living alone or in a boarding-house), social mobility (daily turnover of population, and number of immigrants), and divorce and illegitimacy rates. The suicide rate tended to increase in the middle class and decrease with poverty, and it had no relation to the amount of overcrowding and unemployment in the various boroughs. When, however, the individual records were examined, the frequency of unemployment among the suicides was higher than in the general population—no doubt partly because a man's illness prevented him from working and partly because dismissal from work had helped to provoke gloom or despair.

For convincing reasons, Sainsbury concluded that a lonely way of life and some social disorganization favour the occurrence of suicide. Taken by itself, it is not a startling conclusion, but it must be seen alongside the negative findings—for example that there was no intrinsic connexion between overcrowding and suicide, though it was previously thought that there is; and that drift of predisposed persons into the areas that had high suicide rates did not account for these rates.

An ecological study has serious limitations. It presupposes social homogeneity in the ecological area (Clausen and Kohn, 1954). It cannot penetrate into the details of the nexus between social variables and mental illness rate. It can only in exceptionally favourable circumstances enable us to determine which social variables in an area are responsible for that area's rate of mental disorder. It can, however, indicate where a close search into a presumptive causal relationship is well warranted, and where it has little prospect of reward. It does this best when it deals with a clinical anomaly that can be fairly well defined (like suicide); when it has areas whose relevant social characteristics are distinctive and readily ascertainable; and, most important of all, where there is a well-founded hypothesis to be tested.

In Sainsbury's study the main hypothesis, and the method, derived from Emile Dürkheim (Dürkheim, 1951). Dürkheim had divided the social causes of suicide into three classes: those which promote excessive individualism and isolation; secondly, those which exercise compelling authority over the individual, driving him into conforming or altruistic acts such as suttee or giving one's life for another; and thirdly, those which bespeak social disorganization—anomic forces, as Dürkheim called them, which leave the individual unsupported by the social controls and assurances that should keep him steady and secure. This threefold classification by Dürkheim has commended itself to many subsequent workers, though they have mostly paid more attention to the psychological aspects of the matter than he did.

Sainsbury found social isolation to be the predominant social factor in the populations he studied. A similar conclusion could be drawn from a more exotic study, made in Singapore (Murphy, 1954). The population of Singapore falls into five main ethnic groups—Chinese, Indian, European, Eurasian and Malay, each with a different suicide rate. The Chinese, who make up three-quarters of the total population, have a high suicide rate (21 per 100,000) and so have the Indians, whereas the Malays (like Muslims everywhere) have a low rate—only 1·7 suicides per 100,000 of population. Within the Chinese community there are wide variations in suicide rate (from 12 to 24 in men and from 6 to 16 per 100,000 in women) and these variations are associated with tribal factors: the Chinese are immigrants from five different regions of China, and their place of origin can be recognized from the dialect they speak. The smaller and more economically insecure the dialectal sub-group, the higher the suicidal rate tended to be. Similarly the suicide rate was higher in areas where there was most admixture of the dialectal sub-groups, betokening the insecurity of a transplanted minority. Though isolation was evidently a factor in the causation of suicide, it had less effect (according to Murphy, who made this investigation) upon suicide itself than upon the frequency of manic-depressive psychosis (of which, of course, suicide may be an outcome). Murphy's study in Singapore, to which I have just referred, is a striking example of the application of ecological methods to the study of an ethnically mixed population.

CULTURAL INFLUENCE

This brings us to the anthropological methods and issues that are relevant to the social causes of mental disorder (Hsu, 1951; Opler, 1956). The anthropologists have forced us to re-examine our notions of what is normal and healthy. They have demonstrated that behaviour which in our culture would indicate mental disorder is in other cultures acceptable and healthy. The point has been so often made and is so obvious that I need not labour it. It has reinforced the psychiatric maxim that aberrant behaviour can never be assessed in a social vacuum, but must always be related to its background in time and space: the 'here and now' standpoint is, by itself, misleading. Conversely it is by no means easy to decide whether a particular person, living in a culture alien to him or in a culture alien to the examining psychiatrist, is mentally ill or not. The anthropologist is primarily concerned with groups of normal individuals who fulfil culturally approved roles, whereas the psychiatrist is mostly preoccupied with individuals who are somehow at odds with their cultural environment.

The great difficulties which beset the collection and comparison of statistics about prevalence of psychiatric disorders in European, North American and other 'Western' societies are immensely increased when we wish to compare the frequency of mental disorder, and its particular varieties, in Asiatic or African communities with those in our own countries. Attempts have, of course, been made to do this, even on the evidence available from non-literate, 'primitive' communities where such things as adequate mental hospital provision and censuses are unknown. But the data so presented are untrustworthy, except in the few instances where competent investigators have carried out the study.

An example of the latter is the Formosan inquiry into incidence made by Dr Tsung-Yi Lin in 1946–8 (Lin, 1953). Conditions were rather favourable. The society is homogeneous, except for a few large cities and the mountainous districts where the aborigines live. The population has been static for several generations, and falls into two slightly different ethnic groups, both from South China. The investigators were competent, and were themselves Formosans. Yet even so they concluded that apart from the major psychoses and epilepsy they could not make any reliable comparisons between their estimates of the incidence of neurosis, psychopathic personality, or alcoholism and those available from other communities. For psychoses the rate they found was lower (3·8 per 1,000) than investigators have reported from other countries. But the chief interest of this study lay in its implications for the mental health services. The investigators concluded that the family plays so large a part in influencing behaviour in this Chinese culture that the family pattern should be preserved when mental illness brings the patient to hospital. Consequently the wife or mother of a patient became a nursing aide, so that family care was extended to the ward, earlier discharge was made possible, and the responsible relative learnt how to deal with the patient after he returned home. So we find an ecological survey of mental illness in Formosa leading to an arrangement very similar to that arrived at in another way for children admitted to English hospitals.

The diverse forms of mental disorder in different cultures have been of interest to many psychiatrists, including Kraepelin (1904). Some of the manifestations—like running amok or Latah among the Malays—have become very widely known. These varieties of mental illness, strange to us, could be taken to indicate either inherited differences between Malays and ourselves, or cultural differences. That they rest on specific inherited tendencies is very unlikely. If, as we may safely assume, they rest on cultural influences, it is illuminating to see which of our forms of mental illness they correspond to, and how the particular culture has created their characteristic features.

There is a wide range of these unusual conditions. Windigo among Canadian Indian tribes, Koro in South-eastern Asia and Borneo, Candomblé possession in Bahia (Stainbrook, 1952), and other oddly named forms of very queer behaviour have been described in many parts of the world. The best known, and the prototype of many of them, is Latah: it is a reaction provoked by sudden fright and signalized by automatic obedience to commands, imitation of words and gestures, and obscene ejaculations. It occurs in naïve, poorly endowed persons, and among the Malayans is not regarded as much more than an eccentricity, unless it is severe. It occurs not only in Malaya, but also in Java, the Philippine Islands, Borneo, Burma, Siam, India, Siberia and Lapland, Japan and Africa (Yap, 1952). Always it affects the most neglected or backward people, such as the Ainu in Japan, and many of those exhibiting it show evidence of mild dementia or chronic anxiety. It has often been cited as an example of a special disease, restricted to particular ethnic groups. This view can no longer be sustained. It is closely parallel to conduct observed among some American settlers of European origin, and it is similar to the behaviour of superstitious and illiterate people in many times and countries when under the influence of religious excitement. The more careful the clinical study of the condition, the more does it fit into the categories of conventional psychiatry; the more careful the anthropological study, the more plainly does it reveal cultural influences, working upon suggestible, often defective, psychopathic subjects.

There is, however, a risk in putting too much stress on the cultural aspect of strange forms of mental disorder. A congeries of atypical mental conditions seen on the Gold Coast turned out to be manifestations of trypanosomiasis (Tooth, 1950). But where physical disease had been excluded there were still atypical psychoses; indeed Tooth says: 'One is therefore forced to the conclusion that there are real differences in the quality of the psychotic reactions of individuals with different racial and cultural backgrounds, differences which make it impossible to fit them into the accepted nosological framework.' To examine this conclusion properly, we should have to consider the basis on which we differentiate our accepted nosological classes, but, apart from this fundamental question, the illustrative cases and comments which Tooth provides make his conclusion questionable. It is, at all events, clear from what he tells us in his Report that social influences play a notable part in determining the course and form of mental illness. Thus, apropos of atypical psychoses in which there were delusions, hallucinations, and shallow affect, he writes: 'Most of the individuals came from the Northern Territory and those from the South were found in small villages where their lives, both before and during their illnesses, were relatively simple and sheltered. In only a few instances had any form of restraint been used, and then only by the family within the family compound. As soon as the acute phase had passed, the patient was encouraged to carry on with his usual activities, and, by virtue of his peculiarities, he acquired a certain standing in the community. Thus, without losing the background of family security, he was kept occupied in familiar surroundings, a situation which mental hospitals all over the world are seeking to achieve by artificial means. Contrasting these people living in their homes with those who have strayed to the large towns and those who have been confined to the asylum, one is struck by the dilapidation of the former, and the restlessness and florid symptomatology of the latter. It is suggested that these endogenous psychotics, left to fend for themselves outside the family, would have developed into the dilapidated eccentrics of the market-place but, if transported into an alien and restricted environment, would have produced the symptomatology of one of the familiar varieties of schizophrenia. In short, the form of psychosis had been determined by the treatment.'

The extent to which the form of a psychosis can be affected by the cultural and climatic conditions of a people is well illustrated by the Windigo psychosis of the Chippewa, Ojibwa and Cree Indians (Landes, 1938; Linton, 1956). These people suffer terrible hardships in the severe winters of north-east Canada. The scarcity of game obliges each family to live by itself, exposed to the risk of starvation; cannibalism sometimes occurs. They have myths about a monster, living as an ice skeleton during winter and dying in the spring, who devours human beings. They believe also that human beings may be led, by witchcraft, to develop similar cannibal desires and to have their heart turn to ice. In fact some members of the tribe do become profoundly depressed and excessively anxious about starvation. Their perceptions then become disturbed and they see members of their family as plump, succulent, inviting beavers. Some of those affected have insight into their condition and beg that they should be killed before they give way to their cannibal urge; others actually kill and eat members of their family and eventually other people if they are not caught in time. Normally, if I may use the word in this context, the tribe seize the patient, as soon as he has eaten anyone, and kill him—burning his corpse in order to destroy the hidden ice which they believe to be so potent.

The broad connection here between the physical privations and risks and the form of insanity in these tribes is evident, but as Linton points out, it would be false to attribute this psychotic behaviour entirely to the stresses of the environment. There are many other places where tribes face as grave a risk of cold and starvation as these Canadian Indians, but they have no such cannibalistic psychoses. 'Thus, whereas hunger and ice are ever-present threats also in other areas, this particular psychotic phrasing of the manifestations of ultimate despair is a distinctively localized and cultural phenomenon, closely correlated with many aspects of Chippewa mythology, shamanism, social organization, economy and habitat.'

There are many reports about psychotic behaviour in primitive societies which similarly show how the culture of a people colours and shapes the clinical picture of insanity. It may be objected, however, that such findings have little or no relevance to our problems: these crude people with their fantastic superstititions and simple way of life are too remote from our highly organized, rational, individualistic society to permit us to generalize and apply what we learn from studying them. But the contrast is not so glaring as it seems. Anthropologists have shown that it is false to picture primitive societies as relatively uniform aggregations of custom-ridden savages, and we know well enough how many irrational beliefs and how much irrational conduct can be found in Western societies. Moreover, culture (in the sense in which anthropologists use the term) covers not merely the social organization, the way of life, of a society, but also its symbolism, its language, art, gestures and other modes of expression and communication. The core of a people's culture lies in ideas, values and habits that have been historically selected over a long period. It moulds the individual, brings him into relation with others, and, of course, may itself be modified by what he and other individuals originate or contribute to it. Every cultural system is complex, and cultural similarities turn up in the most unlikely places. The deficiencies in psychiatric studies of 'primitive' cultures lie not in the place or method of study, but in the imperfect knowledge we have of the details of the psychiatric disorders and of the social structure and beliefs in the societies in question. It is hard enough to find out all we should know about mental illness and its background here, where we are at home and have access to so much information: when we come to Latah, or Arctic hysteria, or Koro or Piblotok among the Eskimos of Greenland, we have only approximate information, mostly collected by people with insufficient expert knowledge of what is required.

A special cultural feature to which much attention has been paid is the child-rearing practices of a given society. It is of course a commonplace that childhood is the most plastic and impressionable period of life. Psychoanalytic views put particular stress on certain phases and experiences of childhood as determinants of subsequent personality and of mental abnormalities. A great deal has in consequence been written about the effects of various sorts of infant training and of deprivation of mother love (Bowlby, 1951; Erikson, 1951). Critical examination of this literature (Orlansky, 1949; Lindesmith and Strauss, 1950; Hsu, 1951; Pinneau, 1955; Opler, 1955) shows that it is loosely stated and much of the evidence is inadequate to bear the conclusions drawn. The main inference, that it is beneficial for a child to have been kindly and affectionately brought up, needs no reinforcement since it conforms to universal experience. But when the social implications come to be considered, there is a dearth of well-designed, properly evaluated studies. On the whole this has been, in proportion to the amount written about it, so far an unrewarding field of research in social psychiatry.

THE FAMILY

Family relationships in general, however, are a ground of common concern where the professional interests of psychiatrist, sociologist and anthropologist meet. For the sociologist the family is a nuclear unit; for the anthropologist bonds of kinship are of the first importance; and for the psychiatrist the family is the matrix within which the individual is moulded and developed, the area where his strongest emotional ties are formed, the background against which much of his most intense personal life is enacted. There is therefore need to study the family, not only from the psycho-analytical and psychological standpoint but also to discover how mental illness impinges upon it, and what effects this sort of incapacity has on the family structure.

The problem is obvious enough when neurotic disorders like hysteria or hypochondriasis wear down the patience and affection of other members of the patient's family, or when psychopathic personality, alcoholism or sexual perversions play havoc with family life. Schizophrenia, which may entail many years of continuous mental hospital care, leads to far-reaching changes in the family, which are important in assessing prognosis and especially in regard to the chances of social rehabilitation.

The impact of mental illness, especially schizophrenia, upon the family is now being studied by joint groups of psychiatrists and social psychologists in Washington, and also in London. But as one of the investigators has recently put it: 'One might anticipate that so substantial a practical problem, with so many aspects of significance for understanding the dynamics of human relationships, would have been thoroughly studied by social scientists. Unfortunately, this is not at all the case. With the exception of a few papers . . . there is as yet practically no research literature on the impact of mental illness on the family' (Clausen and Yarrow, 1955). Nevertheless there is no dearth of opinions, based on clinical experience and current assumptions about family relations. It is in the light of these unconfirmed opinions that the clinician usually acts when he attempts to rehabilitate and resettle, say, a schizophrenic who had been for years in a mental hospital and who still has residual symptoms (Carstairs, O'Connor and Rawnsley, 1956). The empirical procedure is often successful. But there is an obvious gulf between these more or less intuitive efforts and the application of assured knowledge about the social meaning, social effects and social possibilities of treatment in mental illness.

The impact of mental illness is, of course, not only on the family, but on wider circles—on the fellow-workers and other associates of the patient; on those who entrust themselves to him (in the way that patients put themselves in the hands of a doctor, soldiers of a general or passengers of an engine-driver); and mental illness has its impact finally on society at large—a paranoid assassin, a psychopathic dictator, a melancholic religious leader, can exert a far-reaching effect even on generations unborn, and mental illness, as an economic and psychological burden, has its cumulative effect on society.

Without ranging too far in place and time, it is useful to examine the extra-familial aspects of social adjustment to mental disorder, and also to mental defect. It was, in fact, work on mental defect by the Social Psychiatry Research Unit (Medical Research Council, 1953; O'Connor and Tizard, 1956) that paved the way for the studies we are now making in the social relations of schizophrenia. It is impossible to develop a sound programme for the social and occupational betterment of high-grade defectives or imbeciles unless one has first examined, and as far as possible measured, the abilities of the affected population, and then organized a training procedure which takes into account these estimates of ability to perform tasks and to learn new ones, and which prepares the defectives, under experimental conditions, to respond adequately to social requirements and to carry social responsibility. The preparation has included group psychological treatment, and a graduated series of rewards and responsibilities; also close examination of the situation in the patients' families and at their prospective residences and places of work. Psychological, clinical and social studies have thus gone hand in hand. The result has been impressive. At the hospital where the work was carried on, many defective patients were resettled in the general community: and in financial terms, the change was from £8,131, earned by the patients on daily licence, in 1948 to £30,000 in 1951. But the result cannot be measured by earnings, but by the well-being of those defectives who return to lead a fairly normal and happy existence in society. Though satisfying, the fruits of this research point to the necessity for further sociopsychological inquiry directed not only at those who have been certified and admitted to an institution but also at the numerous patients who have all along been cared for at home.

SOCIAL ASPECTS OF TREATMENT

The social aspects of psychiatric treatment are manifold. The attitude a society has towards mental disturbance and its treatment is itself an important, far from static, social force, determining how far existing facilities are availed of and how far different or more extensive facilities are demanded. Swayed by the prevailing social attitudes, the patient or his relatives often nowadays put pressure on the psychiatrist to provide electrical convulsant therapy, or tranquillizing drugs, or leucotomy, or psycho-analysis; conversely, the social climate may make them refuse a particular treatment. Leucotomy is legally forbidden in at least one large country, and frowned on in others, for reasons that have little or nothing to do with its therapeutic efficacy.

There are many current developments: the growth of day hospitals, and of interest in mental hospitals as therapeutic communities, the increasing public concern for the corrective treatment of juvenile and other offenders, the public eagerness to know about psychopathology and therapy, and the desire of alarmed parents to be told how they can bring up their children without doing them some irreparable psychological harm. These developments are signs of the interplay between social forces and psychiatry. They are not all equally sound and welcome. Public expectations are sometimes, unfortunately, fed with information that is incomplete or ill-founded. It will be salutary, when this is no longer so. More knowledge of the social, as well as of the somatic and psychological processes that operate in psychiatry, will prevent unreal hopes being fostered and permit more effective measures of prevention and amelioration than we yet have.

REFERENCES

BOWLBY, J. *Maternal Care and Mental Health*, Geneva, World Health Organization, 1951.
BRUGGER, C. *Z. ges. Neurol. Psychiat.*, 1931, **133**, 352.
BRUGGER, C. *Ibidem*, 1938, **160**, 189.
BUCKLE, H. T. *History of Civilization in England*, London, Longmans, 1857.

CARSTAIRS, G. M., O'CONNOR, N. and RAWNSLEY, K. *Brit. J. prev. soc. Med.*, 1956, **10**, 136.
CLAUSEN, J. A. and KOHN, M. L. *Amer. J. Sociol.*, 1954, **60**, 140.
CLAUSEN, J. A. and YARROW, M. R. *J. soc. Issues*, 1955, **11**, 3.
DÜRKHEIM, E. *Suicide: A Study in Sociology* (tr. J. A. Spaulding and G. Simpson), Glencoe, Ill., Free Press, 1951.
EATON, J. W. and WEIL, R. J. *Culture and Mental Disorders: A Comparative Study of the Hutterites and Other Populations*, Glencoe, Ill., Free Press, 1955.
ERIKSON, E. *Childhood and Society*, London, Imago, 1951.
ESQUIROL, E. *Des Maladies Mentales*, Brussels, 1838.
FARIS, R. E. L. and DUNHAM, H. WARREN. *Mental Disorders in Urban Areas*, Chicago, University Press, 1939.
GERARD, D. L. and HUSTON, L. *Psychiat. Quart.*, 1953, **27**, 90.
GOLDHAMER, H. and MARSHALL, A. W. *Psychosis and Civilization*, Glencoe, Ill., Free Press, 1953.
HOLLINGSHEAD, A. B. and REDLICH, F. C. *Amer. sociol. Rev.*, 1954, **19**, 302.
HSU, F. L. K. *Southwestern J. Anthropol.*, 1951, **8**, 227.
KRAEPELIN, E. *Z'blatt Nervenheilk*, 1904, **15**, 433.
LANDES, R. *J. ab. soc. Psychol.*, 1938, **33**, 14.
LEWIS, A. *Brit. J. Sociol.*, 1953, **4**, 109. (See also *The State of Psychiatry*, 1962.)
LIN, T. *Psychiatry*, 1953, **16**, 313.
LINDESMITH, A. R. and STRAUSS, A. L. *Amer. sociol. Rev.*, 1950, **15**, 587.
LINTON, R. *Culture and Mental Disorder*, Springfield, Ill., Thomas, 1956.
MARSHALL, H. *Mental Health Statistics*, Ottawa, Dominion Bureau of Statistics, 1953.
MEDICAL RESEARCH COUNCIL. Report for the Year 1951–2, London, H.M.S.O., 1953.
MOORE, T. V. *Ecclesiastical Rev.*, 1936, **95**, 486 and 601.
MURPHY, H. B. M. *Med. J. Malaya*, 1954, **9**, 1.
NORRIS, V. *J. ment. Sci.*, 1956, **102**, 467.
O'CONNOR, N. and TIZARD, J. *The Social Problem of Mental Deficiency*, London, Pergamon Press, 1956.
ØDEGAARD, Ø. *Emigration and Insanity*, Copenhagen, Levin and Munksgaard, 1932.
ØDEGAARD, Ø. *J. ment. Sci.*, 1946, **92**, 35.
OPLER, M. K. *Soc. Problems*, 1955, **3**, 12.
OPLER, M. K. *Culture, Psychiatry and Human Values*, Springfield, Thomas, 1956.
ORLANSKY, H. *Psychol. Bull.*, 1949, **46**, 1.
PINNEAU, S. R. *Psychol. Bull.*, 1955, **52**, 429.
REGISTRAR-GENERAL, *Statistical Review of England and Wales: Mental Health: 1950–1951*, London, H.M.S.O., 1955.
SAINSBURY, P. *Suicide in London: An Ecological Study* (Maudsley Monograph Series), London, Chapman and Hall, 1955.
SIMMONS, L. W. and WOLFF, H. G. *Social Science and Medicine*, New York, Russell Sage Foundation, 1954.
STAINBROOK, E. *Amer. J. Psychiat.*, 1952, **109**, 330.
STARKEY, M. L. *The Devil in Massachusetts*, London, Hale, 1952.
STENGEL, E. *Attempted Suicide* (Maudsley Monograph Series), London, Chapman and Hall, 1958.
TOOTH, G. *Studies in Mental Illness in the Gold Coast*, London, H.M.S.O., 1950.
YAP, P. M. *J. ment. Sci.*, 1952, **98**, 515.

14

THE OFFSPRING OF PARENTS BOTH MENTALLY ILL

I PRESENT this brief paper diffidently, because of the lapse of time—over 20 years—since the material was obtained.

In 1932 I began to collect information about patients who showed 'conjugal psychoses' and about their offspring. The offspring, however, were in so many instances still young that I thought no statistical legerdemain could be a substitute for patience and complete data such as might be obtained by waiting another ten years, i.e. until 1943, then re-establishing contact with the offspring; and if necessary repeating the process in 1953, by which time almost all the children would have passed the age of risk. However I reckoned without my host: in 1943 we were all otherwise engaged and when I tried to pick up the threads, more recently, I found that in the interval the disruption of communities because of bombing and movements of population, had put it out of my power to find the people again. Searching the central register of all persons admitted to the mental hospitals of England and Wales presented another possible way of discovering the psychotic offspring, but women who had married in the ensuing twenty odd years were untraceable because of the change of surname, and there were other technical difficulties in identifying individuals.

It was plain that the material must be presented as it was in 1933, or not at all. The publication in 1952 of Professor Elsaesser's monograph suggested that even a small further series deserved to be put on record.

The method of collecting the parents was based on a large card-index at the Maudsley Hospital, compiled at the instance of the late Sir Frederick Mott. Mott, deeply interested in the heredity of mental disease, persuaded the doctors of the London County Asylums to send him details of every instance in which a patient admitted to their mental hospital already had another member of his family in a London County Asylum. The system was introduced in 1908, and by 1932, when I wanted to use it, the register was very

This paper was read at the First International Congress of Human Genetics at Copenhagen, August 1956. It is reprinted from *Acta Genetica et Statistica Medica* (1957), **7**, 349–65.

extensive. The doctors had interpreted Mott's request literally, and had therefore included husbands and wives as members of the same family, though Mott had not intended them to do so, wanting only parent and child, sibs, and collateral relatives. The nature of the relationship was always specified, and by going through all the cards I was able to extract the names of 384 husbands and wives (192 couples). The earliest date of admission was in 1862 and the latest 1931. Although many of the patients had blood-relatives also recorded in one of the London asylums, there is no reason to suspect that this influenced the inclusion of the husbands and wives; certainly the existence of any psychotic offspring of such couples was so rare an entry on the cards that it could not have played any part in the selection. We had therefore a pretty clean sample of 'conjugal psychoses' reported in the London asylums (which at that time had in all about 20,000 beds).

Scrutiny of the case records of the 384 patients showed that in 71 couples one or both of the partners had been affected with G.P.I. These were investigated separately, to discover how many of the surviving children had developed neurosyphilis: but I shall not say anything more of these. The offspring of the remaining 121 couples were then searched for, using their original addresses and the addresses of their relatives during the time the patients were in the mental hospital. Bearing in mind the length of time that had elapsed in most cases, the mobility of an urban population and the particular factors favouring the dispersal of families so drastically affected, it is obvious that tracking the offspring down was a most elaborate and often baffling business. In many instances it necessitated visiting eight or nine addresses in widely dispersed areas, searching nominal rolls, and so forth. This skilled and exacting work was carried out by Mrs Janet Jackson, a psychiatric social worker who succeeded remarkably in what is surely one of the most delicate field-inquiries that can be undertaken—a complete stranger calling on the children of parents who have both been insane, explaining to them the reason for the visit which recalls painful memories and personal fears, and then inquiring into their own lives and the mental health of their brothers and sisters. This Mrs Jackson accomplished with such tact and sympathy that many of those whom she had approached wrote appreciatively to her afterwards or invited her to come again: she found that 'those who felt secure in themselves were co-operative because of their security, and those who dreaded the possibility of such trouble (psychosis) in their own cases were often expansive, glad to talk over their anxiety with an impartial stranger'.

Twelve of the couples had had no offspring; others had had children who died before the age of 20 or had not reached that age by the time the investigation was made. These couples were excluded from the inquiry, as were also couples one or both of whom had had epilepsy, senile or arteriosclerotic dementia or other organic disease causing the initial psychosis for which the patient had been admitted to the mental hospital. When these couples had been eliminated, together with those who could not be traced, we were left with 40 couples who had at least one child over the age of 20.

For these 40 couples there were 143 children who had survived until over 20. Nine of the children had passed the age of 60; four were over 70.

Whenever it was known that one of the offspring had been in a mental hospital his case records were of course obtained; any of the offspring not in a mental hospital who showed symptoms suggesting abnormal personality or neurotic or other mental disorder, was seen by me, if he would consent to this.

The diagnosis of the parents' illnesses presented great difficulties. Some of these are common to all family studies: others arose from the special circumstances of this inquiry, depending as it did on the clinical records of London mental hospitals during a period roughly covering the last quarter of the nineteenth century and the first quarter of the twentieth. During that period the terminology and the classificatory outlook prevailing among doctors in English mental hospitals was remote from that now employed: it is therefore impossible to use the diagnoses made by those who knew the patients well, and hazardous to attempt to rediagnose the patient's illnesses in current or Kraepelinian terms. However it had to be done. Like others, I have had special doubts about what to do with involutional melancholia, with the late-appearing paraphrenic forms, and the chronic paranoid psychosis that supervenes on an acute alcoholic hallucinosis. The form and course of the illness rather than its origins or age of onset, or the illnesses of the patient's relatives, have been what I relied on: and in consequence I have usually reckoned the involutional depressions with the affective group, and the paranoid conditions just referred to with the schizophrenias: atypical conditions were distinguished from unequivocal ones, and when both schizophrenic and affective features were equally prominent, I have allowed the course of the illness to decide in which category to place it. As my material is small I have made no further subdivision, such as Schulz used. The clinical records on which any diagnosis must be based in these cases are so defective for the purpose that it would be futile and misleading to try to squeeze inferences out of them by refined analysis or casuistry.

Table 1. Number of parental couples with endogenous psychoses

	Schulz	*Elsaesser*	*Lewis*
Schizophrenia × schizophrenia	20	14	4
Affective psychosis × affective psychosis	17	4	5
Affective psychosis × schizophrenia	15	4	7
Atypical endogenous psychosis in one or both parents	45	15	24
	97	37	40

If it seems that my series is of a respectable size, on the whole, when set alongside Professor Elsaesser's or even Dr Schulz's, I must emphasize that the amount of information I collected about the subjects was much less than they were able to accumulate on their families.

Among the offspring, those who had had signs of mental disturbance without having been admitted to a mental hospital for it, were a further diagnostic problem. In many cases the amount of information about them was enough to raise a doubt, but not enough to resolve it. There is, of course, much to be said in favour of including, for example, brief or mild hypomanic and depressive illnesses in the same category as the manic-depressive illnesses necessitating mental hospital care. If, however, a similar principle were adopted in respect of parents, age of onset in many of them would be pushed back twenty or thirty years; much larger collections of 'conjugal psychoses' could be made, but the comparability of different investigators' findings would become much lower than at present.

In this series, therefore, for practical reasons those children who have had treatment in a mental hospital are dealt with separately and called 'psychotic'. Those whose disturbances of personality and behaviour have been dealt with at general hospitals, outpatient departments, or by general practitioners are listed apart from the 'psychotic', even though their illnesses may have clearly belonged to the schizophrenic or affective category. The reasons for this do not derive from belief in a distinction between neurotic or 'psychogenic' disorders on the one hand, and 'constitutional' or psychotic ones on the other, but from the practical need to have an arbitrary definition of a 'case'. Also for practical reasons, the reported occurrence of ulcerative colitis, asthma and other 'psychosomatic' illness in some of the children has not been included: the information is too meagre and inexact to warrant its use.

To calculate the proportion of children who are affected among those exposed to risk, I have used the shorter Weinberg procedure, taking twenty years as the lower limit of the period of risk, and fifty years as the upper limit. I have reckoned every psychotic child as one, irrespective of his age; and I have throughout taken age as being age at death, or at the latest period for which information is available. The upper limit of fifty was taken for this calculation, in all cases, without regard to whether the parents were schizophrenic or manic-depressive, for the following reasons: the age of onset of the first attack is higher in this material than in a representative sample of all schizophrenic or manic-depressive persons: it is impossible when one parent is manic-depressive and the other schizophrenic, to arrive at a corrected figure for children at risk which would discriminate in respect of upper limit between those who might become schizophrenic and those in danger of affective psychosis; the Strömgren and the Slater devices for calculating the Bezugsziffer seem unnecessary for such small numbers. It is worth noting moreover that in Slater's twins and their relatives he found that as many as 20% of his schizophrenic subjects had first fallen ill after the age of 40; indeed 6% had first fallen ill after the age of 50. Similarly more than half of his subjects with affective illness had not broken down until after the age of 40.

I must return to the age of onset in the parents: it was high. The figure given is that at which indubitable signs of psychosis appeared. Often the record showed that mental abnormality had been evident for years before this but was disregarded because it was inconspicuous or insidious. In others this was not the first attack, but the first to require mental hospital admission. In many of the illnesses classed as affective, beginning in the fifties or sixties, the patient had been discharged 'recovered', and in several of them was known to have been free from illness for up to fifteen years subsequently. When there was serious room for doubt regarding the presence of arteriosclerotic, presenile or senile or other cerebral disease, the pair in question were eliminated from the study, though dementia supervening after, say, ten or fifteen years in the mental hospital was not taken as a ground for exclusion.

Reports of family and twin studies, including Dr Schulz's and Dr Elsaesser's reports on the offspring of psychotic pairs have usually included detailed

Table 2. Children of parents with typical schizophrenia

Parental pair	*Age of onset*	*Children*	*Corrected children at risk*	*Psychotic children*	*Diagnosis of these*	*Age of onset*	*Other children affected*	*Diagnosis of these*	*Total children affected*
N. E.	25, 28	2	2	1	Schizophrenia	26	1	Obsessional attacks with depression	2
W. H.	40, 44	2	0·5	—	—	—	—	—	—
W. M. S.	33, 23	3	1·5	—	—	—	—	—	—
W. G. W.	29, 48	5	4·5	2	1. Schizophrenia 2. Schizophrenia	39 26	1	Paranoid psychopath	3
4		12	8·5	3			2		5

Table 3. Children of parents with atypical schizophrenia

Parental pair	*Age of onset*	*Children*	*Corrected children at risk*	*Psychotic children*	*Diagnosis of these*	*Age of onset*	*Other children affected*	*Diagnosis of these*	*Total children affected*
C. C.	43, 44	5	3·5	—	—	—	—	—	—
J. L.	31, 40	2	1	—	—	—	—	—	—
H. P.	42, 41	8	4·5	1	Schizophrenia	22	1	Severe reactive depression with paranoid features	2
3		15	9	1			1		2

clinical accounts of the persons dealt with in the inquiry, so that others could reconsider the diagnosis, if they wished: and the authors have usually been driven to rather anguished acknowledgment of the misgivings they had felt about the diagnosis in particular instances, and the straits to which they had been put in making up their minds about it. This report is no exception: and I put the tables forward with no claim for diagnostic certitude, though in the psychotic children I have not experienced as a rule any serious difficulty in deciding on the diagnosis, chiefly because the hospital records were much fuller and more satisfactory for the purpose.

Schizophrenic parents

Schulz estimated the probability of schizophrenia in the offspring of schizophrenic parents at 41% if both parents had the disease in typical form, at 30% if one of them had it in atypical or doubtful form. The atypical forms in my series included a husband and wife (C. C.), both aged 44, who were admitted to hospital on the same day in 1906. The wife had belonged to a very narrow sect; both she and her husband had been extremely religious during the twenty years of their married life. Two and a half years before admission, God began to speak to them both. Towards the end of 1904 they burnt their furniture, on divine instructions, and in 1905 God spoke to the husband ordering him to throw up his work and prepare for a special mission. During the ensuing twelve months they remained strictly within their house, reading the Bible and praying, and waiting to be taken bodily to heaven. The Lord spoke to them daily and appeared to the wife in visions. On admission the husband expressed many delusions about his divine mission, said God had thrown him to the floor on one occasion, and constantly spoken to him. He charged his neighbours and his sons (who had supported him during the twelve months he stayed away from work) with plotting against him. The wife told of the same beliefs and experiences—visions, God's voice which had to be obeyed, promises of being taken up into Heaven. She improved and recovered insight faster than her husband: she said her message had begun at an earlier date than her husband's, but that she had been influenced by him. He too improved, but had a relapse: he was not able to leave hospital until after ten months—his wife left after six months. (This pair is rather like the pair IV-16 in Schulz's series of 'querulants and induced insanity', and reminiscent also of his pairs IV-5, IV-7, and IV-17; but there are also considerable differences.)

In another pair (J. L.), the husband had a gross catatonic schizophrenia (punctuated with outbursts of excitement) which lasted from his admission in 1906 till his death in the mental hospital in 1936. His wife was admitted in December 1912: she was much under-nourished, having had great difficulty in supporting her two children since her husband went to hospital. She was said to have starved herself to feed the children and pay the rent. She also had a mitral lesion, was quite deaf and nearly blind: she had had a double iridectomy. On admission, she believed she was receiving messages through a spirit and that blood gushed from her fingers carrying her secrets with it. There was much evidence of thought disorder of the schizophrenic type. She had auditory hallucinations, said the spirits of all her relatives were passing through her body, and talked to herself constantly. After she had been five years in the mental hospital, isolated by her deafness and blindness, but sometimes quarrelling and fighting with other patients, she was taken out by her mother but subsequently had to be readmitted. Subsequent notes record her profound depression, her fights with other patients, hypochondriacal complaints and 'answering the voices all day long'. She died in hospital in 1941. It is clearly impossible retrospectively to judge how far deafness, blindness and malnutrition contributed to the clinical picture, and the classification as 'atypical schizophrenia' could be questioned.

The relation of type of mental illness in the offspring to that in the parents is illustrated by the third pair in the atypical schizophrenic group (H. P.). The husband was admitted to hospital in 1913, with many paranoid delusions—his wife was conspiring with his neighbours to flick pepper into his eyes, the authorities at the Infirmary had tried to murder him by poisoning his food, and so forth. He continued, without much recorded change in his mental state, during the next ten years, and was thought by the doctors who looked after him to be becoming demented. However in 1923 he escaped from the mental hospital and, though he remained hallucinated and muddled, he picked up the threads of his normal life sufficiently, and nine years later was still at home. His wife was first admitted to a mental hospital in 1903, with auditory hallucinations and beliefs that she was being poisoned and defrauded, chiefly by her husband. She improved but was still prone to laugh incongruously and express far-fetched ideas, when her husband took her out of hospital 'not improved' four months after admission. In 1927 she was readmitted, expressing much the same delusions as a quarter of a century earlier—her food was being poisoned, her husband had marked her for death. She said she was older than the Virgin Mary, she misidentified people, and she asserted she was pregnant. She remained in the hospital until her death in 1938: latterly she had occasional fits, probably uraemic, and became demented. The eldest son of this pair was admitted to a mental hospital in 1910, when he was 22. He showed many catatonic features and heard voices telling him he was wicked. He was in a semi-stupor for about a year after admission, he gradually emerged from this, becoming abusive, grimacing and performing antics. He believed his thoughts were read, and that he was being persecuted. From 1914 onwards he was rather more in touch but was considered to show much deterioration. His father took him out of hospital in 1923 (shortly after his own escape!) and the patient remained at home for the next nine years, unoccupied, refusing to get up or wash, and threatening to kill his sister, who looked after the house.

There are similarities here between father and son, but differences in form are also striking: the father's illness was throughout paranoid, the son's catatonic in the main: and the mother's, likewise paranoid, was in the first instance episodic. The prospect of elucidating genetically distinct clinical forms by scrutiny of individuals such as these, is not encouraging.

Table 4. Children of parents with typical affective psychosis

Parental pair	*Age of onset*	*Children*	*Corrected children at risk*	*Psychotic children*	*Diagnosis of these*	*Age of onset*	*Other children affected*	*Diagnosis of these*	*Total children affected*
H. A.	57, 46	3	1·5	—	—	—	2	1. Depression 2. Depression	2
C. H.	55, 52	1	1	1	Recurrent depression	26	—	—	1
J. W.	65, 30	5	3·5	1	Melancholia	30	—	—	1
J. E.	26, 35	7	4	1	Paranoid schizophrenia: alcoholic	33	3	1. Anxiety neurosis 2. Alcoholism 3. Alcoholism	4
T. D.	42, 58	6	5·5	3	1. Recurrent depression 2. Recurrent excitement (mania) 3. Depression: suicide	16 18 42	2	1. Puerperal delirium 2. Alcoholism	5
5		22	15·5	6			7		13

Parents with affective psychoses

In these the preponderance of conditions developing after 50 is obvious. As Schulz and Elsaesser so emphatically pointed out, this is perhaps undesirable, but it cannot be helped. Elsaesser computed that if these and the moderately atypical forms of affective psychosis are excluded from the series, hardly any cases would be left. 'Dass ich die Fälle mit leichten Atypien und die erst im Alter beginnenden manisch-depressiven Psychosen mit zu dem Kreis des eigentlichen MDI hinzugenommen habe ist schon eine Kompromißlösung, um überhaupt eine Berechnung von Belastungsziffern zu ermöglichen. Das ganze manisch-depressive Material wäre ja sonst auf 4 Elternpaare von Schulz und ein eigenes Paar zusammengeschrumpft.'

It is necessary to look at those affective pairs who had a child with a non-affective psychosis. The first of these was a pair (J. E.) of whom the father, first ill at age of 26 with mania, had recurrent mania until his death at the age of 66, and the mother had an attack at 35 of acute self-reproachful depression, from which she recovered after three months in hospital. The eldest son had been steadily working for the same firm for fifteen years prior to his breakdown: he had, however, been drinking ale to excess, in periodic bouts. At the

Table 5. Children of parents with atypical affective psychosis

Parental pair	*Age of onset*	*Children*	*Corrected children at risk*	*Psychotic children*	*Diagnosis of these*	*Age of onset*	*Other children affected*	*Diagnosis of these*	*Total children affected*
C. A.	57, 35	5	3	(1)	G.P.I. (expansive)	40	1	Depression	2
F. C.	48, 31	1	0·5	—	—	—	—	—	—
D. E.	62, 58	4	2	—	—	—	1	Obsessional neurosis with depressive phases	1
A. F.	54, 22	2	2	—	—	—	—	—	—
F. H. M.	55, 33	8	4·5	—	—	—	2	1. Menopausal depression 2. Depression	2
W. N.	44, 51	3	3	2	1. Paranoid schizophrenia 2. Senile paraphrenia	58 67	—	—	2
J. N.	31, 59	1	1	1	Melancholia	58	—	—	1
R. A. R.	18, 33	1	0·5	—	—	—	1	Sexual crimes: psychopathic personality	1
W. A. M.	60, 59	7	4	1	Depression	27	2	1. Dull and backward 2. Anxiety since meningitis	3
W. P.	32, 21	1	0·5	—	—	—	—	—	—
10		33	21	5			7		12

age of 33 he became convinced people were following him about, talking about him and spying on him: he felt they were putting electrical influences on him: he had auditory hallucinations and was excited. He was admitted to a mental hospital, where he remained for eight months, with gradual improvement. On discharge he obtained work in a paint firm where he remained for eleven years, but developed lead-poisoning and had to leave it. For the next six years he was unemployed and subject to spells of mild depression which he coped with without medical aid. Obviously alcohol was an important cause of the transient paranoid condition, which could alternatively be regarded as an alcoholic hallucinosis in a person of depressive temperament.

The child with G.P.I. need not detain us (C. A.). Another affective pair presented atypical features and had two paraphrenic sons. The father had a manic attack in 1862, at the age of 44, from which he never fully recovered, though when he seemed well he was discharged from hospital: he could remain out, however, only a very short time. He died in hospital at the age of 85, after forty years of 'chronic mania'. His wife at 51 became morose, refused to eat, wanted to cut her throat and was convinced that her daughter who died in childbed had been poisoned. While in the mental hospital (1873–85)

Table 6. Children of a parent with typical schizophrenia and a parent with typical affective psychosis

Parental pair	*Age of onset*	*Children*	*Corrected children at risk*	*Psychotic children*	*Diagnosis of these*	*Age of onset*	*Other children affected*	*Diagnosis of these*	*Total children affected*
G. F. A.	39, 50	4	3	2	1. Depression: suicide 2. Depression: suicide	21 24	1	Puerperal depression	3
E. J. A.	32, 36	2	1	—	—	—	1	Cyclothymia	1
W. G. A.	34, 43	4	2·5	1	Depression	19	3	1. Hypomania 2. Hypomania 3. Depression	4
A. A.	52, 43	2	1	—	—	—	1	Reactive depression	1
H. R. H.	34, 45	6	2·5	1	Schizophrenia	31	2	1. Morbid jealousy 2. Violent rages	3
M. M.	37, 50	3	2	1	Schizophrenia	26	—	—	1
J. W.	37, 62	5	3·5	—	—	—	1	Alcoholism	1
7		26	15·5	5			9		14

she wept a great deal, and said she would like to be burned to death. She also believed that people were against her, and at times abused the nurses and doctors, believing they were her enemies. She became as the years went by actively hostile towards anyone who approached her, and during the last few years of her life was solitary, silent and resentful of any intrusion. The eldest son was free from mental illness until the age of 58: he then became agitated and preoccupied with paranoid delusions and after admission to the asylum he came to believe he owned it and had been put in it by the Royal Family.

Table 7. Children of a parent with atypical schizophrenia and a parent with typical affective psychosis

Parental pair	*Age of onset*	*Children*	*Corrected children at risk*	*Psychotic children*	*Diagnosis of these*	*Age of onset*	*Other children affected*	*Diagnosis of these*	*Total children affected*
C. G.	51, 69	2	1·5	—	—	—	—	—	—
D. W. P.	39, 24	4	2	—	—	—	—	—	—
G. P.	58, 52	6	2·5	1	Chronic melancholia: manic phase, infanticide	25	—	—	1
3		12	6	1			—		1

Table 8. Children of a parent with typical schizophrenia and a parent with atypical affective psychosis

Parental pair	*Age of onset*	*Children*	*Corrected children at risk*	*Psychotic children*	*Diagnosis of these*	*Age of onset*	*Other children affected*	*Diagnosis of these*	*Total children affected*
T. B. D.	38, 49	5	2·5	—	—	—	2	1. Violent rages 2. Depression	2
F. V. H.	36, 35	1	1	1	Schizophrenia	22	—	—	1
2		6	3·5	1		2			3

He gradually deteriorated and died after eleven years in the mental hospital. His brother had a similar illness, coming on at 67, necessitating admission to a mental hospital and lasting until the end of his life more than nine years later. It is arguable that these paranoid psychoses coming on in late life, in the setting of severe agitation and excitement, are closer to involutional melancholia than to paranoid schizophrenia: but, in any case, the similarity in form and course between the psychoses of the parents and the offspring here is striking.

Mixed pairs

These may be compared with Schulz's 30 mixed pairs, reported in November 1940. He pointed out the objections to assuming that it is from such marriages

Table 9. Children of a parent with atypical schizophrenia and a parent with atypical affective psychosis

Parental pair	*Age of onset*	*Children*	*Corrected children at risk*	*Psychotic children*	*Diagnosis of these*	*Age of onset*	*Other children affected*	*Diagnosis of these*	*Total children affected*
J. T. L.	38, 27	3	1	—	—	—	2	1. Depression 2. Depression (recurrent)	2
A. M.	47, 44	6	2	—	—	—	1	Depression	1
T. S.	29, 36	3	1·5	—	—	—	1	Excitable psychopathic personality	1
R. J. W.	60, 55	6	3·5	1	Depression: suicide	23	4	1. Alcoholism 2. Anxiety neurosis; alcoholism 3. Anxiety neurosis 4. Unstable psychopathic personality	5
T. W.	61, 62	5	3·5	—	—	—	1	Alcoholism	1
G. T. C.	52, 62	4	2·5	1	Schizophrenia	24	1	Reactive depression	2
6		27	14	2			10		12

that schizo-affective forms could arise, and he left open the question whether the findings ran counter to his suggestion that there is a common genetic determinant for all endogenous psychosis, and that it is an additional 'releasing' factor which determines whether the psychosis shall be schizophrenic or affective. My material is of course too small to be trusted, but the findings do not lend support to Schulz's suggestion; they accord with Elsaesser's on this point.

The proportion of affected children in each group is lower than in Schulz and Elsaesser's series, but high enough to confirm the generally accepted opinion about the inheritable character of these 'endogenous psychoses'. The smaller proportions I obtained may be due to diagnostic bias, leading me to include as 'endogenous psychoses' conditions in older parents which others would list separately or exclude, or it may be due to different practices in regard to mental hospital admission in England and Germany during the periods covered. If the children with psychiatric abnormality, who were not treated for it in a mental hospital, are included, the proportions are appreciably raised. This would accord with Leonhard's proposal that manic-depressive parents dealt with elsewhere than in mental hospitals should be specially sought for: and the same might be said of the offspring.

Table 10. Summary of affected children from various combinations of parental psychosis

Mating	*Number of pairs*	*Corrected number of children at risk*	*Psychotic children*		*Other children psychiatrically abnormal*
			Schizophrenic	*Affective*	
S × S	4	8·5	3	—	2
?S × S	3	9	1	—	1
A × A	5	15·5	1	5	7
?A × A	10	21	2	2	8
A × S	7	15·5	2	3	9
A × ?S	3	6	—	1	—
?A × S	2	3·5	1	—	2
?A × ?S	6	14	1	1	10
	40	93	11	12	39

(S = schizophrenic, A = affective, ? = atypical.)

There are two matters on which this type of study might be expected to throw light: the genetic identity of the clinically recognized 'endogenous' psychoses, and mode of transmissions. The data in this little series can hardly be said to throw light: at most they contribute a feeble taper to the wavering glimmer in which we view these vexed questions. They confirm the similarity of the psychoses of children with those of their parents; but they lend no clear support to the assumption that schizophrenia is attributable to a specific recessive gene, nor indeed to any of the more complicated explanations that have been put forward, touching on the influence of the 'genotypic milieu', the postnatal environment, and so forth. As Elsaesser rightly says on this question: 'Bei dem relativ kleinen Ausgangsmaterial (ist) eine Zufallsschwankung nicht ausgeschlossen . . . Wenn wir nach den zur Zeit stark vertretenen Hypothesen eine rezessive Erbweise der Schizophrenie und eine dominante Erbweise des MDI annehmen, so müßten wir ja überdies sogar mehr kranke Kinder bei den Schizophrenen als bei den manisch-depressiven Elternpaaren erwarten. Die Erbgänge der großen Psychosen sind jedoch noch so wenig bekannt, daß diese Überlegung uns in keiner Weise weiter helfen kann.'

I said at the beginning that I present this material with diffidence. The first reason for my diffidence is the long interval that has elapsed since the data were collected. A second reason is the doubt I have whether the findings can be trusted. The grounds for this misgiving will have been mostly evident in what I have said already. May I briefly recapitulate them. First: the selection of the sample. Even if, as in the series, it is unbiased by any awareness on the selector's part of illness in the offspring of the affected couples, the sample will still be restricted to fertile couples; yet people who became ill before they had procreated or whose children died young may have suffered from specially severe forms of mental illness with a stronger likelihood of manifestation and other genetic features. Moreover any such sample of parents will contain a higher proportion of patients whose illness began in middle life and later, than would be found in the whole population of persons with the relevant 'non-organic' illness.

Secondly: the ascertainment of the offspring is a difficult task. Inevitably many persons are lost through emigration and failure to trace their address.

When both parents have been psychotic, possibly spending the last twenty or thirty years of their lives in the mental hospital, the family will have been disrupted and finding them is exceptionally difficult; some of the children, moreover, will have been taken over or adopted by relatives whose name the child thereafter goes by. Illegitimacy has also been a minor problem in our series. The central register of mental hospital admissions, though a help in tracing some affected children, is of little use—at any rate in England—in finding people who have common surnames, or whose age and full Christian names are not precisely known. It cannot help, either, in finding offspring with psychiatric illness that has not been treated in a mental hospital—psychopathic personality, neuroses and crime are outside its range. (I had one instance of a woman who had attempted suicide and at the same time murdered her child, but because Broadmoor, the State Criminal Asylum, was at that time regarded as part of the Prison Service and not of the Mental Hospital Service, she did not appear in the central register.)

Personal visits are therefore essential for this study, but in England, at any rate, they require an enormous amount of effort and time; and they often expose both the investigator and the investigated persons to an emotional strain which is justified only if the results are of commensurate importance: I am inclined to think they are not.

Moreover, the offspring had to be investigated at a time when many of them were still open to the risk of developing a mental illness later on. None of the devices for getting round this familiar obstacle seems to me satisfactory in the kind of family study we are considering, chiefly because we are ignorant of the genetic relations between parents and child in respect of age of onset of illness, especially when the two parents differ in type and course of illness.

Thirdly: diagnosis is a cause of uncertainty. It has to be made, so far as the parents are concerned, almost entirely from records. In dealing with case notes made forty or fifty or, it might be, eighty or ninety years ago, I found that besides obsolete terms, internal contradictions, very brief histories, and other such deficiencies, I was frequently compelled to ask myself whether drugs (the psychiatrists were fond of sulphonal, for example), malnutrition, and medical and nursing attitudes might not have been responsible for the development of chronic illness, or of 'organic' features, leading to an incorrect retrospective diagnosis. The social, psychological and material environment of some mental hospitals could, and still does, produce artefacts—violent outbursts, withdrawal and preoccupation with fantasies, eccentric habits, despair, distrust, paranoid beliefs, decay of self-respect—symptoms which might not have occurred if the patient had been discharged from the hospital at an earlier stage, and which impose, as it were, a chronic course on what could perhaps have been an acute, transient illness, so that the appearance of schizophrenia is added to an initially affective disorder. All this is in addition to the intrinsic troubles of psychiatric diagnosis, so difficult to resolve when dealing with the psychoses of middle age; involutional psychoses, with paraphrenic features developing in the setting of an agitated depression or an Angstpsychose, are one example of this, and the paranoid schizophrenic illness that ensues upon an acute alcoholic hallucinosis is another.

Finally, there are the difficulties of analysing the material, especially when it is no larger than the series under discussion. Until the clinical entities with which we work are more securely based on objective, unequivocal somatic and psychological observations, we can neither safely add the findings of one series to that of another, nor assume biological identity of syndrome or disease because of clinical similarity. It is sometimes said that genetic studies may serve to define psychiatric diseases and subgroups more effectively than the clinician has so far been able to: this may well be, but it seems unlikely that studies of 'conjugal psychoses' will be the chosen instrument. Much thoroughgoing effort, technical resources, experience in clinical-genetic research, ingenious analysis and reasoning, and critical judgment has been expended on the inquiries by Schulz and Elsaesser to which I have repeatedly referred: but the yield in unambiguous conclusions is meagre.

The work would be easier and more complete in a country which had a central register so organized that it permitted bona fide investigators to ascertain the lifelong record of psychiatric illness for everybody who had been seen at a hospital, clinic or outpatient department of any kind. But even if this improbably complete register were to exist, the other sources of error and misjudgment would still make it doubtful whether a large scale inquiry into the offspring of two psychotic parents can justify itself by its results. It could not, I believe, until we have a surer taxonomy of mental disease.

REFERENCES

ELSAESSER, G. *Die Nachkommen geisteskranker Elternpaare*, Stuttgart, Thieme, 1952.
SCHULZ. B. *Z. ges. Neurol. Psychiat.*, 1940, **168**, 332; 1940, **169**, 311; 1940, **170**, 441; and 1941, **171**, 57.

15

FERTILITY AND MENTAL ILLNESS

ANYONE WHO has the honour of delivering the Galton Lecture has no shortage of topics to choose from, if he assumes that it is his duty to deal with a theme that had interested Francis Galton. In the amazingly wide range of subjects which aroused Galton's curiosity, fertility took a prominent place, and so did mental disorder. But of the fertility of those who fell ill in this way, he did not write, as far as I know, and there has been relatively little attention given to the matter since his time: doubtless the volume of research and discussion would have been greater if there had been the initial stimulus of his ideas and inquiries. I should make it clear that I am excluding mental defect and dealing solely with mental disorders in this lecture.

* * *

A hundred years ago an audience such as this would have taken it for granted that the connexion between fertility and mental disorder could be summed up in the word 'degeneration'. The French psychiatrist, B. A. Morel, had at about that time propounded a doctrine of degeneration which had a strong theological flavour. In some stocks or families, he declared, a morbid deviation from the normal type could occur, most often in the form of mental abnormality. It would then exhibit progressive degradation. In the first generation the abnormality would become manifest as nervous temperament, moral defect, instability and excess (what we should call psychopathic personality): in the second generation, gathering strength, it would appear as severe neuroses, alcoholism, general paralysis: and in the third generation it would burst into full bloom as melancholia, paranoia, hypochondria; a fourth generation, if the stock survived so far, would consist of people with idiocy, gross malformations and other barriers to procreation. For Morel degeneration was a process whereby tainted stocks were firmly predestined to extinction through hereditary disease, a medical counterpart to reprobation in the religious sphere. His definition of degenerative conditions indicates that decay and extinction of the stock was an essential part of the concept. 'Les dégénéra-

---

The Galton Lecture delivered to the Eugenics Society in London in February 1958. It is reprinted from *The Eugenics Review* (July 1958), **50**, 91–106.

tions sont des déviations maladives du type normal de l'humanité héreditairement transmissibles et évoluant progressivement vers la déchéance.'

THE DEGENERATION THEORY

Morel's views, published in 1857, had great influence and were widely accepted. They were reinforced, as time passed, by the convenient fallacy of 'anticipation', which seemed to lend colour to Morel's theory since if hereditary disease appeared earlier in succeeding generations, it would infallibly extirpate the affected stock: the neat model consisted of a first generation characterized by senile dementia supervening on a healthy adult life; in the next generation came involutional melancholia or depression asserting itself in the prime of life; then in the third generation dementia praecox came on in late adolescence or early manhood (it was Morel who coined the term 'dementia praecox', with this connotation): and the fourth generation, afflicted from birth with idiocy or imbecility, was even more completely precluded from reproduction than that which had preceded it. This tidy scheme ignored much evidence, and was of course linked to the notion of a general polymorphous 'neuropathic taint' which could produce any one of several varieties of mental disorder and defect. Indeed Morel held that 'all hereditary diseases are sisters'. In spite of its weaknesses—not all of which could be recognized when it was propounded—his scheme gained much support, outside France as well as within it. Thus Henry Maudsley, then rising into prominence, wrote in 1862: 'Such is the benevolent purpose of nature that no efforts whatsoever can perpetuate a morbid human type; for although the offspring of degenerate parents is a further degeneration, the evil soon corrects itself; and long before man has descended to the animal level, there comes an incapability of producing offspring, and the morbid type dies out. Insanity, of what form soever, whether mania, melancholia, moral insanity or dementia, is but a step in the descent towards sterile idiocy. . . . It is almost impossible to avoid expressing a grateful admiration of the wise, sure and merciful provision of Nature by which degenerate mind is so quickly blotted out.' The theory thus eloquently expounded spread out into literary and other non-medical circles. The ancient argument about the relation between genius and insanity was revived, and seemingly illuminated: the genius and the madman were both seen as degenerates, though the genius was a *dégénéré supérieur* (or, as some now say, a creative psychopath), and both were doomed to extinction. Lombroso gained for the theory some anthropological backing and disseminated it further; Max Nordau vulgarized it until it became, like other discarded theories, a convenient vehicle for prejudice, superstition and facile explanations. It did not die easily even in medical circles, and I find that Adolf Meyer, one of the most enlightened of modern psychiatrists, wrote in 1895 that Morel's description of the successive stages of degeneration through which a 'degenerate' family passes could well be correct, adding: 'I could indeed report as corroborative several instances from my personal experience . . . the scheme is most closely followed by people that live for three generations under the same conditions and where the child is, in every generation, exposed to the same poisonous influences.' Karl Pearson gave one aspect of it qualified assent in his Boyle Lecture: 'We are at present only reaching light on what is a very important principle, namely, that stocks exist which show a general tendency to defect, taking one form in the parent, another in the offspring. Neuroses in the parents become alcoholism or insanity in the offspring. . . . Even now, I doubt whether it is absolutely unscientific to speak of a general inheritance of degeneracy.' And as late as 1926 a prominent German psychiatrist, Hoffman, argued in favour of progressive degeneration in families with mental disorder.

By the turn of the century, however, the fatalistic picture of diminishing fertility, decay, and then extinction of the degenerate stock had been pretty well dropped. An entirely opposite and more alarming view took its place. Instead of the picture of Nature—far-sighted, purposeful Nature—wiping out the hereditarily diseased and insane by a rapid, benignant reduction of their fertility, man was now seen as the blind agent of a social and biological process which would increase the relative fertility of the mentally ill, and consequently the total amount of mental illness. If I had read a paper on Fertility and Mental Disorder fifty years ago, it would have been assumed, I think, that I would address myself not, as in 1857, to the way the mentally ill extirpate themselves, but to the way they threaten to swamp the rest of society through unchecked and probably increasing fertility. That, at any rate, was what people feared in 1907.

FEARS OF EXCESSIVE FERTILITY

The issue was stated, in moderate language, by Dr David Heron in his important *Eugenics Laboratory Memoir*. After setting out his findings, he concluded that 'our present statistics amply confirm the general result reached by Pearson that pathologically abnormal stocks . . . are not less but rather more fertile than the normal stocks in the community. The eugenic importance of this in relation to the insane diathesis is self-evident, for within the community natural selection is largely suspended, and the "insane" restored to family life as recovered.' And later, at the end of the *Memoir*, he states plainly: 'There is no reduction in, possibly rather an augmentation of, the fertility of insane stocks, when compared with that of sane stocks. . . . The normal, or probably more than normal fertility of the insane, notwithstanding their partial seclusion and high death rate, and the fact that insanity is a disease largely of middle life, must make us pause before we acquiesce in the unrestricted return of the "recovered" insane to family life.'

Dr Heron carried out his inquiries under the stimulus of Karl Pearson, in whose laboratory he worked, and Pearson expressed the same warnings in more vivid and urgent language. 'Today we feed our criminals up, and we feed up the insane, we let both out of the prison or the asylum "reformed" or "cured" as the case may be, only after a few months to return to State supervision, leaving behind them the germs of a new generation of deteriorants . . . Education for the criminal, fresh air for the tuberculous, rest and food for the neurotic—these are excellent, they may bring control, sound lungs, and sanity to the individual; but they will not save the offspring from the need of like treatment. . . . They cannot make a nation sound in mind and body, they merely screen degeneracy behind a throng of arrested degenerates.' And elsewhere in the same Lecture occur such passages as 'degenerate stocks under present social conditions are not short-lived, they live to have more than the normal size of family. Natural selection is largely suspended, but not the inheritance of degeneracy nor the fertility of the unfit. On the contrary there is more than a suspicion of the suspension of the fertility of the fit.'

These uncompromising views were reared, so far as the fertility of the insane was concerned, on information about 331 families containing at least one insane member who had been treated at James Murray's Royal Asylum at Perth. In these families Heron found that the mean number of children was 5·97; whereas in ordinary English marriages lasting at least fifteen years, the average gross number of children was 6·58, from which he inferred that marriages in the insane stocks (which had not all lasted fifteen years) were at least as fertile as the sane. He compared the number of children of insane parents who had come into his series with those recorded for a normal group —the Danish professional classes—and found it the same. The normal population, whose marriages had lasted fifteen years or more, were therefore assumed to have a lower fertility than the parents in the families with an insane member.

Now these findings of Heron's are, as he recognized, based on a small material, and take no account of the varieties of mental disorder: thus general paralysis of the insane, other organic cerebral affections, senile demential cretinism, epilepsy, transient depression and recurrent mania, are all lumped together. But a more serious objection was brought forward, first by Weinberg and soon after by Greenwood and Yule. By taking an insane person always as the starting point for study of the fertility of the family or stock, i.e. of the patient's parents, Heron not only excluded all childless marriages but unintentionally ensured that he would have an undue proportion of large sibships since large families have more individuals in them than small families and therefore, other things being equal, more often have an insane member: in the Copenhagen material, on the other hand, parents had been taken as the starting point for the inquiry. When the appropriate statistical c orrection was made (as by Popenoe in 1928) the size of the insane persons sibships tended to be smaller, not larger, than normal.

These objections, however, did not shake the conviction, widespread among eugenists in the earlier years of the century, that social and medical advances, however excellent on humanitarian grounds, were in danger of promoting the fertility of the insane, already high: consequently, it was often cruelly said, they would allow the weeds to choke the garden.

In spite of the eloquence and authority with which the issue was stated and the fervour with which woeful implications were stressed, little was done to amplify the meagre and contradictory data on which the argument rested. Studies by a handful of American and European investigators yielded some information, but it was not until the nineteen-thirties that adequate sophisticated contributions appeared. The first of these was by Professor Gunnar Dahlberg of Upsala.

SYSTEMATIC INVESTIGATION OF FERTILITY IN PSYCHOSES

Dahlberg was acutely aware of the excesses to which eugenic enthusiasm had carried Goddard, Jörges, Estabrook and Davenport. He was alive to the gross statistical and genetical fallacies besetting the interpreter of large pedigrees. He was moreover by temperament and outlook averse from the sombre measures of compulsory intervention that were advocated by ardent believers in the tares-choking-out-the-wheat view of the matter. He therefore set about his inquiry into the fertility of insane women cautiously, and he drew no overbold conclusion.

His propositi were 2,200 women admitted to the Upsala Mental Hospital in the period 1890–1929. Of these 1,219 had been under observation until they had passed the age of forty-five, and were therefore unlikely to have any further children.

These women had borne in all 2,407 children, i.e. the average number of children per woman was 1·97, though of course the younger the women had been when they were first admitted to the mental hospital, the lower their number of children: there is a steady gradient from 0·05 for women first admitted before the age of twenty to 2·45 for women first admitted over the age of fifty. Against the average of 1·97 for these women could be set the average of 3·78 for the general population of Sweden. Insofar as the insane have a higher mortality than the sane, so that some insane women will not have survived to the age of forty-five, the figure arrived at in Dahlberg's count probably, as he points out, overstates the fertility of insane women.

The proportion of single women among the propositi could greatly affect the average in Dahlberg's sample of women observed until past the age of forty-five. There were 551 unmarried and 668 married. This gives 55% married, whereas for the whole Swedish population 81% were married. The married women in his sample had borne, on the average, 3·32 children; for the unmarried the corresponding figure was 0·34. The fertility of the unmarried women being so low, married women are responsible not only for replacing themselves and their husbands but also in large measure for making good the reproductive deficit of the unmarried. This the insane married women were not achieving. Their failure to do so could be attributed in part to the long period many of them spent in hospital, debarred from the possibility of conceiving: on this, however, Dahlberg's statistics could not throw light, except to indicate that the fertility of the insane married women had been lower before their first admission to the mental hospital than the fertility of sane women of the corresponding age group, and that married women discharged from the hospital at some time before the end of their reproductive life had subsequently borne either very few children, or a relatively large number of children.

Dayton, in his analysis of 11,959 consecutive discharges from two large mental hospitals in Massachusetts between 1917 and 1928, had made much the same observation as Dahlberg. Both in the completed and the incomplete families, the average number of children born to married patients having at least one child was decidedly less than the average in the general population for each age-of-mother group. He concluded that 'the stock producing individuals with mental disorder is not on the increase. It appears that this stock is barely holding its own, if not actually decreasing.'

Dahlberg's notable conclusion, coinciding with Dayton's, is in direct contradiction of the alarming view so prevalent in the first decade of the century. His material plainly indicated that mentally ill women, taken *en bloc*, have subnormal fertility. But to take the mentally ill *en bloc* is to ignore the genetic, pathological, clinical and social differences between various types of mental illness. It is, for example, improper to confound the fertility of those with general paralysis—a disease which can limit the fecundity of those affected, making them impotent or sterile—with the fertility of those with recurrent mania. There are, it is true, difficulties in distinguishing between one form of mental illness and another. Karl Pearson was so well aware of this, and so impressed by the frequency with which the same patient would be differently diagnosed by successive doctors, that he deliberately treated all mental illnesses as one illness taking many forms. But methods of diagnosis, though still defective, are more satisfactory now than they were fifty years ago: we have very good grounds for believing the inheritance of the main mental disorders to be distinct: and the natural history of these main disorders is so different that we would expect the reproductive behaviour of affected persons to differ appreciably. Whether this expectation is justified, can be discovered from three major studies, of which the largest and most thorough was carried out by Professor Essen-Möller of Lund.

His propositi were 4,904 persons, of whom 1,679 were manic-depressive, 2,509 were schizophrenic, and 716 were epileptic. They had all been treated in the Munich Psychiatric Clinic between 1904 and 1927. A series of 1,239 normal married people was also investigated, for purposes of comparison. The number of children born to the propositi before the onset of their mental illness was calculated separately from the number born thereafter.

In the manic-depressive group the number of children born before their illness, and subsequently, did not differ from the normal. In the schizophrenic group, however, the number born before the outbreak of illness indicated a curious difference between the sexes: whereas the male propositi lagged behind the general population in the rate at which the birth rate fell during the period covered by their marriages, the women behaved in the opposite way, anticipating the general decline. The schizophrenic men had had much the same average number of children as the rural population before 1904, but a higher rate than the urban population of Munich: in the period 1904–18 they had the rate which the rest of the Bavarian population had shown before 1904, and in the period 1919–30 their rate had fallen only to the level reached by the rest of the population in the previous period 1904–18. The schizophrenic women, on the other hand, showed before 1904 the rate which the rest of the population fell to between 1904 and 1918, and kept correspondingly ahead of the trend in the ensuing period.

Essen-Möller emphasized, in the light of these findings, that it is improper to talk of the fertility of people with a mental illness: it is necessary to take into account the social differences which affect reproductive behaviour at different times. In a stable population, as it appeared from his data, the fertility of married manic-depressives and schizophrenic men before the outbreak of their mental illness does not differ from that of the rest of the population, though the schizophrenic women have only about half the fertility of normal women. But when the birth rate begins to fall in the general population, the schizophrenic men slowly follow suit, while the schizophrenic women, starting with a lower birth rate and declining more slowly than the normal women in this respect, eventually have much the same rate as the normals.

In the number of children born after the outbreak of illness, the married schizophrenics confirmed the expectation that the circumstances and effects of the illness would greatly reduce their fertility: it fell by about 70% when due allowance was made for their age and the duration of their marriage. The exception to this finding lay in the schizophrenics who married after their illness: their fertility approximated to that of the rest of the population, a finding which, taken together with the fact that these patients had spent a relatively short time in hospital, suggests that the schizophrenics who had married after their mental illness had had the disease in a mild form and had recovered.

In this matter of fertility before and after the illness, Essen-Möller's material yielded an interesting further point which illustrates the great risk of jumping to conclusions in such inquiries. He examined the fertility of his propositi during the twelve months before their admission to hospital. He found it higher than expected. He then looked to see if the rate of conception is raised shortly before the onset, or in the early stages, of the illness: if so, an appreciable number of the women would be pregnant at the time of entry into hospital. This was not the case: there was evidence that in fact the rate of conception during the year preceding admission to hospital was depressed. It would seem obvious that if, shortly before admission to hospital, conception was no more frequent but births were more frequent, the explanation must lie in the assumption that a proportion of the illnesses were puerperal, i.e. had been the outcome of childbirth. This easy explanation, however, will not do. It was not only the women who behaved in this way. The married schizophrenic men also showed a rise in births of live children during the three months before admission. The most probable explanation—unless one invents a couvade-psychosis—now becomes the socio-psychological one that in both men and women, when a child is expected admission to hospital is put off, wherever possible, until the baby is born.

From Essen-Möller's masterly study it emerges that (in Bavaria at any rate) the fertility of patients with manic-depressive psychosis did not differ appreciably from that of the general population, but that schizophrenics reproduced significantly less than the general population; the disparity was greater when the general population had a high birth rate. In general the total fertility of schizophrenics was between one-fifth and two-fifths—at most between a quarter and a half of the normal.

At the same time as Essen-Möller's study, a parallel inquiry was made in North Germany by F. J. Kallmann. By agreement their methods of enumeration were harmonized. Kallmann limited his study to schizophrenics admitted to a large mental hospital in Berlin between 1893 and 1902. He subdivided his propositi into two main groups—those with hebephrenic or catatonic forms of schizophrenia, and those with paranoid or mild forms. The former, with typical or 'nuclear' schizophrenia, had on the average only half as many children as the latter; as they comprised 70% of the propositi, the average number of children for the whole population studied was close to that of the typical, less fertile group. The fertility of the propositi, however grouped, was below that of the normal population: the males averaged 3·1 children and the women 3·5 children for 'completed' families. The averages obtained for the prepsychotic period of marriages contracted before the onset of illness did not fall far short of these completed figures: for men the prepsychotic average was 2·7 children and for women 3·4. Almost all the offspring of schizophrenics had evidently been produced before the illness became manifest. The exception to this generalization lay in the sub-group of schizophrenics who recovered from periodic or mild forms of the disorder leaving few traces behind, so that the patients resumed their normal lives in the community; many of them married after their first discharge from hospital and had an appreciable number of children.

Kallmann sums up his findings in terms which agree closely with Essen-Möller's. 'The fertility of schizophrenics lags markedly behind that of the general population. . . . We find the legitimate fertility rate lowered by 1·6 children in comparison with the corresponding average population.'

The only other large study which has provided data on the fertility of schizophrenics has been J. A. Böök's thorough investigation of an isolate, i.e. a population more or less shut off geographically, which is relatively homogeneous in its genotypical structure. He took the people of a rural area in the extreme north of Sweden which has had poor means of communication with the rest of the country: the migration rate was low: and marriages between first cousins accounted for over 2% of all marriages. Through a painstaking combination of interviews and search through appropriate records, all surviving persons who had had a major neuropsychiatric disorder between 1902 and 1949 were identified and examined. Böök found that the fertility of marriages contracted by the schizophrenics (estimated as the average number of children born per year, counting from the year of marriage to the year when the wife reached the age of forty-eight, minus the number of years spent in hospital) was higher than in a control group of mentally normal people in the same area: the differences, however, were not statistically significant. Now this finding is surprisingly at variance with Essen-Möller's and Kallmann's. It was only when Böök took all schizophrenics, and not only those who were married, that he found their fertility to be appreciably lower (by 30%) than that of the normal population. The explanation lay in the very large number of unmarried men (75%) among the schizophrenics. It raises a question of the utmost importance in the whole matter: how far is the reproductive capacity of schizophrenics as a group reduced not because their illness lowers their fecundity but because it lowers their chance of marriage.

MARRIAGE RATE AND REPRODUCTIVE CAPACITY

The high proportion of single men and women among those in mental hospitals has long been observed, and its significance debated.

Thurnam, writing in 1845, found that two-thirds of the patients admitted to the York Retreat had never been married, and that of those who were married one-fifth had never had offspring, and he emphasized that 'many of the cases occur in a class of persons, as regards mental vigour, less likely to be married than the average of the community at large. . . . The celibacy is to be regarded as an effect rather than a cause.'

In all psychoses and at all ages the single outnumber the married among the mentally ill. It can be inferred that this is far more evident in schizophrenia

Table 1. Mental hospitals: admission rates per million 1951 census
(*Population by Sex, Age and Marital Status for Certain Diagnostic Groups, 1950*)

Diagnosis and I.S.C. no.	*Sex*	*Marital status*	20–	25–	35–	45–	55–	65–	*75 and over*
Schizophrenia (300)	Males	S	974	2,204	1,387	586	219	60	—
		M. W. & D.	191	230	185	79	43	20	5
	Females	S	762	1,617	1,160	590	206	93	13
		M. W. & D.	187	296	255	170	104	44	10
Manic-depressive reaction (301)	Males	S	104	360	673	1,005	953	617	145
		M. W. & D.	73	139	267	456	666	491	160
	Females	S	187	534	953	1,268	1,331	723	194
		M. W. & D.	177	372	584	793	919	578	142

(From *Registrar-General's Statistical Review of England and Wales for 1950–1.* Supplement on General Morbidity, Cancer and Mental Health.)

than in other psychoses. If standardized rates of admission per 100,000 per year are calculated, it is found that in schizophrenia the rate for single men is 4·7 times as high as for married men and the rate for single women 3 times as high as for married women: the corresponding rates for manic-depressive patients are 1·6 times higher for single men than for married, 1·5 times higher for single women. These are Scandinavian figures. The corresponding English figures, collected by the late Dr Vera Norris, are even more striking: e.g. first admission rates for schizophrenia six times as high for single men as for married men.

Table 2. Age standardized ratios of the first admission rates of single (R_s) to those for married (R_m) persons

Diagnosis	*Men* R_s/R_m	*Women* R_s/R_m
Schizophrenia	6·2	3·7
Manic-depressive psychosis	1·8	1·6
Psychoses of old age	2·3	1·6
Other disorders	3·0	1·5
All disorders	3·5	2·0

(From Norris, V., *J. ment. Sci.*, 1956, **102**, 467.)

There are three possible explanations for the predominance of the single among psychotic persons: first, that because of their premorbid personality they are less likely to get married; second, that they have not been protected against harmful stresses by the affection and other advantages of married life; and third, that they are more likely to be sent into hospital. In a variety of studies the first of these explanations has been shown to be far the most probable, though the other two factors may play a part. If then the personality of the patients militates against their getting married, why are the single so much more frequent among schizophrenics than among the manic-depressives: and why more frequent among males than females. The answer is that the majority of persons prone to manic-depressive psychosis commonly have, before and between attacks, a sociable, responsive personality that would not be detrimental to their seeking marriage and being sought in marriage. The schizophrenics have, as a group, quite a different mental constitution: morbidly seclusive, shy, sensitive, and socially awkward, they may be heavily handicapped in making and responding to any advances; the men show the discrepancy between single and married more than women because lack of initiative will tell more heavily against their prospects of getting married than the same quality would reduce a woman's prospects. This matter is summed up by Ødegaard, the Norwegian psychiatrist who has studied it closely: 'Certain personality traits reduce the chances of getting married, by making contact with the opposite sex more difficult or less attractive, or indirectly by blocking the way towards social and economic success. Some of these traits are disproportionately common in persons who are predisposed towards certain psychoses, or in the initial stages of such disorders.'

There is another aspect of the relation between mental illness and marriage. When Dr Norris looked into groups of patients who were comparable in previous history, length of follow-up period, legal status, age, sex and diagnosis, she found that single persons stayed longer in the mental hospital than married persons. It may therefore be inferred that they stood a greater chance of becoming chronic hospital patients, debarred from procreation.

The relationship of marriage to the time of onset of the illness has been closely examined by Essen-Möller. He found that whereas before the illness marriage was half as common in schizophrenics as in normal people of their age, it was only about one-sixth of the normal rate after the illness in those who had been single when they were first admitted to hospital. For manic-depressives, before their first admission the marriage rate was, as we have seen, almost identical with that of the normal population, but after the illness it fell to half the normal. It is noteworthy that in a group of schizophrenics whose illnesses had begun with clinical features suggesting manic-depressive psychosis, the prepsychotic marriage rate was as high as in the manic-depressives, but after the illness it fell to the same level as the typical schizophrenics. The length of time before, or after, the illness does not affect the frequency of marriage: thus schizophrenics as a group show the same lowered marriage rate many years before the onset of illness as they do in the period immediately preceding their first admission.

All this points towards the personal characteristics of the patients rather than their enforced residence in a mental hospital, as the main reason for their low marriage rate and low fertility. It is reasonable to suppose that the influence of schizoid personal characteristics on marriage rate will operate differently in diverse cultures, and under different social and economic conditions. This is borne out by Professor Böök's finding in his North Swedish population: the proportion of schizophrenic women married was lower than normal (73% as against 93%) but not nearly as much so as elsewhere. Professor Böök attributes the discrepancy to the fact that this rural and isolated population had been living under relatively primitive conditions where selection of a wife was influenced more by physical strength and capacity for hard work than by psychological oddities: there was moreover a constant shortage of young women because of emigration. Though not in itself of importance, the peculiarity of these schizophrenics living within the Arctic Circle is a warning against generalization based on a few studies. Social factors may greatly alter the picture. Another reminder of this lies in the mortality figures for schizophrenics. In the big German investigations carried out a quarter of a century ago, declared schizophrenics were found to have three times as high a mortality as the normal population; tuberculosis was a very conspicuous cause of this raised mortality—so much so that a close genetical relationship was postulated between the susceptibility to schizophrenia and to tuberculosis. Now tuberculosis has ceased in most countries to be an important cause of death in schizophrenics or indeed in any group of psychotic patients. The change could not have been foreseen, nor its implications for fertility worked out, unless the main social and medical factors determining the course of tuberculosis had been known. Although schizophrenia seems to be substantially the same in form wherever it is met, no matter what the ethnic and cultural diversities of the people affected, any statement about the fertility of schizophrenics must be qualified, and for the present should be restricted to populations of the same sort as the very few that have been adequately studied in this regard—almost entirely West European populations.

The effect of a low marriage rate was, as I mentioned earlier, striking in Böök's investigation. The intra-matrimonial fertility of his schizophrenic propositi was actually higher than that of his normal controls, but the total reproductive capacity of his schizophrenic subjects, married and single together, was reduced to about 70% of the normal, entirely because of the very low marriage rate of his male propositi: three-quarters of them, you will remember, were unmarried. Schizophrenics evidently conform to the hope Charles Darwin expressed in the *Descent of Man*: he wrote that we must bear the undoubtedly bad effects of the weak propagating their kind, but there could be a steady check on this 'by the weak in body or mind refraining from marriage, though this is more to be hoped for than expected.'

It might of course be misleading to assume that schizophrenics who remain single produce no children. Essen-Möller, with his customary thoroughness, looked into this matter. He found that on the average one in eight of the single women among his propositi had produced a child; of manic-depressive women the corresponding figure was four. Kallmann, who counted as illegitimate all children born outside wedlock, even though subsequently legitimized, reports 162 such births among his propositi: seventy-eight of his 537 unmarried female schizophrenics had had an illegitimate child. From these data it would seem that the number of children produced by single women among the schizophrenics is too low to affect appreciably the figure obtained by investigating the fertility of the married women. For men, the findings are equivocal: Essen-Möller inclined to the conclusion that the schizophrenic bachelors had a higher reproductive rate than the spinsters, but Kallmann arrived at the opposite opinion. Clearly it is more difficult to establish the facts for men than for women. In any case they do not, on the information at present available, alter the general finding that schizophrenics of both sexes have a low fertility.

Since the fertility of schizophrenics is so low, the question inevitably arises: how is it that schizophrenia remains as prevalent as ever. Three explanations are possible: (1), it is not, or some varieties of it are not, of hereditary causation; or perhaps (2), though the condition is hereditary, the outwardly healthy carriers reproduce at a higher rate than normal and therefore compensate for the relative infertility of those with the manifest disease; or finally (3), mutations may be constantly replenishing the otherwise dwindling supply of people predisposed to schizophrenia.

Against the first possibility there is a convincing array of evidence. There is still uncertainty as to whether schizophrenia is, as Böök holds, a matter of a major simple dominant gene with a 20% heterozygous penetrance, or, as others believe, is a recessive trait; but as to its being in its typical forms to a large extent genetically determined, there is little room for doubt.

There remain, as possible explanations, the occurrence of fresh mutations, and raised fertility of heterozygous carriers. To inquire into the latter hypothesis, Essen-Möller took the brothers and sisters of his schizophrenic subjects, and ascertained how many of them had married. The proportion of sisters who were married was well below the average figure for the corresponding normal population: likewise with the brothers in the younger age-groups, i.e. under thirty-five. A similar finding was reported by Mertens. In general the probability of marriage in the siblings of schizophrenics is about two-thirds of what it is in the general population. How many children were the offspring of these marriages? Essen-Möller had no count of these, but on indirect evidence concluded that not only the frequency of marriage but also the total fertility of these brothers and sisters was subnormal. Kallmann arrived at a similar conclusion.

It might be supposed that although the sibs failed to confirm the hypothesis, the parents and the children of schizophrenics might. Heron had in fact stated that in his material the parents of his propositi were more fertile than the general population. But Weinberg and others demonstrated the fallacy in his method: as Greenwood and Yule put it: 'The size of family is not, as has been stated, abnormally large. On the contrary, so far as the data go, they seem to support the conclusion that the fertility of such stocks [stocks containing one or more members suffering from the disease] is below the average.' Kallmann studied the fertility of the married daughters of schizophrenics. He found that it was much lower than that of the married sisters of the patients (doubtless reflecting the general fall in birth rate in succeeding generations) and was below normal. It must therefore be concluded that, although the sisters and children of schizophrenic subjects transmit the predisposition to schizophrenia, and do so to a serious extent, their fertility is not sufficient to compensate for the losses entailed by the low fertility of those who manifest the disease.

MUTATIONS

There is left, then, as an explanation of the continuing prevalence of schizophrenia, the mutation hypothesis. The argument is now a familiar one and is more easily tested where dominant or sex-linked characters are in question. For a probably recessive character like schizophrenia, with a possibly deleterious or undetectable heterozygote, calculations are much more difficult, and the assumptions on which they are based more shaky. Böök has critically stated this problem as it affects schizophrenia, and from his North Swedish population has derived a spontaneous mutation-rate of 5×10^{-3} genes per generation. This is higher than Penrose's estimate, which is 1 in 2,000. Much depends on these calculations on the gene frequency, which Böök took as 7%, whereas Nixon and Slater recently assessed it at approximately 3 per cent. Whichever provisional figure is accepted, the spontaneous mutation rate is considerable. It is well to bear in mind Penrose's warning that the rates now calculated may be too high, when it is remembered that suppression of even the most regular kinds of dominant inheritance may mimic mutation, different conditions may be grouped (in the case of schizophrenia very probably are grouped) under one clinical heading, and finally that heterozygotes of recessive traits may have formerly carried slight advantages. But even if the accepted mutation rates are too high, the occurrence of fresh mutations responsible for schizophrenia on a substantial scale must be inferred.

For manic-depressive psychosis, in which the fertility of most of those affected does not seem less than that of mentally healthy people, the mutation rate is much smaller. Penrose assesses it at 1 in 28,000 per gene per generation. Even so the proportion of affected persons in whom the condition is due to a fresh mutation would be high (1 in 70) in each generation.

The possible effect of radiation in raising the mutation rate for hereditary diseases has been considered by the Medical Research Council. Serious as this matter is, it is not strictly relevant to the question of fertility under conditions existing hitherto, with which we are concerned here. It is, however, relevant to quote a passage from the Medical Research Council Report:

> 'We have expressed the opinion that from the standpoint of the social load imposed, mental diseases constitute the most important single category of disease which is determined to a marked degree by heredity and which is serious, in the sense both of being highly harmful to the individual and of making heavy demands on medical resources. We are aware that this is only an opinion and that others may have different views. We believe, however, that it will be conceded by all that the mental diseases contribute a very substantial proportion of the total number of those suffering from serious hereditary disorders.'

This restrained statement indicates the gravity of the problem of fertility in mental disorder, quite apart from the alarming issues raised by possible artificial increase of the mutation rate for this group of diseases.

FERTILITY OF NEUROTIC PERSONS

All the data I have been dealing with so far concern the two major forms of insanity—schizophrenia and manic-depressive psychosis. About the fertility of those with neurotic disorders there is practically no information. The only published material I know which is relevant comes from the Indianapolis Study—Clyde Kiser and C. J. Westoff asked 1,444 'relatively fecund' couples a series of questions about feelings of personal inadequacy. Most of the questions are such as are included in neurotic 'inventories' and although by no means indicative of illness, positive answers may be assumed to indicate an anxious, depressive, worrying, dissatisfied personality of the sort which verges on neurosis. An index was constructed ranging from under fifty to 100 and over, and the replies analysed statistically to see if there was a relation between fertility and this index. The findings were not clear cut. They suggested a slight relationship between size of family and feelings of inadequacy—the more inadequate, the smaller the number of children; but size of family was more closely related to economic security than it was to neurotic feelings.

In view of the extreme dearth of evidence the following unpublished findings, for which I am indebted to Miss Nancy Goodman, are of interest. Miss Goodman looked into the fertility of 375 neurotic married women of forty-five years of age or more who had been seen at the Maudsley Hospital in the years 1954 to 1957.

Table 3. Number of children of married neurotic women aged 45 and over, compared with general population

Family size	MARRIAGES OF 1925–9			MARRIAGES OF 1920–4		
	Family census		*Bethlem/ Maudsley*	*Family census*		*Bethlem/ Maudsley*
	Non-manual	*Manual*		*Non-manual*	*Manual*	
	%	%	%	%	%	%
0	21·5	14·3	14·3	18·3	12·1	25·0
1	27·5	23·1	34·3	25·3	19·1	22·4
2	27·9	23·4	18·6	26·6	21·7	27·6
3	12·8	15·1	17·1	15·2	16·6	13·2
4	5·5	8·9	5·7	7·6	10·8	6·6
5 and over	4·8	15·2	10·0	7·0	19·7	5·3
	100	100	100	100	100	100·1

(Goodman, N. Unpublished.)

The average number of live children born to these women did not differ greatly from that shown for normal women in the Family Census carried out in 1946 for the Royal Commission on Population. In view of geographical limits and difficulties of ascertainment it would be unsafe to stress the apparent difference between the neurotic women, especially of the 1920–4 marriage cohort, and the general population. The same caution applies to the apparent preponderance of small families in the neurotic women of the later cohort. The average age at marriage of the neurotic women was three years less than that of the average bride in England and Wales, but this may reflect only differences in 'social class' composition.

The fertility of neurotic women as a whole could, of course, be less than that of women in the general population if a higher proportion of them remained single. But no clear evidence emerged that this is so.

Table 4. Percentage of single women among neurotic women aged 45 and over, compared with general population

1951 CENSUS

Age Group	*England and Wales* %	*London H.C.* %	*Greater London* %	*Bethlem/ Maudsley* %
45–49	15·2	21·3	17·2	19·9
50–54	14·8	19·9	16·8	21·0
55–59	15·5	19·7	17·0	11·6
60–64	15·5	18·6	16·4	(10·8)
65–69	16·1	17·7	15·8	(12·5)
70–74	15·9	17·4	15·7	
75–79	16·1	18·3	16·3	(20·0)

(Goodman, N. Unpublished.)

The proportion of single women in the whole sample (670 women) was 16·7%, which is the same figure as for Greater London; and for the separate age groups the proportion was not consistently or unequivocally different from that of the normal population. This was disappointing. For if the fertility of the neurotic women in this Maudsley sample had diverged from that of the general population in either direction, some plausible hypotheses could have been suggested to account for it, in the light of psychopathology and social data about women and marriage—but there is nothing as yet to explain.

It is necessary to say 'as yet', because this may be an unrepresentative sample of neurotic women. The exclusion of women who had not yet reached the end of their reproductive life has probably biased the sample in the direction of those whose neurotic symptoms had not become troublesome until middle age. Slater and Woodside who detected 'a suggestion of lower fertility in neurotics', remark that the sexual abnormalities associated with neurosis nearly always 'lie in an impoverishment of sexual life', inhibitions and frigidity. In keeping with this view are the reports put forward by various psychiatrists about the psychological causes and mechanisms of sterility. The evidence in support of the latter, however, is extremely tenuous; and in a society in which family size is deliberately restricted, the influence of neurotic inhibitions would be hard to distinguish from those of prudence and rational restraint. At all events, until we have a clear indication that the fertility of neurotic persons, or of those with a particular variety of neurosis, is restricted, explanations are premature.

We have seen that mental disorder is not associated with higher fertility than normal; the commonest and gravest mental disorder, schizophrenia, is indeed characterized by much lower fertility than normal. The fears so strongly voiced fifty years ago have little substance: society is not in danger of being, swamped by increasing numbers of insane people. But there is still cause for discomfort. Distressing and disabling hereditary mental diseases are being propagated, and it may well be that factors are at work which will increase rather than diminish the fertility of those who are mentally ill or who can transmit the predisposition to mental illness.

It is notoriously perilous to attempt predictions about the future size and genetic composition of populations (Dorn, Glass, Larsson). The effects of mutation, selection, gene flow and genetic drift are hard enough to foresee: harder still the effects of social, cultural, economic, therapeutic and political changes. Here, as Robert Bridges said of the alternative to 'purposeful and wide self-breeding', we see 'complexity irresoluble in obscurity'. But I think there are some recognizable shifts of opinion and practice which could alter in an unwelcome direction the reproductive behaviour of those prone to mental illness.

DANGERS AND OPPORTUNITIES

Because of the irrational fears and misunderstanding about mental disorders which have clogged progress and made the lot of the mentally ill needlessly hard, great efforts are now being made to instil into the public a more sympathetic and informed understanding of the nature and course of these illnesses. Such activities, responsibly conducted, obviously do much good. They could, however, result in a rise in the proportion of married people among those with schizoid personality or with a history of manic-depressive attacks, because the lesson that 'mental illnesses are illnesses like any other' will have been so well learnt by the public that existing social and psychological barriers to such marriages will become much weaker. I am aware that intrinsic biological and psychological factors in the affected persons may be much the most powerful determinant of whether they marry, far outweighing conscious beliefs and attitudes. But the findings of Böök to which I have referred, and Essen-Möller's demonstration of the way in which the birth rate of schizophrenics slowly or hastily followed the trend downwards in the general population suggest that extraneous influences cannot be safely minimized. This applies not only to the proportion of marriages among the patients and the number of children they produced but also to the fertility of their sibs and children: these refrain to some extent from marriage and procreation for reasons which could be weakened if there were widespread acceptance of the view that mental illnesses are illnesses like any other, without reference to the need for caution because of the strongly hereditary character of some of them. I wish enough were known about the mode of inheritance of mental disorders and about the factors which determine fertility, to offer clear guidance to those who engage in education of the public on matters of mental health and mental illness: but in the light of present knowledge I think it is reasonable to urge that the hereditary aspect of these illnesses should be fairly stated, neither slurred over nor unduly stressed. There is little doubt that it is now often played down in mental hygiene campaigns: thus the National Association for Mental Health tells the public that 'heredity plays a less important part in insanity than is popularly supposed. . . . This age-old question has not yet been completely answered, but more harm is done by worrying over possible inherited factors than by the factors themselves' and goes on to say on the following page, with contrasting assurance, that 'it is quite certain that the surest defence against mental illness is to have a secure and happy childhood'. Unfortunately the issue is fogged by misunderstanding and the adoption of an extreme position by some who concentrate on the psychodynamic aspect of causation. 'The genetic approach to the problem of schizophrenia and manic-depressive psychosis is not so pessimistic, deterministic or sterile as many psychiatrists are still inclined to believe. . . . Nor is there any conflict between a genetic theory and the idea that psychological and other factors may precipitate . . . psychoses, which appear in persons having a specific genotype.' (Böök, 1952.)

There is now a strong move towards keeping the mentally ill in the community if at all possible. The many virtues in this movement need no emphasis. It coincides with a disposition in psychiatrists to discharge patients from mental hospitals soon after the acute symptoms of their attack have subsided, even though there is a recognized possibility of relapse within a short time. The development of therapeutic methods in the last twenty years has promoted the tendency towards much shorter periods of stay in the mental hospital. All in all, the chances of a particular patient with schizophrenia or melancholia spending a substantial part of his life in uninterrupted residence in a mental hospital are becoming much less. This may increase the fertility of schizophrenics; it seems unlikely, however, that it would greatly do so, since, as I mentioned earlier, Essen-Möller had found that there was little relation between duration of hospital stay and fertility after the onset of illness. The question is still open, and important. We have unfortunately only the German inter-war data to go on, which may not correspond to post-war experience in various countries.

Sterilization is a topic impossible to ignore when discussing the eugenic aspects of the fertility of mentally ill persons. We have, it is clear, abundant evidence that many schizophrenics need no such surgical aid to sterility. There are, however, also the manic-depressives, with their approximately normal fertility. It is generally agreed that sterilization would not appreciably reduce the amount of schizophrenia and manic-depressive psychosis in the population, even if it were carried out with the abominable thoroughness and compulsion which the National Socialists employed in Germany. But this does not preclude the employment of voluntary sterilization in individual cases. Even so severe a critic of many eugenic proposals as Professor Haldane has said, of metabolic and other abnormalities inherited as autosomal recessives, that though negative eugenic measures like sterilization would be of little value in reducing the frequency of these abnormalities 'doubtless parents who have produced one child with a grave recessive defect should have no more children'. He advocates, of course, persuasion and not compulsion, to this end.

There is a place for persuasion and advice in this matter of reducing the fertility of those who have had a mental illness. I doubt, however, if we know enough to advocate celibacy and childlessness to many of those who seem to us *predisposed* to mental illness, in the light of their family history and constitutional traits: there are too many opportunities for error in judging that a 'schizoid' or 'syntonic' personality or a particular bodily habit forebodes mental illness, and there are too many valuable qualities closely allied to supposedly premorbid ones, to justify such a step in most cases. But once a man or woman has been overtly ill with one of the illnesses that are genetically controlled, advice about having children may be called for: and it may prevent much individual unhappiness. This presumes, of course, restraint and sound judgment in the advising physician—the antithesis of the irresponsible attitude sometimes shown when a depressed or neurotic woman is advised to become pregnant so that she may have a child to interest her.

There are, of course, psychiatrists who believe that most of the evidence put forward in favour of hereditary transmission of mental illness is better interpreted as evidence of the paramount influence of upbringing and personal relations within the family. To them the fertility of the mentally ill is of little or no consequence, except insofar as the patient is likely, or unlikely, to bring up her children well, in the light of accepted psychodynamic principles. Such a view is unwarrantably one-sided. The fertility of those with mental illness is important, and is not less so because it carries implications that we cannot fully assess at present because our information about relevant biological, demographic and social facts is too scanty. Not only eugenists but all compassionate and reflective people must surely be concerned at an increase in the number of children born to parents who are themselves affected by a prolonged mental illness or who are destined to become mentally ill—perhaps many times—before they reach old age. Because of this much further inquiry is needed into the biological, social and psychological factors that control fertility in the mentally ill.

SUMMARY

A hundred years ago mental disorders were believed to occur in 'degenerate' families, which tended to die out. By the turn of the century this was replaced by the opposite view, that the hereditarily diseased and insane would multiply until they swamped the rest of society. Systematic investigations have shown the falsity of these extreme views. Of the two commonest and gravest mental disorders, manic-depressive psychosis is characterized by approximately normal fertility, and schizophrenia by much lower fertility than normal, largely because of lessened capacity for marriage. Very little is known about the fertility of people with neurotic disorders, but there is no evidence that it differs greatly from the normal.

The hereditary transmission of mental disorder is still a grave problem, though often slurred over in mental hygiene campaigns. Schizophrenia is largely a hereditary disease or group of diseases; since it remains as prevalent as ever in spite of the relatively low fertility of those who suffer from it, fresh mutations are evidently replenishing the otherwise dwindling supply of people predisposed to it: the same might be said, though to a much lesser extent, of manic-depressive psychosis. Radiation may be raising the mutation rate for these hereditary diseases.

We do not know enough to warrant our making firm predictions or advocating celibacy and childlessness to outwardly healthy people who seem predisposed to mental illness, but once a man or woman has been overtly ill with one of the mental disorders that are genetically controlled, advice about having children may be called for: it should be cautious and should draw on the best available genetic and psychiatric information.

REFERENCES

BÖÖK, J. A. 'A genetic and neuropsychiatric investigation of a North-Swedish population', *Acta Genetica*, 1953, **4,** 133.

DAHLBERG, GUNNAR. 'Die Fruchtbarkeit der Geisteskranken', *Z'schr. f. d. ges. Neurol. u. Psychiat.*, 1933, **144,** 427.

DAYTON, NEIL A. 'Size of family and birth order in mental disease', *Studies in Quantitative and Cultural Sociol.*, 1930, **24,** 123.

DAYTON, NEIL A. *New Facts on Mental Disorders*, Baltimore, Thomas, 1940.

DORN, H. F. 'Pitfalls in population forecasts', *J. Amer. Stat. Assoc.*, 1950, **45,** 311.

ESSEN-MÖLLER, ERIK. 'Untersuchungen über die Fruchtbarkeit gewisser Gruppen von Geisteskranken', *Acta Psychiat.*, Suppl. 8, Copenhagen, Levin and Munksgaard, 1935.

ESSEN-MÖLLER, ERIK. 'Die Heiratshäufigkeit der Geschwister von Schizophrenen', *Arch. f. Rassen u. Gesell. Biol.*, 1936, **30,** 367.

GLASS, BENTLEY. 'Genetic changes in human populations', *Advances in Genetics*, 1954, **6,** 95.

GREENWOOD, M. and YULE, G. UDNY. 'On the determination of size of family', *J. Roy. Stat. Soc.*, 1914, **77,** 179.

HALDANE, J. B. S. *New Paths in Genetics*, London, Allen and Unwin, 1941.

HERON, DAVID. *A first study of the statistics of Insanity and the Inheritance of the Insane Diathesis*, London, Dulau, 1907.

KALLMANN, FRITZ J. *The Genetics of Schizophrenia*, New York, Augustin, 1938.

LARSSON, TAGE. 'The interaction of population changes and heredity', *Acta Genet. et Stat. Med.*, 1956/7, **6,** 333.

MAUDSLEY, H. 'The genesis of mind', *J. Ment. Sci.*, 1862, **8,** 61.

MERTENS, K. 'Untersuchungen über die Heiratshäufigkeit der Schizophrenen und der Manisch-Depressiven sowie deren Geschwister', Würzburg, Inaug. Dissert., 1939.

MOREL, B. A. *Traité des Dégénérescences physiques, intellectuelles et morales de l'espèce humaine*, Paris, Baillière, 1857.

NIXON, W. L. B. and SLATER, E. 'A second investigation into the children of cousins', *Acta Genet. et Stat. Med.*, 1958, **7,** 513.

NORRIS, VERA. 'A statistical study of the influence of marriage on the hospital care of the mentally sick', *J. Ment. Sci.*, 1956, **102,** 467.

ØDEGAARD, O. 'Marriage and mental disease', *J. Ment. Sci.*, 1946, **92,** 35.

ØDEGAARD, O. 'New data on marriage and mental disease', *J. Ment. Sci.*, 1953, **99,** 778.

PEARSON, KARL. 'The scope and importance to the state of the science of national eugenics', 14th Robert Boyle Lecture, London, Frowde, 1907.

PENROSE, L. S. 'Estimate of the incidence of cases of schizophrenia and manic-depressive reaction due to spontaneous mutation: Appendix E', *Hazards to Man of Nuclear and Allied Radiations*, H.M.S.O., 1956.

PENROSE, L. S. 'Mutation in man', *Acta Genetica*, 1956, **6**, 169.

POPENOE, PAUL 'Fecundity of the insane', *J. Heredity*, 1928, **19**, 73.

Registrar-General's Statistical Review of England and Wales for the two years 1950–51: Supplement on General Morbidity, Cancer and Mental Health, London, H.M.S.O., 1955.

WEINBERG, WILHELM. 'Die Rassenhygienische Bedeutung der Fruchtbarkeit', *Arch. f. Rassen u. Gesell. Biol.*, 1910, **7**, 684.

WESTOFF, C. F. and KISER, CLYDE V. 'Interrelation of fertility and feeling of personal inadequacy', *Milbank Mem. Fund. Quart.*, 1952, **30**, 239.

16

DEMOGRAPHIC ASPECTS OF MENTAL DISORDER

I SHOULD like to begin by quoting a passage in Graunt's *Observations on the Bills of Mortality*:

'The Lunaticks are also but few, viz. 158 in 229,250, though I fear many more than are set down in our Bills, few being entered for such, but those who die at Bedlam; and these all seem to die of their Lunacy, who died Lunaticks; for there is much difference in computing the number of Lunaticks, that die (though of fevers and all other Diseases, unto which Lunacy is no Supersedeas) and those that die by reason of their madness.

'So that, this Casualty being so uncertain, I shall not force myself to make any inference from the numbers and proportions we find in our Bills concerning it: only I dare ensure any man at this present, well in his Wits, for one in a thousand, that he shall not die a Lunatick in Bedlam within these seven years, because I find not above one in about one thousand five hundred have done so.

'The like use may be made of the Accompts of men that made away themselves, who are another sort of Mad-men, that think to ease themselves of pain by leaping into Hell; or else are yet more Mad, so as to think there is no such place.'

This is a guarded and qualified conclusion. Graunt recognized that bills of mortality would give little information about the frequency of a group of diseases which are not as a rule directly lethal; and that, as long as he had to depend on the insane admitted to Bethlem (then the only mental hospital in London) for any estimate of prevalence he could not calculate the risk of insanity for the ordinary people of London, but only their risk of being admitted to hospital and dying there.

These seem very obvious considerations, but many assertions since Graunt's day about the incidence and the frequency of mental illness have been based entirely on the people admitted to mental hospitals, who are, of course, only a proportion of all mentally ill people. Moreover, Graunt by his reference to 'Lunaticks' and his inclusion of people who commit suicide, reminds us that some definition of mental illness is requisite, and may be disputable. There has been—and still is—a good deal of fog about where the limits are to be set, so

---

This paper was delivered to a meeting of the Royal Society in November 1962. It is reprinted from the *Proceedings of the Royal Society* (1963), B, **159**, 202–20.

that it is necessary to add to any demographic statement on this topic an explicit note regarding the criteria of inclusion in the category of mental disorder. The chronic psychoses that are compatible with life in the ordinary community, the neuroses that shade off into minor anomalies of personality that are very widespread, the so-called psychosomatic disorders like asthma, and psychopathic aberrations of personality—all of these present formidable problems of delimitation.

Since the beginning of the last century, the question has often been asked: is mental disorder on the increase? Thus in 1810 Dr Richard Powell, who was secretary to the Metropolitan Commissioners in Lunacy, came to the conclusion, after a careful analysis of the registers between 1775 and 1809, that insanity was 'considerably upon the increase'... 'for if we compare the sums of two different lustra, the one beginning with 1775 and the other ending with 1809, the proportion of patients returned as having been received into lunatic houses during the latter period is to that of the former period nearly as 129 to 100'. (Powell, 1813.) In France the issue was debated hotly, from 1820 onwards. As adequate figures were not available, theorizing was rampant, and prejudices about the effect of changing conditions of society had a generous airing. Those who doubted whether any real increase in mental disturbance had taken place, suggested that the rise in the number of insane persons admitted to hospital—in Paris it had doubled between 1786 and 1813—could be accounted for by the larger accommodation and better care, the improved survival rate, and the greater willingness of patients' relatives to bring about inpatient treatment. On the other side it was urged that social and psychological influences play an important part in causing some very common forms of mental disorder, and that the stressful times which ensued upon the French Revolution and the Industrial Revolution must have had their toll in more and more breakdowns. Yet another line of unsupported argument assumed progress in the direction of lessened hereditary disease, improved sexual behaviour, and a reduction in alcoholism, insecurity and material cares.

These profitless disputes continued throughout the century. As more sophisticated methods came into play, employed upon census and other data fuller than those available early in the century, it became clear that extraneous factors were at work to increase the number of mentally ill persons admitted to hospital, without necessarily any increase in the proportion of mentally ill in the whole population. An Official Report on this subject to the Lord Chancellor in 1897 listed thirteen such factors, including among them the increasing numbers of elderly people requiring admission, the greater accessibility of mental hospitals, a change in the attitude of the public towards the prospect of treatment and recovery, and a wider conception of the range of disorders which could properly be cared for in a mental hospital.

But the question whether mental illness is on the increase seems of perennial interest. The best known answer is that of Goldhamer and Marshall (1949) who compared the age-specific first admission rates to mental hospitals in Massachusetts between 1840 and 1885 with those for 1940. They found that for people under fifty the rates a hundred years ago were just as high as now; though for older persons the first admission rates have become much higher. The patients admitted in the last century were, however, more severely ill, because the limited number of beds imposed the need to select those whose violence, suicidal efforts or other gross disturbance of behaviour made their reception essential. The findings justified the conclusion that there had not been a secular increase during the last hundred years in the incidence of psychoses of early and middle life requiring admission to a mental hospital.

Admissions to English mental hospitals do not tell quite the same tale. In a comparison of age-specific rates of admission in a first attack in 1907 with the corresponding rates for 1937 I found that there had been an appreciable decline in the rates for men during these 30 years, though for women the rates in the various age-groups between 35 and 65 were virtually unchanged (Lewis, 1946). Since the war the rates have been much higher. Thus the first admission rate of men per 100,000 of population in 1951 was, for all ages, 79, but by 1959 it had risen to 102; and in women the rate was 99 in 1951, but 139 in 1959—a rise of 40%. Such an increase during a single decade could hardly signify an equivalent rise in incidence. It was probably due in part to the reception of categories of psychiatric patient previously seldom taken into mental hospitals: there was a demonstrable rise in the proportion of first admissions attributable to neuroses and abnormalities of personality, though it is not the whole story. Other factors were also at work: thus general paralysis of the insane has become a rarity since syphilis was brought under control. Mental disorder now has a wider range. To determine the size of the mentally abnormal population information must be drawn not only from mental hospitals but also from general hospitals, outpatient clinics, general practitioners, educational authorities, and samples of the general public. The paucity of objective evidence for these elusive abnormalities bears hardly on the investigator.

The most detailed studies come from Scandinavia. Essen-Möller (1956) in an exceptionally thorough study of a rural Swedish population numbering 2,550, all but thirty of whom were personally interviewed by him and three of his colleagues, determined that 2·3% of the female and 1·4% of the male adult population were suffering from neurotic illness at the time of the investigation. When he included those who had previously had such an illness from which they were now recovered, the figures rose to 8·2% for the women, 4·4% for the men. Fremming (1951), who examined similarly a Danish population, recorded a lower frequency of incidence—2·8% in women, and 1·8% in men.

For the psychosis schizophrenia, Essen-Möller established in the same rural population a frequency of 0·9% of the adult population. Böök (1953*a*), studying the population of an isolated area of North Sweden, found the frequency of schizophrenia to be 0·95% and Fremming's figure was much the same for Denmark. For manic-depressive psychosis the frequency was about 0·9% in the various Scandinavian investigations. There is sufficient concordance of findings regarding the psychoses for it to be fair to assume that Scandinavian investigators are using similar criteria for the recognition of psychoses, though where the neuroses are concerned such community of outlook and method is doubtful.

When we look at British and American findings the area of doubt on this score is much wider. The American data come chiefly from Baltimore, Tennessee and New York. In a survey of a district of Baltimore in 1936 (Lemkau, Tietze and Cooper, 1943) the prevalence rate of schizophrenia was 2·9 per 1,000, whereas in the Tennessee survey (Roth and Luton, 1943) it was 1·7. For psychoses of every kind it was 6·7 per 1,000 in Baltimore in 1936, but in a post-war study of another sample of the Baltimore population (Pasamanick, Roberts, Lemkau and Krueger, 1957) it was only 4·3. For psychoneuroses the rates were, in Baltimore in 1936, 3·1 per 1,000, Baltimore 1952, 52·6 per 1,000. There were other large differences.

It is highly improbable that the discrepancies reflect gross diversity in the psychiatric state of the population of Baltimore in 1936, of Tennessee in 1938, and of Baltimore in 1952. Evidently different concepts of morbidity, and different methods of finding affected persons, contributed largely to the divergency. This is what we find when we come nearer home and consider in particular the prevalence of neuroses.

Seven years ago a survey of a large sample of the population of England and Wales was made, in which the observations of 171 practitioners were pooled (General Register Office, 1962*b*). It was found that during 12 months 4·8% of the population at risk had sought medical advice for a psychoneurotic condition. A further 0·4% did so because of a psychosis or some disorder of personality and behaviour. In another survey, however, made at about the same time among 750 families living in a new housing estate, the frequency of neurotic symptoms was estimated at 22% of the population at risk (Martin, Brotherston and Chave, 1957); this extraordinarily high figure, based on replies to a direct inquiry about particular symptoms on a check list, was put into its place when it was found that in the same survey the prevalence of neuroses, if determined from the practitioners' records on the same population, was only 5·6%—much the same as in the 1952 Baltimore inquiry. In a slightly later study of 9,000 people living in a south London suburb, the period-prevalence of psychiatric morbidity in the year 1956–7 amounted to 7% of the men on the practitioners' lists, and 11% of the women (Kessel, 1960). Those included had a neurotic illness that was disabling in some degree; if to them were added the patients with distinctly abnormal traits of personality, not necessarily disabling, the total prevalence rose to 14% of the people at risk. Some investigators like to include in the psychiatric category the so-called psychosomatic or stress disorders—such as asthma—which are supposed to be partly caused, and appreciably influenced, by psychological factors: this extension of the field swells the figures of psychiatric morbidity inordinately, so that, as one investigator puts it, 'it coincides with the popular estimate that one-third of the patients seen in general practice are suffering from a psychogenic and mental illness' (General Register Office, 1962*b*). Whether popular or not, this estimate is built on a flimsy foundation: sober demographic observations are best restricted to the established categories of outright neurotic and psychotic disorder. It is quite hard enough to draw the limits for these, and to decide what anomalies of conduct, mood and thought are to be judged pathological. Even with so striking a criterion of disease as an epileptic fit ascertainment presents many uncertainties; thus the prevalence rate of epilepsy was 6·2 per 1,000 population at risk in south-east England (Pond and Bidwell, 1960), whereas in Minnesota (Kurland, 1959) it was only 3·6; for the population under the age of 20 the English rate was nearly double the American, and for people over 60 it was very much higher even than that. The discrepancies do not point to differences in the incidence of epilepsy in Minnesota and Surrey, but to differences in ascertainment procedure.

The extent to which social factors can affect the enumeration of mentally ill persons in a census or survey is suggested by the differences between certain countries in the prevalence and incidence rate for men and women respectively. In England and Wales in 1959 the rate of first admission to mental hospitals per 100,000 population was 102 for men and 139 for women, the preponderance of women being evident at all ages; in the resident population of the hospitals the rates were similarly heavier among women (341 per 100,000, contrasted with 272 for men) (General Register Office, 1962*a*). In a nearby country, Denmark, the total proportions are similar: the prevalence rate determined by a census taken on a given day in 1957 was 211 per 100,000 men, 245 for women (though in the age-group 25 to 44 the men had a higher rate—190 as against 167 for the women) (Arentsen and Strömgren, 1959).

In the United States the picture is startlingly different. In 1955 the first admission rate of men to public mental hospitals was 108, whereas the rate for women was only 78. But in the resident population of the mental hospitals in that year the rate per 100,000 of total civilian population was practically the same for both sexes (442 and 440): though the rate for men was higher in the age-group under 44, this was reversed in the very large contingent of people over 55, mostly suffering from the mental disorders of old age. I would emphasize that these are age-specific rates: in actual numbers the women preponderated in all the age-groups over 35, e.g. there were 88,013 women over 65 in the mental hospitals, as against 67,000 men (Kramer, Pollack and Redick, 1961).

Though there may be some differences in the frequency of occurrence of mental illness at various ages in the two sexes in America and this country, it is more probably a reflexion of differing social conditions, public attitudes, medical organization, including admission and discharge policy, and changes in the prospect of survival for those in mental hospitals.

The figures from the United States draw attention to the age distribution, and particularly to the large contingent of elderly people, in the total population of mentally ill persons. The statistics of mental hospitals in all countries which have a well-developed psychiatric service show this preponderance.

In Western Europe the first admissions for senile psychosis amount to about 10% of all first admissions to mental hospitals. In order to see how far this indicates the prevalence of senile psychoses in the whole community, Sjögren and Larsson (1959) examined the relevant findings in a rural Swedish population of about 25,000 people; in such a population the proportion of those with senile psychoses who would be cared for in a mental hospital would be lower than in the cities, because the available hospital beds are fewer, the distances to the mental hospital greater, and there are readier facilities for accommodating and caring for a debilitated relative at home. They found that the morbidity risk of senile psychosis up to 80 years of age was 0·6% for men, and 0·8% for women. This may be compared with a morbidity risk of 1·6% for schizophrenia in both sexes, and of 0·9 and 1·2% for manic-depressive psychoses in men and women respectively. Norris (1959), on the basis of mental hospital admissions in the London area, concluded that the expectation at birth of being admitted to hospital for psychiatric treatment after the age of 60 is 2% for men and 3% for women: not all of those so admitted would, however, have senile psychoses, some would have vascular disease of the brain, and others might have depressive or other transient disorders.

At the other extreme of life there are to be considered the place the mentally ill occupy in the order of births, and the age of their mothers at that time. It has been observed that schizophrenia tends to occur more often in the later-born than in the earlier-born of families numbering four or more brothers and sisters. This might be connected with the age of the mother at the time when the future patient was born. It has been found, by Goodman (1957), that, in comparison with all children who were born during a given period, schizophrenic patients show a deficit of young mothers, a shift of the 'peak' age for births towards the older ages, and (except for men from small families) an excess of older mothers. The interpretation of this finding is obscure.

The fertility of the mentally ill and defective has been a disputed topic for more than half a century. Much of the contention has been emotionally coloured. The old views of progressive degeneration and sterility wiping out a diseased stock had a considerable vogue in the latter half of the nineteenth century. Then the opposed view gained an ascendancy: instead of the doom of dwindling fertility, decay and then extinction for psychopathic families, people feared the consequences of unchecked fertility in the mentally ill and the mentally defective. Insanity and imbecility, it was supposed, would spread, putting an ever greater burden upon the rest of the population. David Heron, who made an investigation of the matter under the stimulus of Karl Pearson, stated the prevalent belief in 1907: 'Our present statistics amply confirm the general result reached by Pearson that pathologically abnormal stocks . . . are not less but rather more fertile than the normal stocks in the community. The eugenic importance of this in relation to the insane diathesis is self-evident, for within the community natural selection is largely suspended and the "insane" restored to family life as recovered.' And, in another passage, he concluded, 'There is no reduction in, possibly rather an augmentation of, the fertility of insane stocks, when compared with that of sane stocks. . . . The normal, or probably more than normal fertility of the insane, notwithstanding their partial seclusion and high death rate, and the fact that insanity is a disease largely of middle life, must make us pause before we acquiesce in the unrestricted return of the "recovered" insane to family life' (Heron, 1907). Since then the wheel has come full circle: we aim at getting the maximum number of such patients, recovered or unrecovered, back to family life, and we do so without fear of their undue propagation.

The collection of satisfactory evidence on their fertility began in the nineteen-thirties. Dayton (1930) in Massachusetts, and Dahlberg (1933) in Upsala, ascertained that mentally ill women have subnormal fertility: more of them are single than is the case in the general population, and they bear fewer children. To determine whether this general finding holds good for the individual mental disorders, and especially for those which can be inherited, Essen-Möller (1935), of Lund, has inquired into the fertility of three groups: those with a manic-depressive psychosis; the schizophrenics; and the epileptics. In the manic-depressives the number of children born before their illness, and subsequently, did not depart from the normal. The schizophrenics showed a surprising difference between the sexes in the number of children born to them before the onset of their illness: the men showed a higher rate than the rest of the population, whereas the schizophrenic women had a lower rate or to put it more exactly, they had a lower birth rate than the normal population at the beginning of the century but declined more slowly than normal women in this respect during the ensuing 30 years, so that their pre-illness rate, at the end of this period, was much the same as that of the rest of the female population.

The fact of illness had exerted, as might be expected, a profound effect upon the women's reproduction. The fertility of the married women who were schizophrenics fell by about 70% after their breakdown, when the necessary allowance was made for their age and the duration of their marriage. If they lived in a community where contraception was not practised, their total fertility was only a quarter of that of the normal population; in a community which used contraception, it was about half the normal. The number of illegitimate children is small and does not appreciably alter the finding. In another large inquiry upon a North German population, the fertility of the schizophrenics was similarly low, and a very high proportion of the offspring of schizophrenics had been produced before the illness became manifest. An exception to this was found in the subgroup of schizophrenics who recovered from mild or periodic forms of the disorder so that they could resume their customary lives afterwards, and in many instances get married.

It is plain that social factors can play a large part in reducing the fertility of schizophrenic persons of either sex. The crudest example is that of the patient whose illness necessitates his remaining in hospital for many years, perhaps until death. Other influences may be intimately connected with the determinants of marriage. It is clearly of importance to see whether the reproductive capacity of schizophrenics as a group is reduced not because of any biological reduction of their capacity to procreate but because the illness, or the personality that preceded it, lowered their chance of marriage.

The first admission rate of single men who have to enter an English mental hospital is, for almost all ages, very much higher than the rate for married men: for single women it is higher than for married women, though the disparity is less than in the men (Brook, 1959). When the data are analysed, to show the rates for individual forms of illness, it is in schizophrenia that it is most prominent: there the age-standardized first admission rate for single men is six times that for married men, and for women 3·7 times higher in the unmarried (Norris, 1956). Scandinavian, American and German figures show the same heavy preponderance of single people among those who enter hospital with a schizophrenic illness.

The question arises: does the illness preclude marriage, or is it that marriage reduces the risk of illness? The former explanation is, on many grounds, the more probable, so far as schizophrenia is concerned. The characteristics of personality which often precede overt illness of this kind militate strongly against marriage. Moreover, once the illness has become manifest, the chances of marriage are further reduced. Whereas before the outbreak of schizophrenic illness, marriage is half as common in the schizophrenics as in normal people of the same age-group, it falls to only about a sixth of the normal rate after the illness in those who had been single at the onset of the attack (Essen-Möller, 1935). This is in contrast with manic-depressive patients who have, before their illness, a marriage rate almost the same as that of the normal population, and after the illness a marriage rate which is about half the normal.

It is, of course, to be expected that the marriage rate of schizophrenics and other mentally abnormal people would vary with social conditions: in a remote self-contained rural community, for example, it would be higher than in a large city. In the geographically isolated north Swedish population that Böök (1953*a*) investigated, he found that although the proportion of schizophrenic women who were married was lower than normal, the disparity was far less than in the rest of Sweden, and this he attributed to the selection of a wife being more influenced by her physical strength and capacity for hard work in the arduous and primitive conditions of life in this area than by her psychological attributes. The schizophrenic men, on the other hand, were mostly unmarried.

In spite of their low fertility, the proportion of schizophrenics in all countries shows no diminution. This could be first, because heredity has very little to do with its causation, or at any rate with its manifestation: or secondly, because outwardly unaffected persons who transmit it reproduce at an abnormally high rate and so compensate for the relative infertility of those with overt schizophrenia; or, thirdly, because mutations replenish the supply. The first two of these explanations seem, on present evidence, inadequate. There are good grounds for believing that in its typical forms schizophrenia is to a large extent inherited and that although environmental influences may affect its form, course, and time of occurrence, the illness will not occur unless there is a genetic predisposition. Such slender data as we have on the second possibility suggest that heterozygous carriers cannot be making good the reduction in size of the schizophrenic population that would be expected from the reduced fertility of schizophrenics. There remains the third explanation. There is at present no unanimity as to the spontaneous mutation rate, since it depends on estimates of the gene-frequency, and on a gross clinical grouping of conditions which cannot be regarded as genetically homogeneous. But that there is a considerable spontaneous mutation rate is hardly to be questioned (Böök, 1953*b*). This is true also of manic-depressive psychosis, though the rate is probably much smaller than for schizophrenia.

Manic-depressive psychosis and schizophrenia are, apart from the disorders of old age, the common psychotic conditions and they are largely of hereditary causation. The neuroses, which are responsible for so much psychiatric invalidism and incapacity, are of more uncertain etiology. The hereditary factor in them does not seem strong enough to make their fertility an important influence upon the psychiatric composition of the next generation (except in so far as upbringing by a neurotic parent may bring about neurotic illness or other mental abnormality in the offspring). So far very little has been done to determine the fertility of neurotic persons as a group: from preliminary studies it does not seem to deviate from that of the normal population (Lewis, 1958).

The duration of life of the mentally ill has been the subject of a number of studies, which dealt, however, almost entirely with the patients in mental hospitals. In 1841 William Farr wrote a paper for the Statistical Society in which he examined the number of deaths of persons resident in the asylums, and concluded that 'the mortality of lunatics in asylums is much higher than the mortality of the general population, and the excess cannot be ascribed entirely, though it may partially, to the confinement, the unwholesomeness, or the usages of mad-houses'. In modern studies his finding has been confirmed many times. It has been established that the mortality in mental hospitals is highest during the first year of hospital stay (13 times as great for men, and 8 times as great for women as it is in the general population), and that it is higher for those mental disorders dependent on physical disease affecting the brain than for manic-depressive psychosis and schizophrenia. The causes of death have, of course, changed in their relative frequency: thus, whereas intestinal infections with bacillary dysentery, were, over a long period, endemic and lethal, and tuberculosis accounted for very many deaths, these diseases have ceased to give any serious trouble. In most respects, though not in all, the mortality of those resident in mental hospitals follows the trends in the general population: diseases of the cardiovascular system are now the most frequent cause of death, but neoplasms are twice as common in the general population as in the mental hospital patients. The mortality rate in the mental hospitals has been reduced by more than half in the last eighty years, but their relative mortality has decreased only slightly (Ødegaard, 1952).

Ascertaining the mortality of those in mental hospitals is a poor substitute for knowledge of the mortality rate of all who have a mental disorder, since a majority of psychiatric patients now either do not enter a mental hospital or, if they do, leave it, sooner or later, to return to the general community. The only estimate available for the total psychiatric population comes from Sweden where Larsson and Sjögren (1954) have made observations covering the span 1900–44: they found that schizophrenic men had, after the date of onset of their illness, a mean expectation of life which is 75% of that of the general population, while schizophrenic women had only a 64% residual expectation of life. Those with manic-depressive psychoses had a much smaller reduction in their expectation of life: it was, for men, 91%, and for women 87% of that of the general population. Larsson and Sjögren infer that the relative mortality of people with endogenous psychoses will remain much what it was during the first half-century since, in spite of considerable changes in the general mortality rate during the period studied, the ratio of the number of years survived by these psychotics to the years they would have survived with the mortality rate of the general population had fluctuated little. The changes in general mortality would, however, lead of course to a higher number of senile and arteriosclerotic psychoses. Similar conclusions have been drawn by Ødegaard in Norway, where the relative mortality of psychotic patients has declined very slowly during the 80 years between 1870 and 1950. No one has so far studied the mortality of neurotic patients.

That the mortality of manic-depressives should be so nearly that of the general population seems strange when it is considered that these are the people most prone to suicide and other forms of self-injury. Graunt, as we saw, regarded all suicide as a form of madness, but did so for reasons which were theological rather than medical. The numbers of suicides in different countries appear to vary enormously. In the most recent report from the World Health Organization (1961) the death rate from suicide per 100,000 of population ranged from 35·6 for West Berlin, 28·4 in the German Democratic Republic and 25·7 in Japan to only 2·7 in Ireland: the United Kingdom and the United States were mid-way between these extremes (11·7 and 10·7 respectively). The method of ascertaining and recording suicide is, however, as a rule biased and incomplete: little reliance can be placed on prima facie disparities between the official statistics of different countries. There are, however, some detailed *ad hoc* studies which point to considerable differences in the suicide rate of communities living in the same area but with diverse cultural and social backgrounds: this has been seen in Ceylon, and in Singapore, for example. Sainsbury (1955) has shown that in London the suicide rate for different boroughs was correlated with indices of social isolation, mobility, divorce and illegitimacy, but not with unemployment or overcrowding. Graunt said of the Bills of Mortality that he intended they should 'not be only as Deaths heads to put men in mind of their Mortality, but also as Mercurial Statues to point out the most dangerous Waies that lead us into it and misery'. The close study of deaths from suicide and of the social and psychological conditions evidently predisposing to it, may serve the purpose Graunt had in mind, acting as a signpost to preventable causes of this form of death.

Turning from mortality back to morbidity, we have to take into account a further social factor, that of class.

It is notoriously difficult to define social class satisfactorily. The criteria used in different countries vary, though in all occupation is a prominent or decisive constituent. In England and Wales, where the five social classes of the Registrar General's reports are based on occupations, it has been clear for years that the total first admission rate to mental hospitals from Class 5 (which includes labourers, kitchen hands and other unskilled workers) is about double that from other classes. For schizophrenia the disparity is much greater, the Class 5 rate of male first admissions being more than three times that for Social Class 1 and nearly five times the rate for Social Class 2 (General Register Office 1961). Since this association of schizophrenia with lower social class has been found in other countries, notably the United States, efforts have been made to determine its significance. Inquiries have been mainly directed towards discovering whether the unfavourable social circumstances in which they live cause breakdown in predisposed persons, or whether their illness, and the anomalies of personality that have led up to the illness, have brought about a decline in their occupational level by the time they receive psychiatric attention. The latter interpretation has received most support. A downward drift can be discerned in the work record of many of the patients, and a decline also in the level of the patients compared with that of their fathers at the same age (Morrison, 1959). American investigators do not agree with this, but their diagnostic and social class criteria, method of ascertainment, and scope of population studied differed appreciably from those of the English investigators.

To test the strength of the ecological assumption that the inception rate of schizophrenia (as distinct from its prevalence) varies according to the social characteristics of the district, a comparison was made between a group of five west London boroughs which were outstanding in their high proportion of men in social classes 1 and 2, and a group of four east London boroughs outstanding for their high proportion of men in social classes 4 and 5 (Stein, 1957). If, as American investigators had concluded, adverse socio-ecnomic conditions breed schizophrenia, the inception rate should have been higher in the east London group of boroughs. Standardized first admission rates were therefore calculated for the two groups of boroughs for the years 1954 and 1955. It emerged that for schizophrenia the first admission rate was actually higher in the western than in the eastern group (although within each borough the social class gradient was on the same lines as for England and Wales as a whole). Whatever the causes of this disparity—there was, for example, a much higher proportion of migrants from other countries and from other parts of the United Kingdom in the western group of boroughs—it cannot be held that relatively poor socio-economic conditions in London breed more schizophrenia than more favoured neighbourhoods. The social complexities are too great, obviously, for a crude differentiation by occupation, or by any single social attribute, to suffice for study of the effects of contrasted environments upon the incidence of schizophrenia or other mental disorder.

The high proportion of migrants in some areas was mentioned as a relevant social datum. Entry into a strange environment can obviously put a strain on individuals' capacity to adapt. The immigrants from Norway who came in a steady flow to Minnesota from 1870 onwards have been shown to have had a higher first admission rate to a mental hospital than had the population in Norway from which they came: this could have been due mainly to the stresses of settling in a new country, or to some selective factor which caused less stable Norwegians to emigrate to America. Ødegaard (1932), who investigated this, found strong support for the latter explanation; schizoid personality and even schizophrenia were disproportionately frequent among the emigrants before they arrived in the United States. It is necessary, however, to add that in a study published last month (Malzberg, 1962) another Scandinavian group of immigrants, who came to New York State, have been shown to have had (in 1949 to 1951) a higher incidence of mental disorder than native-born Americans of Swedish parentage living in the same state: for schizophrenia the Swedish born had a standardized first admission rate of 63·4 per 100,000 population, whereas the native born of Swedish parentage had a rate of 40·3. Malzberg, who reports this, infers that, since ethnic origin was a constant, the native born are showing the effects of living in a more favourable environment. The study does not profess to throw light on which features in the environment are thus favourable to mental health, and it is unlikely that demographic data will avail to do so.

The size and characteristics of the mentally defective section of the population can be determined with a greater approach to accuracy than can the assessment of mental illness. Nevertheless, the World Health Organization paper on Prevalence (Tizard, 1953) said bluntly that the 'criteria of mental subnormality are complex, uncertain, and not self-consistent. Confusion arises because of errors of measurement, faulty standardization of tests and measurements, differences in growth patterns, environmental influences, and lack of agreement between the different criteria for diagnosis. Fluctuations in the threshold of community tolerance make the term "mental subnormality" only a relative one, useful mainly for administrative purposes.'

After such a broadside, to pay attention to estimates of prevalence seems perhaps futile. But there have been studies which stand up to severe scrutiny. The best known and most thorough is that made by Lewis (1929) on the population of six areas in England and Wales in 1925–7. He concluded that just under 1% of the population was mentally defective; the incidence, especially of the milder forms, was considerably higher in rural than in urban areas (probably because of selective migration), and the prevalence apparently varied with the age-groups, being at its maximum during school-age. Among the mentally defective, people of idiot grade made up only 5%, the imbeciles amounted to 20%, and the remaining 75% were feebleminded. A Baltimore study (Lemkau, Tietze and Cooper, 1942) showed a similar pattern, though the total prevalence in the age-group 10 to 19 was much higher than in the English inquiry. There have been several Scandinavian studies; they, too, give a prevalence rate between 1 and 1½%, and broadly the same age-distribution.

The most recent survey is that of Äkesson (1961) in rural southern Sweden. He defined his grade in terms of Stanford-Binet Test rating: a reduction of more than twice the standard deviation from the mean indicated defect; a reduction of between two and three times the standard deviations amounted to high-grade defect (or feeble-mindedness), and a reduction of more than three times the standard deviation denoted a low-grade defective (imbecile or idiot). He found a prevalence rate of 1·8% for all forms of deficiency; 67% of them were feebleminded, 28% imbeciles, and 5% idiots. The fertility of the defectives was low.

The demographic picture of mental defect is changing because of the fall in death rates in infants and young children. Carter (1958) has shown that the proportion of mongoloids among 10-year-old children in 1949 was twice what it had been in 1929 (1 in 2,000 as against 1 in 4,000). Now it is double the 1949 proportion. This fourfold increase is attributable to the large decrease in their mortality—20% less in the 11 years 1944 to 1955. This greatly improved survival of the children with mongolism is not paralleled by a comparable change in the rest of the defectives of imbecile and idiot grade, leading to increased numbers. The prevalence rate of low-grade defect, apart from mongolism, in Middlesex, in children between the ages of 10 and 14 years, appears to have declined by a third since 1929, if the present rate can safely be compared with the 1929 rate for urban areas (Goodman and Tizard, 1962). There is speculation, but as yet no evidence to indicate how this apparent decline has come about, at the same time as mortality has been reduced.

It is plain from this rapid survey that much attention has been given to the demographic aspects of mental disorder, but the results are still discrepant in many particulars, the discrepancy arising primarily because there is no sure and practical way of finding out all those who have some form of mental disorder, and counting them.

REFERENCES

ÄKESSON, H. O. *Epidemiology and genetics of mental deficiency in a Southern Swedish population*, Upsala, University Press, 1961.

ARENTSEN, K. and STRÖMGREN, E. *Acta Jutlandica*, 1959, **31,** 1.

BÖÖK, J. A. *Acta genet. stat. med.*, 1953*a*, **4,** 1.

BÖÖK, J. A. *Acta genet stat. med.*, 1953*b*, **4,** 133.

BROOKE, E. M. *J. ment. Sci.*, 1959, **105,** 893.

CARTER, C. O. *J. ment. Def. Res.*, 1958, **2,** 64.

DAHLBERG, G. *Z. Neurol. Psychiat.*, 1933, **144**, 427.

DAYTON, N. A. *Stud. Quant. Cultural Sociology*, 1930, **24**, 123.

ESSEN-MÖLLER, E. 'Untersuchungen über die Fruchtbarkeit gewisser Gruppen von Geisteskranken', *Acta Psychiat.*, Suppl. 8, Copenhagen, Levin and Munksgaard, 1935.

ESSEN-MÖLLER, E. 'Individual traits and morbidity in a Swedish rural population', *Acta Psychiat.*, Suppl. 100, Copenhagen, Munksgaard, 1956.

FARR, W. *J. statist. Soc.*, 1841, **4**, 17.

FREMMING, K. H. *The expectation of mental infirmity in a sample of the Danish population*, London, Cassell, 1951.

GENERAL REGISTER OFFICE. *Registrar-General's statistical review of England and Wales for the two years 1957–1958*, Supplement on Mental Health, London, H.M.S.O., 1961.

GENERAL REGISTER OFFICE. *Registrar-General's statistical review of England and Wales for the year 1959*, Supplement on Mental Health, London, H.M.S.O., 1962*a*.

GENERAL REGISTER OFFICE. *Morbidity statistics from general practice*, vol. 3, *Disease in General Practice*, Studies on Medical and Population Subjects, no. 14, London, H.M.S.O., 1962*b*.

GOLDHAMER, H. and MARSHALL, A. *Psychosis and civilization*, Glencoe, Ill., Free Press, 1949.

GOODMAN, N. *Brit. J. prev. soc. Med.*, 1957, **11**, 203.

GOODMAN, N. and TIZARD, J. *Brit. med. J.*, 1962, **1**, 216.

HERON, D. *A first study of the statistics of insanity and the inheritance of the insane diathesis*, London, Dulau, 1907.

KESSEL, W. I. N. *Brit. J. prev. soc. Med.*, 1960, **14**, 16.

KRAMER, M., POLLACK, E. S. and REDICK, R. W. 'Studies of the incidence and prevalence of hospitalized mental disorders in the United States', in *Comparative epidemiology of the mental disorders* (Ed. P. Hoch and J. Zubin), London, Grune and Stratton, 1961.

KURLAND, L. T. *Epilepsia*, 1959, **1**, (4), 143.

LARSSON, T. and SJÖGREN, T. 'A methodological, psychiatric and statistical study of a large Swedish rural population', *Acta Psychiat.*, Suppl. 89, Copenhagen, Munksgaard, 1954.

LEMKAU, P., TIETZE, C. and COOPER, M. *Ment. Hyg., N.Y.*, 1942, **26**, 275.

LEMKAU, P., TIETZE, C. and COOPER, M. *Publ. Hlth Rep.*, 1943, **58**, 1909.

LEWIS, A. J. *J. ment. Sci.*, 1946, **92**, 150.

LEWIS, A. J. *Eugenics Rev.*, 1958, **50**, 91. (See also this volume pp. 285–305.)

LEWIS, E. O. *Report on an investigation into the incidence of mental defect in six areas, 1925–1927: Report of the Joint Mental Deficiency Committee, Part IV*, London, H.M.S.O., 1929.

MALZBERG, B. *Acta Psychiat. Scand.*, 1962, **38**, 79.

MARTIN, F. H., BROTHERSTON, J. H. F. and CHAVE, S. P. W. *Brit. J. prev. soc. Med.*, **1957**, **11**, 196.

MORRISON, S. L. *J. ment. Sci.*, 1959, **105**, 999.

NORRIS, V. *J. ment. Sci.*, 1956, **102**, 467.

NORRIS, V. *Mental illness in London. Maudsley Monograph*, no. 6, London, Chapman and Hall, 1959.

ØDEGAARD, O. 'Emigration and insanity', *Acta Psychiat*, Suppl. 4, Copenhagen, Levin and Munksgaard, 1932.

ØDEGAARD, O. *Acta Psychiat. et Neurol. Scand.*, 1952, **27**, 353.

PASAMANICK, B., ROBERTS, D. W., LEMKAU, P. V. and KRUEGER, D. E. *Amer. J. Publ. Hlth*, 1957, **47**, 923.

POND, D. A. and BIDWELL, B. H. *Psychiat., Neurol., Neurochir*, 1960, **63**, 217.

POWELL, R. 'Observations upon the comparative prevalence of insanity at different periods'. Read before the College of Physicians, April 1810 (*Med. Trans.* 1813).

ROTH, W. F. and LUTON, F. H. *Amer. J. Psychiat.*, 1943, **99,** 662.

SAINSBURY, P. *Suicide in London*, Maudsley Monograph, no. 1, London, Chapman and Hall, 1955.

SJÖGREN, T. and LARSSON, T. *Bull. Wrld Hlth Org.*, 1959, **21,** 569.

STEIN, L. *Brit. J. prev. soc. Med.*, 1957, **11,** 181.

TIZARD, J. *Bull. Wrld Hlth Org.*, 1953, **9,** 423.

WORLD HEALTH ORGANIZATION, *Epidem. Vital Statist. Rep.*, 1961, **14,** 144.

BIBLIOGRAPHY

1926

With CAMPBELL, T. D. The aborigines of South Australia: dental observations recorded at Ooldea. *Aust. J. Dent.*, **30,** 371–6.

With CAMPBELL, T. D. The aborigines of South Australia: anthropometric descriptive and other observations recorded at Ooldea. *Trans. T. Soc. S. Aust.*, **50,** 183–91.

1928

Traumatic pneumocephalus. *Brain,* **51,** 221–43.

1930

An investigation into the clinical features of melancholia. M.D. Thesis; Univ. Adelaide.

1931

Paranoid disorders. *Gen. Pract. Fr.-Br. med. Rev.*, **7,** 311–15.

Genetic problems in psychiatry: and their solution by the study of twins. *Eugen. Rev.*, **23,** 119–25.

1932

The experience of time in mental disorder. *Proc. R. Soc. Med.*, **25,** 611–20.

1933

Inheritance of mental disorders. *Eugen. Rev.*, **25,** 79–84.

1934

Melancholia: a historical review. *J. ment. Sci.*, **80,** 1–42.

Melancholia: a clinical survey of depressive states. *J. ment. Sci.*, **80,** 277–378.

The psychopathology of insight. *Br. J. med. Psychol.*, **14,** 332–48.

Mental reactions to bodily injury. *Med. Press,* **188,** 511–12.

Acromegaly in one of uniovular twins. *J. Neurol. Psychopath.*, **15,** 1–11.

German eugenic legislation: an examination of fact and theory. *Eugen. Rev.*, **26,** 183–191.

Inheritance of Mental Disorders. In *The Chances of Morbid Inheritance,* ed. BLACKER, C. P. London: H. K. Lewis.

1935

Psychological syndromes in central nervous disease: a genetic interpretation. *Eugen. Rev.*, **27**, 213–15.
Neurosis and unemployment. *Lancet*, **2**, 293–7.
Prognosis in schizophrenia. *Lancet*, **1**, 339–41.
With Minski, L. Chorea and psychosis. *Lancet*, **1**, 536–8.

1936

Melancholia: prognostic study and case material. *J. ment. Sci.*, **82**, 488–558.
Prognosis in the manic-depressive psychosis. *Lancet*, **2**, 997–9.
Problems of obsessional illness. *Proc. R. Soc. Med.*, **29**, 325–36.
A case of apparent dissimilarity of monozygotic twins. *Ann. Eugen.*, **7**, 58–64.
Psychiatry and general medicine. *Med. Press*, **192**, Symposium No. 2, 1–3.

1937

With Samuel, N., and Galloway, J. A study of cretinism in London with especial reference to mental development and problems of growth. *Lancet*, **1**, 1505–9 and **2**, 5–9.

1938

States of depression: their clinical and aetiological differentiation. *Brit. med. J.*, **2**, 875–8.
The diagnosis and treatment of obsessional states. *Practitioner*, **141**, 21–30.
Some recent aspects of dementia. In *Festskrift tillägnad Olof Kinberg*, pp. 238–44. Stockholm: Asbrink.
Paranoia and paranoid states. In *The British Encyclopaedia of Medical Practice* (1st ed.), **10**, 292–301. London: Butterworth.
Alcoholic psychoses. In *The British Encyclopaedia of Medical Practice* (1st ed.), **10**, 332–41. London: Butterworth.

1940

With Jackson, J. Psychiatric comparison of artificial menopause and the effects of hysterectomy. *J. Neurol. Psychiat., Lond.*, **3**, 101–10.

1941

Psychological Medicine. In Price's *Textbook of the Practice of Medicine*, 6th ed. (and subsequent editions). London: Oxford University Press.
Psychiatric aspects of effort syndrome. *Proc. R. Soc. Med.*, **34**, 533–40.
With Jones, M. Effort syndrome. *Lancet*, **1**, 813–18.

1942

Discussion on Differential Diagnosis and Treatment of Post-contusional States. *Proc. R. Soc. Med.*, **35**, 607–14.
Incidence of neurosis in England under war conditions. *Lancet*, **2**, 175–83.
With Slater, E. Neurosis in soldiers: a follow-up study. *Lancet*, **1**, 496–8.

1943

Social effects of neurosis. *Lancet*, **1,** 167–70.
Mental health in war-time. *Publ. Hlth, Lond.*, **57,** 27–30.
With GOLDSCHMIDT, H. Social causes of admissions to a mental hospital for the aged. *Sociol. Rev.*, **35,** 86–98.

1944

Depression (In 'Recent Progress in Psychiatry'). *J. ment. Sci.*, **90,** 256–65.
The psychological aspects of indigestion. *Practitioner*, **152,** 257–60.
With GOODYEAR, K. Vocational aspects of neurosis in soldiers. *Lancet*, **2,** 105–9.

1945

The industrial resettlement of the neurotic. *Labour Mgmt*, **27,** 40–3. Also in (1946) Supplement to *Brit. med. J.*, **1,** 197–9.
Psychiatric investigation in Britain. *Amer. J. Psychiat.*, **101,** 486–93.
On the place of physical treatment in psychiatry. *Br. med. Bull.*, **3,** 22–4.
Psychiatric advice in industry. *Br. J. ind. Med.*, **2,** 41–2.
The treatment of alcoholism. In Interim Supplement to *British Encylopaedia of Medical Practice*, pp. 11–12. London: Butterworth.
Sobre el lugo del tratamiento físico en psiquitría. (i) *Revta. Asoc. méd argent.*, **59,** 1235–7, and (ii) *Gac. méd. españ.*, **19,** 494–7,

1946

Early recognition of disease; mental disorders. *Practitioner*, **156,** 459–63.
Ageing and senility: a major problem of psychiatry. *J. ment. Sci.*, **92,** 150–70.
Memorandum to the Royal Commission on Equal Pay. Appendices IX and X to Minutes of Evidence taken before the Royal Commission on Equal Pay, pp. 130–4. London: H.M.S.O.

1947

The education of psychiatrists. *Lancet*, **2,** 79–83.

1949

Philosophy and psychiatry (Manson Lecture). *Philosophy*, **24,** 99–117.
Postgraduate study in mental health in Britain. *Br. med. Bull.*, **6,** 185–7.
With DAVIES, D. L. Effects of decamethonium iodide (C 10) on respiration and induced convulsions in man. *Lancet*, **1,** 775–7.

1950

Mental disorders. Section in *Chambers' Encyclopaedia*, **9,** 258–64. London: Newnes.

1951

Henry Maudsley: his work and influence (Maudsley Lecture). *J. ment. Sci.*, **97,** 259–77.
Social aspects of psychiatry (Morison Lecture). *Edinb. med. J.*, **58,** 214–47.
Medical psychology. In *A Century of Science*, ed. DINGLE, H. London: Hutchison.

1952

Classification of schizophrenia. *Proceedings of the first World Congress of Psychiatry* (*Paris* 1950). Part 2. Paris: Hermann.

With Slater, E. Psychiatry in the Emergency Medical Service. In *History of the Second World War: United Kingdom Medical Series. Medicine and Pathology*, ed. Sir Z. Cope. London: H.M.S.O.

Paranoia and paranoid states. In *British Encyclopaedia of Medical Practice* (2nd ed.), **10,** 362–70. London: Butterworth.

Alcoholic psychoses. In *British Encyclopaedia of Medical Practice* (2nd ed.), **10,** 394–402. London: Butterworth.

1953

Health as a social concept. *Brit. J. Sociol.*, **4,** 109–24.

Letter from Britain. *Amer. J. Psychiat.*, **110,** 401–5.

Hysterical dissociation in dementia paralytica. *Mschr. Psychiat. Neurol.*, **125,** 589–604.

Research in occupational psychiatry. *Folia psychiat. neurol. neurochir. neerl.*, **56,** 779–86.

Advances in psychological medicine. *Practitioner*, **171,** 403–12.

Contribution to Points of Research into the Interaction between the Individual and the Culture. In *Prospects of Psychiatric Research*, ed. Tanner, J. Oxford: Blackwell.

1954

With Fleminger, J. J. The psychiatric risk from corticotrophin and cortisone. *Lancet*, **1,** 383–6.

Aspetti psicosomatici della medicina clinica. *Recenti Prog. Med.*, **16,** 434–53.

1955

Philippe Pinel and the English. *Proc. R. Soc. Med.*, **48,** 581–6.

Mental aspects of ageing. *Ciba Fdn. Colloq. Ageing*, **1,** 32–48. London: Churchill.

The relation between operative risk and the patient's general condition: alcohol, other habits of addiction and psychogenic factors. *Sixteenth International Congress of Surgery, Copenhagen*. Brussels: Imprimerie Medicale et Scientifique.

1956

Sigmund Freud, 1856–1939. *Discovery*, **17,** 181–3.

Statistical aspects of suicide. *Can. med. Ass. J.*, **74,** 99–104.

Rehabilitation programs in England. In *The Elements of a Community Mental Health Program*. New York: Millbank Memorial Fund.

1957

Social psychiatry. In *Lectures on the Scientific Basis of Medicine, 1956–7*, **6,** 116–42. University of London: Athlone Press.

The offspring of parents both mentally ill. *Acta genet. Statist. med.*, **7,** 349–65.

Jung's early work. *J. analyt. Psychol.*, **2,** 119–136.

La enfermedad obsesiva. *Acta neuropsiq. argent.*, **3,** 323–35.

1958

Between guesswork and certainty in psychiatry (Bradshaw Lecture). *Lancet*, **1**, 171–5 and 227–30.
Resettlement of the chronic schizophrenic. (i) *J. all-India Inst. ment. Hlth*, **1**, 22–8; (ii) (1959) In *Report of the Second Internat. Congr. Psychiatry: (Zurich 1957)*. Zurich: Orell Fussli. **1**, 223–8.
J. C. Reil's concepts of brain function. In *The History and Philosophy of Knowledge of the Brain and its function*, ed. POYNTER, F. N. L. Oxford: Blackwell.
Fertility and mental illness. *Eugen. Rev.*, **50**, 91–106.
A psychiatrist looks at a layman. *Oxf. med. Sch. Gaz.*, **10**, 124–6.

1959

Families with manic-depressive psychosis. *Eugen. Q.*, **6**, 130–7.
The impact of psychotropic drugs on the structure, function and future of psychiatric services in hospitals. In *Neuro-Psychopharmacology*, eds. BRADLEY, P. B., FLÜGEL, F. and HOCH, P. Amsterdam: Elsevier Pub. Co.

1960

The study of defect (Adolf Meyer Research Lecture). *Amer. J. Psychiat.*, **117**, 289–305.

1961

Agents of cultural advance (Hobhouse Memorial Trust Lecture). London: Oxford University Press.
Amnesic syndromes; the psychopathological aspect. *Proc. R. Soc. Med.*, **54**, 955–61.
The chemical treatment of mental disorder. *Biology hum. Affairs*, **27**, 19–26.
Psychiatric education and training. In *Psychiatrie der Gegenwart*, eds. GRUHLE, H. W., JUNG, R., MAYER-GROSS, W. and MÜLLER, M., Band 3. Berlin: Springer.
Current field studies in mental disorders in Britain. In *Comparative Epidemiology of Mental Disorders*, eds. HOCH, P. H. and ZUBIN, J. New York: Grune & Stratton.
Psychiatry in Great Britain. In *Contemporary European Psychiatry*, ed. BELLAK, L. New York: Grove Press.

1962

Ebb and flow in social psychiatry (Bertram Roberts Memorial Lecture). *Yale J. Biol. Med.*, **35**, 62–83.
Inaugural speech of the scientific session. In *First Pan-African Psychiatric Conference 1961*, ed. LAMBO, T. A. Ibadan: Government Printer.
What are the foreigners up to? *Amer. J. Psychiat.*, **118**, 751–2.

1963

Medicine and the affections of the mind (Harveian Oration). *Brit. med. J.*, **2**, 1549–57.
Research and its application in psychiatry (Maurice Bloch Lecture). Glasgow: Jackson.

The psychoses. In *Cecil-Loeb's Textbook of Medicine*, 11th ed. (and 12th ed.), eds. BEESON, P. B. and McDERMOTT, W. Philadelphia: Saunders.
Symposium: Training for child psychiatry. *J. Child. Psychol. Psychiat.*, **4,** 75–84.
Demographic aspects of mental disorder. *Proc. Roy. Soc.*, B.**159,** 202–20.
Henry Maudsley. In *Grosse Nervenaerzte*, ed. KOLLE, K. Band 3. Stuttgart: Thieme.

1964

Health in 1984: changes in psychiatric methods and attitudes. *New Scient.*, **21,** 423–4.
Health. In *A Dictionary of the Social Sciences*, eds. GOULD, J. and KOLB, W. L. London: Tavistock.
Depression. In *Depression. Proc. Symposium, Cambridge, 1959*, ed. DAVIES, E. B. Cambridge: University Press.

1965

J. C. Reil: Innovator and battler. *J. Hist. Behav. Sci.*, **1,** 178–90.
A note on personality and obsessional illness. *Psychiatria Neurol. Basel*, **150,** 299–305.
The Medical Research Council Social Psychiatry Research Unit. In *The Organization of Research Establishments*, ed. Sir J. COCKCROFT. Cambridge: University Press.
The Psychology of Shakespeare. In *Shakespeare: the comprehensive soul*, PRITCHETT, V. S. *et al.* London: British Broadcasting Corporation.

1966

Dogma disputed: Psychiatric dicta. *Lancet*, **1,** 974–5.
Survivance de l'Hystérie. *Evol. psychiat.*, **31,** 159–65.

INDEX

(*Authors' names are in italics*)